WINNING COLOURS

WINNING COLOURS

Selected Racing Writings of
Edgar Wallace

Edited & Introduced by
John Welcome

BELLEW PUBLISHING
London

CONTENTS

INTRODUCTION

EDGAR WALLACE was a phenomenon in his lifetime both in his writing and his racing, the one for his immense output, the other for his keeping and running a host of moderate horses which he believed in and backed on a monumental scale. Paradoxically, his lack of success both as an owner and gambler did not prevent his writing about the sport he loved with skill, accuracy and an authority which was often laced with wit.

Racing had fascinated him from the first and was to remain an all-consuming passion to the end. The illegitimate son of an unsuccessful actress he was boarded out early to a family in the East End of London but he did not remain there long. By his own talents and push and the discovery of a fluency with the pen, he fought his way out of poverty. From the unlikely position of a private in the R.A.M.C. in South Africa his freelance efforts and the journalistic contacts they made enabled him to buy himself out and commence a full-time writing career which was to sustain him throughout the many ups and downs of a comparatively short life.

He remained in South Africa for some years earning a living, much of which he gambled away as a reporter, editor, freelance journalist and versifier of jingles in the Kipling manner which he could turn out apparently at will. Returning to England he continued in journalism and published the first and one of the best of his many thrillers, *The Four Just Men*, which was a financial disaster owing to over-enthusiastic advertising paid for by himself.

It is, however, with his racing and racing writing that we are concerned here. A chance meeting at the Press Club with Meyrick Good, for many years the chief racing reporter of *The Sporting Life* and with whom he was to form a friendship lasting until his death, gave him his first insider's view of the sport and enhanced his already consuming passion for everything concerned with it.

Meyrick Good was one of the most knowledgeable and experienced racing writers of his day. Born into a racing tradition – he was the grandson of William Day of Danebury – Good knew racing in all its aspects. As well as writing of it he rode as an amateur with some success and as an owner had had a hand in the training and shrewd placing of his horses. He was attracted by Wallace from the first and captivated by his enthusiasm and ready charm, as indeed most people were when he cared to exert it.

He took him racing and for years he and Wallace together with another Turfite, 'Gipsy' Lyndall, shared a flat over Boots in the High Street for the big Newmarket meetings. There they would sit up far into the night discussing the racing, arguing and swapping stories as racing people will the world over. With his reporter's instinct fully alive, Wallace absorbed the lore of the thing and learnt and retained in his memory the jargon of track and stable, becoming more and more fascinated with it all and determined sometime to become an owner and a personage of the Turf. From this it was but a step to turn his journalistic talents to writing about it. Soon there appeared, too, the first of his novels with a racing background *Captain Tatham of Tatham's Island*. It made little stir but it and Good's patronage brought his name to the attention of racing people and, more important at that stage, of other racing journalists and editors, all of which helped him to sell his racing pieces and further his career.

In 1913 John Corlett, owner and editor of *The Sporting Times*, or 'Pink'un', the slightly risqué sporting and dramatic paper beloved by the Edwardian clubman, suddenly sold it behind the backs of his devoted staff and without notice to them. The purchaser was a young man about town of dubious reputation called de Wend Fenton under whose proprietorship the staff did not care to continue. They therefore decided to set up a new paper to be called *Town Topics* which would carry on the old tradition. Its editor was to be Arthur M. Binstead, 'Pitcher' of the 'Pink'un', raconteur, roué and wit, who obtained the necessary backing from Kennedy Jones, a financier of plays and papers and a man of influence in Fleet Street. It is a measure of the success which Wallace's writings had brought him that at the first meeting of the convenors Jones declared: 'Where is

Wallace and what is he doing? We must get hold of him, he's just the man we want.' Get hold of him they did at eight guineas a week, which was gratefully accepted since his reckless gambling had been going unusually badly even for him.

Binstead, however, began to wonder, on Wallace's first day in the office, if they had picked the right man. Meeting the office boy on the stairs at mid-morning bearing a glass of milk, he enquired what he was doing with it. On being told that it was for Wallace, Binstead, who was accustomed to greet each midday with a pint of champagne, exclaimed, 'Good God, isn't he weaned yet!'

But in fact Wallace was an immediate success on the paper and the staff soon learnt that he could turn his pen to anything, though his chief interest and delight was to cover racing. They also discovered to their pleasure and indeed profit his talent for light verse on topical matters. Soon after he joined news broke of the sudden scratching from all his engagements of The Tetrarch, 'the spotted wonder', the ante-post Derby favourite on which thousands had been wagered. No hint had come from the stable or owner that anything was amiss. Despite rumours that all was not well with the colt, money continued to flood in. Forgotten now, the scratching created a sensation then and did nothing to enhance the popularity with the public of the trainer, H.S. 'Atty' Persse or the owner, Captain (as he then was) Dermot McCalmont. Wallace promptly penned his own comment with one of the neatest of his verses:

> I turn my head; through the stable door
> There's a glimpse of yard and a hint of Down –
> (O heath and down and crowded moor,
> Where the gold is wrought for the Triple Crown!)
> And here I am in my lonely stall,
> What do I think – if I think at all?
>
> Far away at this moment's space,
> Horses stand at a white-webbed gate,
> Fit and fancied and eager to race . . .
> Hill . . . and Corner . . . and into the Straight . . . !
> I – who have met and beaten them all.

When war broke out it took its toll of the staff. Binstead, whose health had been failing, died and others enlisted, but since Wallace was over-age he was not recalled to the colours. He took over the editorship and, indeed, in an effort to keep it going, wrote most of the paper himself. Then, as always, what he really enjoyed writing about was his beloved sport of racing and he wrote about it well. It is important to emphasise this since a myth has grown up – fostered by his almost manic belief in and management, or rather mismanagement, of his own horses once he became an owner, and his failure as a tipster (although many knowledgeable racing men have been woefully bad tipsters) – that he knew nothing about the nuts and bolts of racing.

There was then on the staff of *Town Topics* Horace Lennard, who had been assistant racing editor to John Corlett on the old 'Pink 'un'. He had owned and managed racehorses and bought and sold them too – he just missed buying the 1914 Grand National winner, Sunloch, for a song – and was, the historian of the paper says, one of the soundest writers on the Turf of his time. Although on *Town Topics* he was mostly concerned with the theatre, he would scarcely have allowed Wallace's racing writings to pass without protest had they not been founded on informed knowledge and judgement.

All this time, too, Wallace was making acquaintance with the highest and the lowest on the Turf and revelling in their company. His possession of a Press pass enabled him to mix freely with and talk to jockeys, owners and trainers, at the same time never neglecting those on the underside of the Turf, little bookmakers and their runners, silver-ring tipsters and the like – the sort of men whom his earlier experience as a police court reporter had brought him into contact with, who never ceased to fascinate him and of whom and whose quirks, trickeries and peculiar camaraderie fostered by a common passion for racing he was to make good use of in his plays, short stories and novels later on. But those in high places came to take to him and talk to him too. It was during this period that he first met Lord Derby and an unlikely friendship was forged between the illegitimate son of the East End and one of the leaders of the ruling few of his day. The bonds of friendship thus forged lasted and Lord Derby never forgot him. Writing a foreword to Meyrick Good's reminiscences many years after Wallace's death, Lord Derby paid him this tribute which is worth reprinting: 'Your remarks about Edgar Wallace especially interest me. He was, as you know, a private soldier in the Boer War. He was somewhat shabbily treated with regard to his medal. I was able to get that put right and he remained a friend of mine to his dying day.'

Inevitably, Wallace was betting, mostly unsuccessfully, and to keep pace with his losses and his increasing lifestyle he was writing thriller after thriller for a host of publishers, selling the entire copyright for ludicrously low sums. Suddenly he woke up to the fact that other authors were drawing royalties from their books and through the good offices of a leading agent, A. P. Watt, Sir Ernest Hodder Williams of the leading firm of Hodder and Stoughton – whose thriller stable included such as John Buchan, Sapper, A. E. W. Mason and Dornford Yates – took him on. Not only that but Sir Ernest decided, in modern parlance, to hype him, and from that moment Wallace was made. Immediately, with the prospect of a vast increase in income, he plunged into ownership. Of the first two horses he owned – named respectively Sanders and Bosambo after two of the chief characters in his West African stories – the first was useless but the second won a few races and whetted his appetite for more horses and a larger string. From then on he was embroiled in all the perils of ownership, made far worse for him by his undying belief that the magic gift he displayed in his writings was carried over to his string; one and all he backed them time and again as if defeat was out of the question, and his losses were enormous. 'I am living on crusts of bread and raw apples until my royalty cheques come in,' he wrote plaintively to his publisher.

Of course he was doing nothing of the kind. He had indulged himself by taking a box of Ascot, something he had always longed for, so as to place himself amongst those who had really arrived on the Turf. There he entertained lavishly, providing badges as well as champagne for his guests. When Sir Patrick Hastings, the leading K.C., protested that with all this hospitality at least he could pay for admission, 'You can,' Wallace told him, 'but there are others who cannot and it means a lot to them and it would be unfair and hurtful to make exceptions.' This was typical of him, since however high he rose he never lost the common touch. And in the midst of his success he did not forget his comrades of the press. When he published *The Flying Fifty-Five* – the best of his racing novels and one of the best of his many books, full of what we should now call 'one-liners' devised with the wit which was one of his many attractions as an author it was prefaced with the words, 'To my friends and colleagues on the sporting press this book is affectionately dedicated.'

The press did not forget him, either. The following year he was
elected chairman of the Press Club and it was in this office that he
established and left behind him a lasting memorial to his career on
the Turf. This was the Derby lunch which, with the assistance of
Lord Derby, he installed as an annual event. To it on the Monday
before the race all the leading owners, trainers and pressmen were
invited and entertained to a menu carefully chosen by Wallace
himself. At the lunch speeches were made and tips lightly and
publicly proclaimed. It was such a success that the tradition was
maintained after Wallace's death and the luncheon as an annual
sporting gathering has continued to this day. He was also at this
time to perform an even more important service to the sport. It had
long been an anomaly which worried Wallace, owners, members of
the Jockey Club and those of the racing public who cared to think
about it, that all classic engagements were made void on the death
of an owner. No one, however, appeared willing to do anything to
think of a way round it until Wallace came along with his brain-
wave. The rule had its origin in the assumption made at the time of
the passing of the Gaming Acts that forfeits were irrecoverable at
law by the Jockey Club since they were believed to be part of a
gaming and wagering contract. Wallace took the view that this was
not so and that it could and should be challenged. By reason of his
friendship with Lord Derby he was able to enlist the assistance of
the Jockey Club in the matter and it was agreed that he would be
the defendant in a test case. Accordingly, he incurred forfeit by
scratching two of his runners at the Newmarket Spring Meeting
and refused to pay it, whereupon the Jockey Club issued a writ.
The sum involved, incidentally, was £4! It is not necessary to go
into the legal arguments here – the case was fought through two
courts but the Court of Appeal upheld Wallace's arguments and the
rule was rescinded with consequent benefit to racing and to bloodstock owning and breeding.

The case gave Wallace the idea for a play which he subsequently
dashed off in his impulsive fashion. It turned out to be *The Calendar*, one of his best plays and arguably the best racing play ever
written. By now into his middle fifties, with the reading public at
his feet and money for all his extravagances in his pocket if not his
bank balance, his output of books and plays was prodigious. Plays,
films, serials, his invention never flagged and money poured in but

nothing could quench his itch to spend or his lust for gambling. On his last ill-fated trip to America he sent a radiogram to Meyrick Good from *The Empress of Britain* to put £50 on whatever he fancied for the Manchester November Handicap for him. Anxious to do the best he could for his old friend, Good narrowed the choice to two and then at the last moment backed the wrong one!

It looked as though Wallace's ill-luck at gambling was following him across the Atlantic but, in fact, just before the end there was a turn for the better. In the few days before his final, swift, fatal illness he paid a visit with friends to a race meeting in California at Aqua Caliente. On arrival he was delighted to find that he had been made an honorary steward of the meeting and that the principal race was called 'The Edgar Wallace Stakes'. To cap it all he picked and backed three winners. Hardly had he returned to California than he fell ill, contracted pneumonia and on 10 February 1932 he died aged only fifty-seven. It was fitting that the funeral arrangements in America were placed in the hands of another old racing friend, the jockey, Steve Donoghue, who was in Hollywood at the time and had been with him not long before that last illness started.

His estate was hopelessly insolvent, though nothing was owing to the bookmakers, with whom as a matter of honour he had settled promptly. He left behind him a warmth in the hearts of all who knew him on the Turf or off it and a body of popular literature which has seldom or ever been surpassed, for he was a far better writer than he has been given credit for. His inventiveness never flagged, he could turn a phrase, enliven a page with wit and, when he tried, create a character of which the *Educated Evans* stories here reproduced, together with his sharp pen-portraits, are good examples. It was his tragedy that his fluency ran away with his other, possibly greater gifts. But such was the power of his name that the books did not suffer the usual fate of those of a popular author by disappearing immediately after his death. He was not forgotten; they continued to be reprinted and to sell to the extent that in two years the then vast sum of £140,000 in debts was satisfied and thereafter royalties continued to accumulate.

Racing, as we have seen, remained an enduring passion to the end. Nothing would have pleased him more than to see these racing stories and articles, long-forgotten, back in print under his name.

THE 'PAT' BARRIE
REMINISCENCES

PETER CHRISTIAN BARRIE, *known to his intimates as 'Pat', was a cheerful Turf crook who deserves immortality, if for nothing else, for his answer to the examining magistrate at his trial. When asked, 'What is your idea of a good thing in racing, Mr. Barrie?' he replied, 'A useful three-year-old in a moderate two-year-old race, your Worship.'*

It was a theory he exploited to the full, as his 'memoirs', ghosted for him by Wallace, amply show. He had brought the business of camouflaging one horse to look like another, or 'running a ringer' as it is known in racing parlance, to what amounted to a fine art, so much so that he became known after his trial, when his audacity had led to his downfall, as 'Ringer' Barrie.

Where or when Wallace originally met him, and conceived the idea of ghosting his memoirs, is not known but it was probably at the trial of Barrie and his associates at the Old Bailey in 1923, which lasted nineteen days and created a sensation at the time. He was sentenced to three years' hard labour and served this, with remission, in Dartmoor, emerging with his spirit unbroken and his cheek unimpaired. Once free Wallace and he somehow made contact and the memoirs appeared in serial form in John Bull, *a sort of scandal sheet of the day, from which Horatio Bottomley, another cheerful trickster, shortly to enter prison himself, had recently relinquished the editorship.*

Apart from their intrinsic interest showing how a clever and audacious crook could drive a coach and horses through the rules, the memoirs have a certain topical value, too, in view of recent allegations of ringing and doping. Barrie's account of the doping of The Panther, for instance, is almost certainly accurate. The Panther had won the Two Thousand Guineas of 1919 and started favourite for that year's Derby at the astonishingly short price of 6 to 5 against. His victory would have cost the bookmakers a fortune. But, as Vincent Orchard in his history of the Derby records, he behaved atrociously at the start, broke the tapes, ran, 'like a mad thing' and was soon beaten.

The ghosting of Barrie's memoirs had several effects on Wallace's life and writing career. When Barrie came out of prison he set up a tipster's business which he ran from a room over a stable in Brick Lane, Piccadilly. Wallace was fascinated by this and also by the sidelights his acquaintanceship with Barrie gave him into the underside of the racing world. He also fancied himself as a tipster and made an offer to Barrie to take over the business and set up himself as a tipster with Barrie as a sort of unofficial and occasional consultant and adviser. Wallace, as we know, was hopeless in picking winners. Although he gleaned much entertainment and copy from finding that Barrie's clients numbered all sorts of people he would have thought unlikely – such as country parsons, maiden ladies and husbands and wives anxious to use accommodation addresses to keep their little flutters secret from their spouses – the business, profitable enough under Barrie's control, went sadly astray once Wallace's idiosyncratic tips, some of them on his own 'hair trunks', went out to clients. Protests began to pour in and after six months Wallace had to admit defeat and hand the business back to Barrie. They remained friends, however, and from this friendship and all the lore he absorbed Wallace's fertile brain conceived and produced one of the liveliest and best of his series characters – Educated Evans.

Like many truly original fictional characters, Evans, the cockney tipster of the stories, owed something to a real-life model, in this case Barrie. Something – but no more. There was an indomitable quality about Barrie, the ability to bounce back after his time in prison, which Wallace, who had a fair amount of that quality himself, admired. That resilience, coupled with his ebullience and sheer cheek, were also qualities which endeared him to Wallace. These were all embodied in Evans but there the resemblance ended, for Wallace gave to Evans a life entirely his own. His inventiveness combined with the humour which was one of his greatest gifts as a writer enabled him to make of Evans one of racing's unforgettable characters and to turn the anecdotes Barrie graphically recounted in their conversations into a series of skilfully crafted tales of the seamier side of the Turf which bear comparison with the best that Damon Runyon was producing in America.

As usual with Wallace, however, he was writing in such haste that at first he regarded these stories as throwaway pot-boilers to help to pay his gambling debts, which were then becoming too formidable for comfort. In that year, to pay his way, he produced no less than seven novels and wrote a racing column for The Racing Specialist *under the pseudonym of 'Nick*

O'Lincoln'. It is no wonder then, perhaps, that the Evans stories were so lightly regarded by him that he sold them for £100 a time to a little racing paper run by a friend, Alec Webster, called Sports Pictures. *So short was he of the readies and so pressing his debts that he frequently had to ask Webster for an advance against the next instalment. It was not until Webster later collected them and published them in book form that Wallace realised that in Evans he had a character to rival or exceed in popularity his other though very different creations, Mr Commissioner Sanders and his sidekicks Lieutenant 'Bones' Tibbets and Chief Bosambo of the River. He then followed them up with two more hastily written 'Evans' collections, neither of which quite rival the freshness, wit, cheerfulness and cheek of the original stories reprinted here.*

A further word needs to be said about the dramatis personae *of Barrie's story. Barrie himself was born in Australia of English parents. He had been brought up with horses, served in Gallipoli as a trooper in the Australian Light Horse, been badly wounded and discharged as unfit. Coming to England, he returned to the first and real love of his life – horses and racing. Endowed with undoubted charm, he bluffed his way along and before the first of his coups he had eight horses in his wife's name for which unpaid bills were mounting up, a suite at the Queen's Hotel in Leicester Square, and patronised the best tailors. Gilbert Marsh, whom Barrie mentions frequently and who appears to have been in charge of the betting, was a con man, a crook and a thorough-going wrong 'un. Barrie never appears to have been on good terms with him and why he employed him remains a mystery. He posed as all sorts of things, amongst them being, 'a millionaire metal merchant in the city', and it was he who roped in the 'mug-punter', Norman Weisz, to join in the swindles. Weisz was the one man of means in the whole entourage, being a substantial pearl merchant in Hatton Garden. Born in Hungary in humble circumstances he became a naturalised British citizen and by his own efforts had made a fortune. At the time of the ramps he was in receipt of an income of £10,000 a year, a large sum indeed in those days and some of which he was anxious to spend on horses. He fell more or less eagerly into Marsh's and Barrie's clutches, who saw this transparent innocent as an admirable front man for them. Barrie, in his memoirs, clears him of any fraudulent interest or involvement and says he was wrongly convicted. But as time went on Weisz, who had ambitions to be known on the Turf, may not have been quite the innocent Barrie makes out. There is no doubt that he was involved to some degree in the Silver Badge affair and in one or two of the other swindles. He was described in the trial as 'an absolute ass on the racecourse' and there were many character witnesses. It was stupidity and cupidity that undid him and he went down for fifteen months in the second division. Barrie, however, may well have been right in that he owed the severity of the sentence at least to the venom with which C. F. Gill, Q.C. pursued him in the box. Weisz was an unconvincing witness but Gill certainly showed him no mercy. Gill was the standing counsel to the Jockey Club and a relentless, some would say an unfair, prosecutor and in this instance he appears to have determined to make Weisz pay for his folly.*

The detective, whom Barrie does not name and who was able to protect Marsh and keep him out of the prosecutions, is unidentified still but there was at that time a detective much connected with the Turf whom he may have had in mind, and nemesis, in the end, as Barrie points out, did catch up with Marsh and he was sent down for several years.

One or two other points deserve mention. The Douglas Stuart referred to on pages 57 and 102 was a leading bookmaker whose slogan was 'Duggie never owes', but whose entertaining advertisements for years enlivened the back pages of the Tatler *and the* Illustrated Sporting and Dramatic News *when those illustrated papers were in their heyday. Gerald L., the four-year-old whom Barrie tipped for the National, never quite fulfilled that ambition, though he ran prominently in the race and in the Gold Cup and was ante post favourite in 1923 until taken out owing to injury. Captain 'Tuppy' Bennet won the Grand National in 1923 on Sergeant Murphy and was leading amateur that year. He died from a fall at Wolverhampton when he was kicked in the head and never recovered consciousness, an accident which led to the compulsory wearing of crash-helmets.*

Richard 'Dick' Wootton, whom Barrie refers to as having caught the camouflaged Mexican Belle formerly in his charge, and indeed once owned by him, was one of the most astute and hardest men on the Turf – it was he, for instance, who brought down Bob Sievier. Since he failed to recognise the ringer one must assume that Barrie was indeed a near genius at his self-appointed trade and perhaps express a tinge of sympathy when his own recklessness and over-confidence, perhaps encouraged by the then laxity of the laws and their enforcement combined with the fact that too many were in the plots and someone squealed, finally brought him down.

MY CONFESSIONS OF TURF SWINDLES

EVERY man who starts off to tell the story of his life, and particularly such a life as mine, begins either with an apology for the poor way in which he has told his history, or else an even more abject apology for his own shortcomings as a law-abiding citizen.

I noticed the other day the biography of an ex-convict, which draws attention to the fact that all these so-called true stories begin with a declaration of innocence. These ex-inmates of Dartmoor and Parkhurst have been wrongly accused, and are the victims of a miscarriage of justice.

I will not be such a hypocrite. I have had my packet, and, to a great extent, deserved it, and I have neither squeaked nor squealed, except in so far as this, that I have a genuine grievance against certain police officers – a grievance which I hope soon to ventilate in the most startling fashion.

And really, this is not intended to be the story of my life, because I am perfectly sure that the readers are not interested in my relations, my schooling or my early literary tastes. What I am going to tell is the true and inside history of the racecourse swindles which, if I was not the instigator, I was one of the principal instruments of carrying out.

Why tell them at all? some may ask (and particularly some who are trembling in their shoes at the thought of all I may, and can, tell). And my answer to these is a very simple one.

I owe it to myself that I should give the fullest details of events which have only been scrappily and inaccurately reported in the course of my trial.

I am not proud of my achievements, but at the same time the law and the rigours of Dartmoor make it wholly unnecessary that I should profess repentance.

Any man who serves three years' penal servitude has his repentance ready made for him, unless he loves prison, as quite a sensible proportion of the people who go into the convict establishments of England apparently do.

I came from Australia during the war with a very complete knowledge of the racing game. I had ridden winners down under, including the winner of an Australian National.

Without knocking my country, I would say that any man who has graduated on an Australian race-track knows as much about the crooked side of the game as he is ever likely to learn. This in spite of the vaunted stipendiary stewards, which certain press-writers, in their dementia, imagine would purify the turf in this country.

I had with me, when I came to London, an introduction to a man whom I will describe, without feeling that I exaggerate, as a master crook. The master crook is at present serving a sentence of five years in one of His Majesty's prisons, and as the extent of his shadiness is public property, I shall not add any great stigma to his well-blemished character when I give his name – Gilbert Marsh.

Gilbert is a story in himself – an unscrupulous, heartless man with few, if any, redeeming features. Men who live the precarious kind of life that Marsh was living, have one very important quality – the power of lying calmly, and with conviction, and I must confess that I myself was deceived when he told me that he had plenty of money and unlimited capital to work the ramp which I was called upon to engineer.

And here I might say, in passing, that, when the crash came, and I appeared in the dock of the Old Bailey, Gilbert Marsh did not stand by my side. Why he did not appear with me, a police official, who is no longer in the service, could tell. I could tell also, for I know very nearly the amount of money that Marsh paid to keep out of the 'boob', though all his bribery did not serve him, for he was later arrested on another charge and went to prison for a much longer term than was awarded me.

When, in 1919, I first met Marsh I was under the impression that he was a very wealthy crook, for undoubtedly he had, at various periods of his life, come into possession, legitimately or otherwise, of enormous sums of money. I knew, of course, just the character of the man; and, with very little preliminary, we decided upon our plan of campaign.

Marsh had a stable of horses at Epsom. I had taken up my quarters in a small stable, with insignificant animals, half-an-hour from his Epsom headquarters. It was not necessary that I should have a trainer's licence, for there is no law in England to prevent any man from training under National Hunt rules.

When the principle – or rather, the lack of principle – had been agreed to, it was arranged by Marsh that I could take over any horse that happened to be in his stable. He had a very excellent lot of animals, including a Derby candidate in Bruce Lodge. The horse I chose for my purpose was Mexican Belle.

Mexican Belle was a bay filly by Beau Bill out of Navaho, and she was trained in Wootton's stable, and had, I think, been a source of some disappointment to that astute trainer.

The stable had betted on her once or twice, but on each occasion she had disappointed. However, they got her right and entered her for a race at Folkestone on Friday, 5 October, 1919. She won the race from Double Deck and old Prevoyant, who was giving her nearly two stone and finished three lengths behind her.

Wootton, not wishing to keep the horse at his stable, allowed it to be sold, and eventually it came into the care of Godfrey (whose other name, by the way, is Lovelock), Gilbert Marsh's trainer.

I chose her because she bore some resemblance, in point of colour and size, to a two-year-old filly I had in my stable – La Lune filly, by Gentle Shepherd. She was a moderate animal, who had never run, and even if she had, it was extremely unlikely that she would ever win.

The point was that she was quite unknown by sight to anyone who ever went racing; and it was a very simple matter, by giving a little additional hair to Mexican Belle's tail, and by a judicious application of dye, to make the three-year-old look as much like La Lune filly as possible.

What I certainly could do, and what I did, was to change Mexican Belle's appearance so effectively and completely that anybody who had seen the horse every day of his life would not recognise her.

Now the changing of a horse's appearance requires a tremendous amount of skill and care. The ordinary dyes which come readiest to the mind would be absolutely useless, because the faked horse might be caught in a shower of rain, and is very liable to be covered with a white sheet, whereupon the dye would come out and the whole trick would be exposed.

Therefore, I would say to those who too readily condemn the officials for being imposed upon by horses which have passed through my hands, not to be too ready in their condemnation.

Later I will deal with this branch of the 'science' more fully. At present it is only necessary to make a passing reference to the care I took with my first coup, Mexican Belle.

I had already entered La Lune in two selling races at Doncaster: The Milton All-Aged Selling Plate over five furlongs on the Wednesday, and the Selling Nursery Handicap on Friday, La Lune being in with 8.7, which was practically top weight.

The reason she had top weight was, of course, because she was an unknown quantity, had never run in public before the Doncaster meeting, and the handicapper was taking no risks.

But the question of weight never bothered the confederation, because we were going to win one of those races, *not with the two-year-old that was entered, but with the three-year-old, Mexican Belle!*

How carefully were the plans made, and how tragically did the first of the great coups come unstuck! Marsh came to Doncaster, and we agreed upon our scheme, which was to give the faked La Lune a 'stopper' in the first race (on the Wednesday) and to stick her full of dope on the Friday and win a packet.

There was no human chance of a defeat – she was running against young horses; there wasn't a two-year-old in the field that had any pretensions to beat a three-year-old. The money was almost as good as in my pocket.

All I had to do was to carry out my plans carefully and await results. How was I to anticipate the startling turn events were to take?

HOW I FOOLED WOOTTON!

It was bad luck alone that queered my first big exploit, the substitution of the three-year-old Mexican Belle for the two-year-old filly, La Lune, entered to run in two races at Doncaster.

The plan my friend Gilbert Marsh and I had formed was simply to run a good horse under the name and reputation of a poor one, so that its chance of winning would be increased a hundredfold.

When Mexican Belle came to me she was a bay with two white legs and a big white face. Once seen she would never be forgotten – unless her appearance were drastically altered.

That is exactly what I did.

Two days before the race I dyed her from bay to brown, carefully touching up her face and legs to match La Lune filly.

Mexican Belle was not the exact replica of La Lune, but the resemblance was good enough to pass muster, and, what was much more important, the disguise was complete. I had no fear that Dick or Stanley Wootton, who I knew were present at the meeting, would recognise the selling plater they had parted with at Folkestone.

We put up K. Robertson, the champion lightweight of his day, and one of the cleverest jockeys I have ever known, though somewhat small – fatally, as it proved to be. Robertson, of course, knew nothing about our little scheme.

The filly was to run on Wednesday and again on Friday. Being an unknown quantity, it was our intention to give her a 'stopper' in the first race, so that she would make a poor show, then with the assistant of some gee-up dope let her come away on the Friday and rake in the winnings.

The stopper which we gave the filly was a dose of laudanum. This I have found makes a horse run sluggishly and sleepily.

On the Wednesday Robertson got La Lune away well, and kept her in the first three until the final stretch.

I had no qualms about what the result would be, though I heard Marsh softly swearing. He knew that if the filly romped home a winner in the first race, it would queer the price for Friday's coup.

His fears were groundless, however, for the best La Lune could do was to finish sixth, and we breathed easy again.

We got her back to her box quickly, and next morning I found her none the worse for her sleeping draught. She was eating well and was frisky, as I like to see a horse, and I was satisfied that she could do the trick on Friday.

The great day dawned, wet and miserable, sloppy underfoot and grey overhead – the sort of day when none but the needy and greedy would go racing except in a case like Doncaster, which, though not a national event, is a county function and attracts thousands of people.

Marsh and I took the filly on the course in the morning, gave her a pipe-opener, and she went freely and pulled up as sound as a bell.

I did not keep her very long in the open, for it was raining heavily, and I was taking no chances with that dye. Besides, I had yet to administer the 'gee-up' dope which would put her in the finest fettle.

I performed this operation half-an-hour before the race. With a hypodermic syringe I gave her four grains of cocaine under the skin.

I then saddled her and left her in charge of a boy, with instructions that he was to hold her head if she got at all excited, and soothe her or send for me.

The filly did get excited, but she soothed herself in a way which proved to be our undoing. The idiot in charge of her evidently did not notice that while she was standing there in the box she was chewing away at one of her reins, which she had got into her mouth.

If he did notice, he must have thought she was partial to leather, and felt that he was rendering us a good turn by indulging her. It is extremely unlikely that he thought at all. I remember the boy; he did not look as if he were capable of any sustained mental effort.

★ ★ ★

The saddling bell rang, and along came Robertson. We led the filly out, and he was hoisted up into the saddle, with instructions to keep with his field, and to come away at the distance and win as far as he liked. I also told him that I could account for her poor show on the Wednesday, and he would find that she ran a different animal from what she was on that day.

In the meantime Marsh was doing the commission. A lot of it was put on 'away', but a considerable amount went on the course, without, however, shortening her price.

There were two very strong favourites in the race, a horse called Magic Wire, trained by Kingsley, which was a hot order at 5 to 4, and Ridgeway, one of Gwilt's, which was at 3 to 1. A third favourite was found in Lovely Nightie, which was 4 to 1.

And it says something for the miserable character of the field that not one of the horses that ran in that race ever won a race of any description except the winner, and he never won afterwards. The betting was 5 to 4, 3 to 1, 3 to 1, and 12½ to 1 others, in which last lot La Lune filly figured, and when I saw the way they were betting, it looked as though a big stake was coming my way.

Now that the race was about to begin, all feeling of tension or suspense left me. I always feel confident that a horse I have set out to win a race with will succeed in romping home, barring accidents. If an accident occurs, that is not my fault and it cannot be helped.

★ ★ ★

The accident to La Lune occurred as soon as the gate flew up and the filly leapt away in front.

I was standing with Marsh near the winning-post, and for a few seconds I couldn't understand what was happening, and wondered what on earth was the matter with Robertson in allowing La Lune to flounder about from one side of the course to another in the way she was doing.

It flashed through my mind that the dope had gone to the filly's head, but I had such complete knowledge of the action of cocaine on horses that I knew that something else must be causing her strange antics.

Then as the field drew nearer I saw that Robinson was leaning over her head as if he were trying to grab something, and all at once I realised the truth.

The chewed rein was broken.

I turned to Marsh. He was staring absolutely dumbstruck at La Lune as she zigzagged down the course.

'It's all up, Marsh,' I muttered. 'The reins are broken. Our luck's dead out.'

He gave a groan and then a mighty swear, for he knew that there was no hope now of our coup coming off.

The filly was absolutely out of control and the cocaine intended to bring the very best out of her succeeded only in making it impossible for Robertson to grab that dangling rein.

If only the jockey had been a little bigger, if only he had been able to get hold of that broken end, we would have won a fortune.

I felt a queer sickening feeling in my stomach as the field flashed past the post with La Lune last.

She was completely out of control and pranced on beyond the post with Robertson quite unable to stop her.

Suddenly Marsh grabbed my arm and pointed to a man running across the track to try to stop the filly.

'Look, Pat,' he gasped. 'Dick Wootton. It's all up now.'

My heart was in my mouth. Did ever any man have such infernally bad luck?

Surely it was bad enough to lose the race after having laid our plans so carefully and spent so much time on their preparation – not to mention the money we had laid out in expenses and most of all in bets. These things in themselves were enough to make a saint swear – but on top of them all a misfortune far more serious seemed about to befall us.

If Dick Wootton stopped La Lune, there was a big chance that he might be struck by a resemblance to Mexican Belle, which he himself had owned.

My mind pictured in that instant everything that would take place – recognition, the discovery that the horse had been dyed – exposure and imprisonment.

'He's caught her!' ejaculated Marsh. 'I think it's time we went, Pat.'

I kept a grip on his arm and stood still. Somehow I felt that we had had enough bad luck for one day.

Dick Wootton held the filly while Robertson dismounted.

'Come on,' I said; 'the sooner we get her away the better.'

I ran over and grabbed La Lune's bridle with a word of thanks to Dick Wootton.

To my amazement he said nothing.

He had not spotted his own horse.

I hurried her away, feeling thankful at least for this good fortune, and got her safely in her box.

Marsh was there waiting for me, and he almost chuckled when I told him how Dick Wootton had been deceived.

Now, you might imagine that I would be in particularly bad odour over this ghastly failure. I refer more especially to the people who had backed the horse knowing it was a fake. Instead of which I had nothing but sympathy, and from people in the know, whose names, were I to mention them, would make your hair stand on end.

It is not my practice, however, to allow myself to be upset by small failures, and in the notorious 'Coat of Mail' case, which figured so prominently in my trial, I succeeded in amply covering my losses.

MY £6,000 SWINDLE

THERE are certain clever authorities who say that the criminally-minded are not sensitive. Personally, I would not confess that I am criminally-minded, even though the sensitiveness which was suspected in me had, as a matter of fact, no existence.

'Pat,' said one of my confederates when we had completed the arrangements for our Stockton job, 'don't you feel scared when you get on to a racecourse, knowing that you've "rung in" a horse, and that at any moment somebody might recognise the animal for what it is?'

My prophetic reply was: 'If I ever go to Dartmoor, I certainly shall not feel embarrassed because I'm amongst thieves.'

As a matter of fact, though all race-goers cannot be classed as thieves, there are few bookmakers who would worry greatly if they learned that a horse was not trying. My exploits were hardly any less honest.

★ ★ ★

And now I come to the Coat of Mail ramp. Coat of Mail was a two-year-old colt in my stable, who had been bought for £40 from a well-known Newmarket trainer. In my handling of Coat of Mail I was a public benefactor, and there are certain fashionable trainers who might profitably follow my example. He was useless for racing, and I did not run him. If all the useless horses that are now being entered for expensive races were similarly treated, the public would lose less money.

We entered Coat of Mail in a race at Stockton. It was my intention from the very start to substitute an older horse for that race, and so to doctor and paint him that his own mother wouldn't have known him. We had a long discussion as to the horse we should choose for the purpose, and it was I who decided upon Jazz, and in these matters my word was law. I chose Jazz because he had an excellent record. He had been beaten a short head by Little Cell, at Gatwick, with Ramboda behind him; while at Stockton he had been beaten three-quarters of a length by Woodhall, with the fast Mount Lebanon beaten out of a place.

From the point of view of his then owner, Sir Hedworth Meux, he wasn't much good for racing. From our point of view, he was an ideal horse. Negotiations were begun, but I refused to accede to the suggestion that Jazz should come straight away to us.

'I want that horse only a few days, and only a few hours before the Stockton race,' I said.

'Are you racing him at Stockton?' asked somebody in horror. 'Why, he was beaten there when well backed, and they are certain to recognise him!'

I laughed. I always had to laugh at their shivers and shrieks.

'That's the place to run him,' I said, 'where all the clever ones are, and there are two or three Stewards of the Jockey Club looking on.'

That is my theory. And it is a sound theory, because, if you take a horse to a little wayside meeting, you're apt to be careless, thinking that it really doesn't matter; there'll be nobody there who will detect you. Whilst if you race at Newmarket, and work a ramp under the eyes of the Stewards of the Jockey Club, you'll not only be careful, but you have the added security that there are so many authorities in the Birdcage that, if one says, 'That isn't the horse it is represented to be,' there will be a hundred other clever ones who will swear that it is.

Two days before the race, Jazz was brought up from Stockbridge and handed over to me at Waterloo Station. He was in excellent condition, as, of course, all horses are that are trained by Persse, who, in addition to being a great trainer, is a great horse-master.

I took the colt from a boy and had a man walk him across London to the station for Stockton, where I put him in a loose box for an hour.

I have a good look at a horse before I start doctoring him; and the sight of Jazz filled me with every confidence. He lay down and rolled, drank a bucket of water and had a feed of oats – just as a horse in good health should do.

I had him boxed myself and accompanied him on the journey to Stockton. He went into the horse-box Jazz, a brown colt by Mushroom, out of Fizzer. He came out Coat of Mail, a bay colt by Roquelaure – Queen of the Dell.

I did all the faking in the box on the journey, and Jazz submitted to his disguising without giving any trouble. Once he turned his head round and had a look at himself, and I thought I detected the look of surprise in his eyes! Perhaps that was imagination.

At any rate, he must have thought it was all for the best, because he gave no trouble, and when I unboxed him at midnight and took him off to the racecourse stable, he was as lively as a cricket, fed up well, and slept like a top.

I saw Gilbert Marsh in the early morning, and told him there was no question as to what the result of the race would be.

'What about the betting?' I asked. 'And how many people are in the secret?'

Of course he protested, like he always protested, that only two or three knew, and that he himself would get all the money on at a remunerative price. The truth was that Gilbert Marsh was so broke, and owed so much money to bookmakers, that he had no credit at all; and, so far from there only being a few people in the swindle, there were 75!

That may sound astonishing, but it is a fact.

★　★　★

I will leave to another chapter the story of Norman Weisz, the unfortunate mug whom we had roped in to help us in our adventures. It is sufficient to say that Weisz was a very rich man – a pearl merchant of Hatton Garden – a mug gambler (he had £200 on a race without taking the trouble to enquire whether he was backing a horse or a cow); and it was through him that Marsh intended doing most of the betting.

It was a case there of 'Heads I win, tails you lose', because if Coat of Mail had been beaten, Weisz would not have got a cent of money from any of us. And, being a mug punter, it followed naturally that his methods were alarmingly crude. I was soon to learn that the big price I expected was a dream.

'Who have we got to ride him?' I asked Marsh.

'William Griggs,' he replied. 'I have arranged that.'

★　★　★

At the subsequent trial, Griggs stated that I had made all the arrangements, and here I think his memory is at fault. Indeed, most of the
witnesses at that trial seemed to forget the existence of Gilbert Marsh
or any part he played.

Just before the race, I went and had a look at Jazz *alias* Coat of
Mail. He was such a good, honest horse – and the issue was so far
beyond doubt – that I did not trouble to give him any 'hurry-up
stuff'. There is a saying: 'Never flog a willing horse.' I will add to
that a new one: 'Never dope a horse that can "do it" without.'

I am not a betting man, but on this occasion I took £100 to £20
on my own, and was very glad I did, because soon after the numbers
went up, telegrams began pouring on to the course from all the
starting-price offices, backing Coat of Mail. The 75 honest gentlemen who were in Gilbert Marsh's secret were laying down the
money with a vengeance, and if the race had been delayed a few
minutes' longer, there is no doubt that Coat of Mail would have
started odds on.

I saw Marsh, and had a long talk with him.

'You're a great organiser,' I said sardonically, as the price began
tumbling down.

I told Griggs to stay with his horses until they were well in the
line for home, and then to come away and win by a length or two;
but as soon as the gate went up, Coat of Mail leapt forward like a
shot from a gun, and a yell came from the ring: 'It's not a horse;
it's a blinking aeroplane!' He won the race from start to finish,
ending up three lengths ahead of the second.

★   ★   ★

Of course, there was a crowd round the unsaddling enclosure to
have a look at this wonder horse. A certain writer in a well-known
sporting newspaper wrote a paragraph to the effect that this was
one of the best two-year-olds seen out in the North since the beginning of the season, and held out rosy prospects for his future!

Griggs, when he got down, said:

'This is the best two-year-old I have ever ridden. What is he
worth?'

'Thousands,' I said solemnly, and I hoped I was speaking the
truth. But he only started at 5 to 2, though he opened in the
market at 20 to 1. If fewer people had been in the secret, and the

commission had been worked intelligently, we should have packed up £40,000. As it was, we cleared about £5,000 or £6,000.

It was not much of a secret; for, in addition to the 75, there must have been 75,000 hangers-on who knew all about the horse, and, after the event, whenever I walked down Coventry Street, I was certain to meet half-a-dozen people who would pull me up, and, fingering my jacket, would say:

'That's a nice coat of mail you've got on, Barrie. But you've had it dyed?'

★   ★   ★

My share of the swag was £500, and I think that I was about the only member of the gang who earned it. We had made enough, however, to show what could be done, and then and there we began to plan for ringing in Shining More at a race at Cheltenham; and the story of Shining More is the most remarkable and, to me amusing, story of Turf fraud that has ever been told.

FAKING A 10 TO 1 WINNER

I AM now going to tell you the story of a horse – one of the many that came under my care – that had the faculty of being in two places at once. In fact, I'm not sure that, on occasions, Shining More wasn't in three places!

In what follows I have set out the particulars of the Cheltenham race in which Shining More ran as Silver Badge so that the reader can follow my narrative with greater ease. Shining More was a bay mare, and extremely suitable for our purpose.

'What are you going to do with her?' asked one of my over-anxious friends.

'I'm going to run her at Cheltenham,' was the reply, and there was a gasp of horror.

'But Shining More has won at Cheltenham, and Gwilt, her former trainer, is a great patron of the meeting, and he's certain to recognise her. Besides, everybody in racing – including the Stewards of the National Hunt Committee – will be there.'

So they argued, and I listened patiently, for patience is my long suit. When they had all finished, I said:

'Shining More runs at Cheltenham. I haven't decided what she will run as, or what sort of appearance she will make; but this I guarantee that neither Gwilt nor any other person will recognise Shining More by the time I've done with her!'

★ ★ ★

I think I have mentioned before that Gilbert Marsh was incapable, owing to his bad credit in the ring, of working the commissions which he had so glibly promised should be put on at the last moment. We had found a gentleman who I will describe as 'the prize-mug of the world', and this in no spirit disparaging to him, for Norman Weisz was a good fellow, sublimely ignorant about racing, though he thought he knew a great deal. Incidentally, Weisz was the most innocent man that has ever been sent to prison, for he was neither in our swindles, nor was he aware that the horses we told him to back on our behalf were anything but straight propositions.

Weisz was practically ordered to go to Cheltenham, with instructions to back the horse on the course, and when she won, to buy her in, for we intended to run her in a selling plate, where she would be meeting a much lower class of animal than she had ever met before.

I was never wholly in favour of Weisz being entrusted with these commissions, and what little uneasiness I had was due to this reason:

'Gilbert,' I once said to Marsh, 'I would sooner have a rogue than a fool in this business.'

But he was much too hard-pressed to change his plans; besides which, if we hadn't had Weisz, I don't exactly know who we would have got to do the betting.

The 'character' in which Shining More was to make her appearance at Cheltenham gave me considerable thought. The glamour of the Army was still upon the people, and I decided upon the most picturesque disguise that I had ever yet attempted. Shining More must appear as a cast-off Army horse; and, having found a nominal owner, we also found its name, because the man who was supposed to be the proprietor of this gallant charger was an ex-officer who was running a factory which he called the Silver Badge factory.

'That is what we will call her – "Silver Badge",' said I.

★   ★   ★

And now that I had made up my mind on this point, I entered light-heartedly into the business of disguising the horse.

And here I might remark that it is no offence to dye a racehorse, unless one is, as I was, in the secret of the swindle that was about to be attempted. First of all, Shining More had to have the Army brand on her quarters; and I hasten to add, lest there be any idea that I hurt the horse, that I did no more than singe the hair – it would have been bad business to have done anything else, because I had need of Shining More for future engagements. Similarly, I lightly burnt military numbers on her hoofs, with a jolly old broad arrow to show that she was genuinely released from military service.

In all these ramps, timing is everything, and I arranged to bring Shining More to Cheltenham about half an hour before the race started. I brought her down myself in the horse-box, and in the course of the journey changed her colour to black, stained her hoofs, and completed the alteration of her appearance – which included a shaping of her mane and tail; this was done, however, before the journey started.

On to the course at Cheltenham came Silver Badge, black mare, pedigree unknown. She had not to walk in the ring for very long, but during that brief space of time she attracted considerable attention, and I, for one, did not quiver so much as an eyelid when Mr. Gwilt, who had had her in his stable for some time, strolled across and had a good look at her.

★ ★ ★

Weisz had gone into the ring, and his first bet was made under peculiar circumstances, which, at first glance, would suggest that he knew all about the 'ring in'. He approached a bookmaker and asked the price of the favourite and when this was offered, shook his head.

'Give me some good outsider I can get 10 to 1 about,' he said, and the bookmaker, looking at his card, pointed: 'Here's one – Silver Badge,' he said, and Weisz took 500 to 50.

Of course, he was only being tactful and 'clever' for he believed me implicitly when I told him that I had found this extraordinary horse by chance, and that he had cleared out everything in the stable.

'There is one thing you must do, Norman, and that is, buy the horse in, whatever she fetches,' I told him earnestly, just before the betting started. 'We may have a Grand National winner, and I don't want to let her go.'

And he, poor soul! believed that our anxiety to retain the horse was due to its superlative merit. There was another cause!

I put up Hulme to ride her, and he looked disgustedly at the Army marks just before he mounted.

'There will be a little present for you when you win,' I said.

'A little present!' he scoffed. 'Do you think I'm going to win on this poor old hair-trunk?'

'Never mind about "hair-trunk",' I replied. 'This mare can jump and go.'

'Do you want her ridden any particular way?' he asked, and I told him to come away for the first mile, then ease his horse, and bring her along at the last mile to win, and the sound of his sarcastic laughter is in my ears as I write.

Well, to cut a long story short, old Silver Badge, most wonderful of remounts, won in a hack canter, starting at 10 to 1. It cost Norman £600 to retain the animal, but we could well afford that little outlay, for we had won a tidy stake. As soon as the sale was over, I had her sheeted and taken straight away off the course to the railway station.

Weisz, of course, was delighted. He was a man who had consistently lost money, and the fact that he had won a bit – and a big bit – gave him the greatest satisfaction. But I always think that it was the knowledge that he owned this wonderful horse which was his chief source of gratification, particularly when some of the newspapers came out the next day with graphic and glowing stories of the old remount, who, rescued by a clever trainer from the ignominious end which awaits old Army horses, had come out of fashionable Cheltenham and beaten selling-plate brothers at their own game.

★   ★   ★

How innocent Weisz was! He was so completely in the dark as to the swindle that, on the following Sunday, when we were working Heaven knows how hard to get the dye off the mare in order to prepare her for another race in her own name, along he came with a friend of his.

'Barrie, I've brought Mr. —— over to see that old Army horse that everybody's talking about. Bring her out, and let us see her, will you?'

I looked at him open-mouthed. Bring out a horse that was black in one place and bay in another? Bring out that dappled and fearful-looking beast for the friends of Weisz to see? Not much!

'I'm very sorry, Mr. Weisz,' said I, in my best trainer manner, 'but the mare's leg has filled, and I've sent her away into the country to recuperate. We shall certainly get another race out of her,' I said, when I saw the look of consternation in his face, 'and don't worry about her. She's quite all right, and I think I've dealt with the disease in time.'

So Weisz had to be content and go away, leaving us to the arduous business of restoring Shining More to her old colours. And it was some job! When I dye, I dye, and neither rain nor thunder nor lightning can change the horse's colour. Nothing but week after week of hard rubbing, with special chemicals, can change his appearance.

I had entered Shining More in her own name for a race at Plumpton, and we had engaged that famous and brilliant amateur, Captain Bennet, to ride her. This was the Saturday following Good Friday of 1920. We had also entered her for a race at Manchester. There was some doubt as to which Manchester race we should choose, but the moment I saw the list of races I fixed on one.

MY MOST IMPUDENT SWINDLE

I ALWAYS planned every coup from start to finish except the betting; and if the betting had been in my hands and I'd had time to scheme out that side of the business, not only should we have been rich men, but we should never have been caught.

The Shining More campaign was my own; and naturally, those who were in with me began to get scared when they saw the difficulty we had in restoring Shining More to her natural colour.

'You'll never get that dye off in time for Plumpton,' said Marsh irritably. 'We shall have to give that race a miss.'

★   ★   ★

But I was particularly anxious not to give Plumpton a miss. The race was on the Saturday following Good Friday, when all the lovers of the jumping game were assembled, and I wanted them to see Shining More, in the same way as a conjurer wishes the audience to see the inside of a hat to show that there is no deception!

We got Shining More clean at last, and the old mare – she didn't seem to care very much what colour she was – went well in a gallop a few days before the race, and I thought that, if she didn't win, she would be placed. To leave nothing to chance, half an hour before the race I gave her just a gentle 'gee-up' with a couple of grains of cocaine.

Captain Bennet was put up to ride Shining More, and a real good race she ran, though she did not win, finishing third in a huge field. But Plumpton was not my objective. My eyes were steadfastly fixed upon the Cheetham Handicap at Manchester on the following

Monday; and in order to win that race, and to supplement our gains, I had planned the most audacious piece of villainy in my career.

*   *   *

As usual, when a big coup was in the course of organisation, the nerves of the confederacy got on edge. There was one big book-maker in our gang (he has since died, and no useful purpose would be served by throwing mud at his memory) who was absolutely terrified.

'I shall be betting at Kempton,' he said, 'and all the time I shall be worrying what's happening at Manchester. Don't you realise, Barrie, that the whole National Hunt Committee will be in the North, watching the Lancashire Steeplechase?'

'That's what I like,' I said. 'If I knew any of the National Hunt Committee weren't going to be present I'd send them a wire!'

'You're raving mad,' said Marsh. 'I agree with ——. You're too reckless. Can't you keep these fakes for smaller meetings?'

It was the same old story, and I was wearied of hearing this ancient argument, wearied of returning my inevitable reply.

'I hope,' said I, 'that when Shining More comes back into the unsaddling ring, every member of the National Hunt Committee will have a front place on the rails. I should like Shining More's previous owner and trainer to be in the unsaddling enclosure to give her a good look over. I hope the Press will be there in force, and that Shining More will be photographed from every angle. I never feel so confident as when I am surrounded by clever people.'

What was the trouble about? What was the cause of the agitation? It was simply this, that, whilst I had taken Shining More to Chelten-ham and called her Silver Badge, I was now going to take another mare to Manchester and call her Shining More!

Accurate timing was everything. Horses must be at a certain place at a certain moment, so that the change could be made without anybody being the wiser.

*   *   *

The mare I had fixed upon as being as nearly like Shining More as possible was a mare that was running in Ireland – a most excellent performer, fast over hurdles, a safe jumper, and, in her class, infi-nitely better than anything in the Cheetham Handicap. I had been over to Ireland before the Plumpton race and completed my arrangements.

And here let me say, in case you are disappointed because I do not give you the name of the mare, its owner and its trainer, that in these reminiscences I steadfastly refuse to 'shop' anybody who has not already been in the limelight. They were as guilty as me, but that has nothing to do with the matter. It is not my job to play policeman.

So tremble not in your shoes, dear Irish friends, at the thought that Barrie is going to give you away. And you, member of a great family, respected from one end of the country to the other, do not go abroad hurriedly, for Barrie is no squeaker! You were in the fraud and you got away with the stuff – good luck to you! I did three years, and I am not going to say anything that will bring the gates of Dartmoor any nearer than they are to you.

★ ★ ★

One look at the mare was quite good enough for me. She was the ideal animal for my purpose. I examined her from head to foot, noted how she walked, made a mental photograph of her legs, her hoofs, the colour and length of her mane, the stance of her tail, the prick of her ears; and I was satisfied that, with a little change here and a little twist there, Shining More would be reborn in this good performer.

She arrived at Liverpool and went on to a place near Manchester. Shining More, after the Plumpton race, was officially reported to have gone on to the same venue, but in reality the old mare travelled westward; and when she was supposed to be engaged in the strenuous business of race-running, she was, as a matter of fact, kicking up her heels in a paddock and enjoying herself as a thoroughbred horse can enjoy itself, even on Easter Monday.

★ ★ ★

It was I who brought the mare on to the Manchester racecourse, for I had decided that on this occasion it would not be wise to put up Captain Bennet, who was a keen horseman and, although he might be deceived by appearance, would not be so easily deceived once he got astride of something which he was supposed to have ridden on the previous Saturday.

I brought her out ready saddled, got into my riding kit, and weighed out. On the way to 'get up' an acquaintance stopped me.

'I see you're riding Shining More today, Barrie, but I don't think you'll do much better than Bennet did. He was rather surprised to hear you had sent her up after that severe race on Saturday.'

'Is he riding?' I asked, for I did not until then realise that he had a mount in the race.

As it happened, we both mounted at the same time and went out of the paddock together. Bennet took in the mare at a glance.

'That's a nice little thing you're riding, Barrie,' he said. 'What is it?'

'Well, you ought to know – you rode her on Saturday,' I replied, as bold as brass.

His eyebrows went up.

'Oh! Is that Shining More? I never had a good look at her before. I thought she was a bigger animal than that.'

'She'll be big enough by the time this race is over,' said I, and cantered away from him, for I wasn't anxious to continue this conversation.

He was riding Wisp, which shared joint favouritism with Piggott's mount, Palmer's Hill. The other horse, ridden by Watkinson, Corso, was second favourite; whilst Shining More, ridden by that redoubtable gentleman jockey, Mr. Peter Christian Barrie, opened at tens and came down to 6 to 1. The distance was two miles four furlongs; and with the exception of Palmer's Hill, I was giving weight away all round.

I knew what a good 'un I was on the moment my knees gripped her, but I had no idea how good she was until the flag fell and we went over the first flight of hurdles together. Thence onwards I had all my work cut out to hold her, for she was a two-stone-better mare than anything in the race. Eventually I shot out, and, despite all my efforts to lessen the distance, won in a hack canter by ten lengths.

'Bravo, Shining More!' said some mug who had backed her, as I rode into the paddock.

'That's a good horse you rode, Mr. Barrie,' said an official of the Manchester executive after I had weighed in. 'Do you know that I've backed her every time she's run?'

'I'd like to bet that you haven't!' said I to myself – but I was wise enough not to speak my thoughts aloud.

★ ★ ★

There, so far, ends the history of Shining More. I took her eventually to Scotland, where there occurred an incident which may be briefly recorded before I get on to the next swindle.

Shining More was extensively tipped to win a Scottish race, and I went there with the intention of winning. When I arrived on the course, I was approached by a big bookmaker, who said significantly. 'Is a monkey any good to you, Barrie?'

I replied that £500 was always good to me, under any circumstances.

'Where is the money?' I asked.

He handed over five £100 notes and I put them into my pocket and no other word was uttered. But I am well acquainted with the methods of a certain type of bookmaker. I lost my race, but it was a devil of a job to lose it!

To this day I recall the howls of the frenzied backers of Shining More.

HOW WE TRICKED DONOGHUE

A T this moment Steve Donoghue is engaged in writing the story of his life. But Donoghue can only write what he knows. The secret history of events which affected him is unknown to this brilliant rider, and I now tell him that, on one occasion unknown to him, he was engaged to help me carry out a swindle! For at Liverpool, in November, 1919, Donoghue won a race on a dyed horse and was none the wiser! Yes, innocent of the fact that he was being victimised by my little gang, he rode a horse to victory.

He can put that in his reminiscences – I present him with a romance from real life.

★ ★ ★

This was one of the fakes I worked in 1919–20 during which £119,000 passed through my banking account, £39,000 going into one account (I had several) in the first six months of 1920. And Donoghue, unwittingly, contributed at least a thousand! It happened in this way.

I had in my stable, round about this time, a little horse, the name of which I will not divulge because it is still racing 'in another place'. He was the cheeriest, most honest little fellow that ever looked through a bridle. Sometimes he ran in his own name, but more than often he ran in names that never were on land or sea. No swindler ever stood up in the dock of the Old Bailey with more aliases than my little fellow had!

If I had put him in a selling race under his own name, we should have had to buy our money. He would have started at 3 or 4 to 1 on, all the opposition would have been frightened away, and it would have cost more to buy him in than we could possibly have won. I could, and did, race him under his own name, and win with him. But when we had our betting boots on, we did not want any might-have-beens.

★   ★   ★

Any trainer I employed who came to me and said: 'I think your horse has a wonderful chance of winning, but, of course, I can't be absolutely certain', would have been as much use to me as a boil on the neck. I very very seldom bet, but when I do, I want some-thing that has got the race won before the tapes go up. And my little friend usually supplied that certainty whenever he was slipped into a selling race.

Our coups were often made at short notice; which meant a tremendous amount of work for me; for not only had a horse to be dyed the colour required, and his appearance so altered that he could not be recognised, but there came in the question of the meeting of trains, the exact arrival of the interchangeable horses at the selected rendezvous, and all that entailed a tremendous amount of organisation.

One day, looking through the Calendar, I saw a little selling race at Liverpool, the Ford Welter Handicap.

'What chance has The Squire of winning this race?' I asked Marsh.

'Let me have a look at the Calendar,' he said, and after a glance he shook his head. 'I shouldn't think Squire had got an earthly chance,' he added, and looked up the book.

The Squire had won an apprentice race at Newcastle, beating a lot of shockingly bad horses. Previously to that he had run unplaced.

'He might win it, of course,' said Marsh, 'but he's nothing to bet on. He's been heavily backed before, and has failed. I wouldn't like to risk a monkey on him.'

I turned up the book and found that he was in Burns' stable in Scotland. That night one of the crowd got on to Burns, calling him out of bed, and pitched a tale about a man who wanted to buy a little horse that might possibly win a race, asking if The Squire was for sale.

The long and the short of it was that, a day or two afterwards,

The Squire, who was a brown gelding, was purchased and was ordered to be sent down to Liverpool to fulfil his selling-plate engagement.

★　★　★

This was on 5 November. In the meantime the little changeling had run under his own name at Alexandra Park, and had run very well, being close to the winner.

Once The Squire was obtained, my little horse had to be changed to a nice rich brown, and I made a hurried journey, though the innocent Mr. Burns was not aware of the fact, to have a look at The Squire at exercise, and take a mental photograph of his points, peculiarities and colour. This done, I got back to Liverpool.

The two horses arrived in that town within an hour of one another. I took delivery: the real The Squire was sent to a quiet place, whilst the camouflaged The Squire, looking remarkably like the horse he was impersonating, was taken up to the course.

In the early morning one of the crowd came to me in a state of agitation.

'Burns is here,' he said. 'Can't you get him back to Scotland?'

This wasn't as difficult a proposition as it sounds. When we ran La Lune filly at Doncaster (or rather when we ran Mexican Belle as La Lune filly) we found that Farquharson was on the spot, and he was the one man who, it was very necessary, should not see the filly, because he had had her in his stable for some time, and he knew that she was a little horse, whilst Mexican Belle was fully grown. If Mr. Farquharson will recall the circumstances of that day at Doncaster, he will remember that, just before racing, he received an urgent wire from his home calling him back – only to discover that the wire was a fake, and that not only was there nothing serious at home, but nobody knew anything about the wire.

I, myself, followed him to the station, and saw him get into the train. Thus I have pleasure in solving one little mystery in Mr. Farquharson's life, and I take this opportunity of apologising to him, a real good sportsman, an honest trainer and a gentleman, for the trick which we played.

★　★　★

But it was impossible to get to Scotland in time to recall Burns. Nor would I have done so if I had had the time.

'Never mind about Burns,' I said. 'I defy him or anybody else to distinguish this horse from the one he sold. What is more important, go along to Marsh and find out who is going to ride The Squire. If he hasn't engaged anybody, tell him to put up Steve Donoghue.'

'That'll bring the price down a bit,' said my assistant, to whom I replied that the horse would be a short price anyway, for the field had dwindled down to nothing, and we only had such animals as Skookum Joe to beat.

Steve had to be approached with the greatest caution. He was then, as now, the most sought-after jockey of the day. It was close to the end of the season, when jockeys were striving hard to bring themselves to as near the head of the winning list as possible, and anything that looked like a winning ride was eagerly snapped up by the best of them.

My agent approached Donoghue. He had promised to ride in the race a horse that had not arrived.

'I'll ride The Squire – has he a winning chance?' he asked, and was told that 'The Squire' represented real good business. So the engagement was duly marked down in his book.

We kept the spurious The Squire out of sight until it was necessary to bring him into the ring, and then only when Donoghue was waiting to mount.

'You've got a winning ride here, Donoghue,' said I.

Steve, who knows the book of form backwards, was not so confident. I gave him no instructions, because a man of his ability doesn't want to be told.

★　★　★

However cold-blooded you may be, there is a thrill in a race under the conditions I raced my horses that is like no other. Will he get away? Will something knock him over at the start? Will some unforeseen accident happen, as in the case of La Lune filly at Doncaster? Will the jockey twist the book on you?

With Donoghue up, the first and last-named possibilities could be dismissed. The horse was pretty sure to get away, and Steve was above any doubtful practice.

The delay at the post was a short one. Suddenly there was a flash of white tapes as the 'gate' shot up, and then into his stride dashed The Squire.

What a game little fellow my horse was! I could see him through my glasses, pulling double! The distance was a mile, and Steve had him well placed from the start – the race, I knew, was all over, and I turned with a sigh of relief to Marsh.

'Go and collect your money,' I said, before the field was half-way home. Our horse won in a canter by a length and a half – it might have been ten if Steve had pushed him.

★   ★   ★

So impressive was his performance that it cost us £600 to buy him in. He started at 2 to 1, and Burns was given as the trainer in *Racing Up to Date*, but of course, Burns had nothing whatever to do with the horse when he won at Liverpool. Both he and Donoghue were completely ignorant of the 'ramp' we worked with their assistance.

ATTY PERSSE BLUFFED

AFTER we had worked the Coat of Mail swindle at Stockton, it was suggested that the horse Jazz (who was really Coat of Mail) should be taken out of the country. But Jazz was too good a horse, and much too consistent, to be surrendered by me. The horse had been bought on the understanding that it was not to race on the flat again. It was permissible to run the animal over hurdles; and during the winter that followed, Jazz was turned over to a straight trainer and put into training as a hurdler. He ran twice, without, however, gaining place honours.

He was now, of course, a four-year-old; and whilst I prefer putting a three-year-old into a two-year-old race, as offering the finest margin for successful operations, there is a lot to be said for putting a four-year-old into a three-year-old handicap in the early part of the year, since this at least gives a 14lb. pull.

★ ★ ★

There were two handicaps I had my eye on in the beginning of 1920. The first was the Prince of Wales Stakes at Epsom; the second was a three-year-old handicap at Alexandra Park.

'You can cut out Epsom,' said Marsh immediately. 'I train there and I live there, and I certainly am not going to run a horse under the eyes of trainers and stable-boys who know my animals by sight.'

'It is the last race of the day,' I said, 'and nobody is going to stop behind to have a look at the winner – the stands will be empty when the horse comes back and there'll be practically nobody at all in the unsaddling enclosure. We ought to get a packet, if the commission is properly worked.'

Without worrying very much about what they thought, I had

entered The Clown in the Prince of Wales Stakes. The distance was a mile, which was well within the compass of Jazz, and The Clown had the advantage of having run before, though he had never yet won.

★ ★ ★

He was a brown colt by Black Jester practically the same colour as Jazz, so there was no dyeing required, though it was necessary to make some 'structural alterations' by trimming the mane and tail and by other little touches to bring Jazz into likeness with the substitute horse.

It was, I admit, a pretty audacious scheme of mine to run Jazz, with little or no disguise, under the eyes of trainers who knew The Clown by sight as well as they knew their own horses. Marsh and our trainer were in an agitated state of mind when the horse cantered down to the post. But, as I had prophesied, there were few people in the stands, even to see the last race, for Viaduct, who won the Metropolitan Handicap that afternoon, had hit the majority of punters a real good left-handed one, and it gave me particular satisfaction, when I gazed upon the serried ranks of the bookmakers, smoking their big cigars, to know that, figuratively, I would walk into them in a few moments and bleed them as nearly white as was possible with my bank.

When I say 'I', it is, of course, a figure of speech, for the betting was not done by me, though on this occasion I had £200 on the horse. Marsh, I believe, had considerably more.

There had been a long discussion as to who was to be engaged to ride the horse, and, of course, Donoghue's name had been mentioned.

'No more Donoghue for me, thank you,' I said firmly. 'You can buy security at too heavy a price – I don't want any more 2 to 1 winners!'

Donoghue, of course, was a champion at Epsom, and anything he rides is certain of a large and, from our point of view, unprofitable following. He had won for us on The Squire, and now, by the irony of fate, we were to come up against him and beat what was regarded as one of the greatest racing certainties that had ever run at Epsom.

★ ★ ★

On the morning of the race, our trainer came to me, rather troubled.

'Donoghue is riding Mapledurham, one of Lord Rosebery's horses,' he said, 'and they think it can't get beaten.'

Mapledurham was a four-year-old who had only been beaten a head by Blue Dun, giving weight to that mare. This was at Liverpool, and she had run unplaced since. She had now to give mine well over a stone, and in spite of the fact that she had the great Donoghue up, I was not in the least degree worried as to whether The Clown would beat her.

Remember this, that in the faking of racehorses, it is absolutely necessary that the substitute horse should be a good one. Mere substitution and dyeing and doping will not turn an unfit animal into a winner. There is no magic in racing, not even in crooked racing. But in Jazz I had the goods; he was as fit as hands could make him, and I pacified our unhappy trainer.

'Never mind about your Donoghues and your Mapledurhams,' said I. 'Put Frank Bullock up, and Donoghue won't see the way he's going!'

I based my opinion upon the fact that Mapledurham was a bit jady. I may be mistaken in this, but she certainly ran a jade in the only other race I had seen her running, and, if I remember rightly, she never ran again after Epsom.

★ ★ ★

Marsh was by my side when the race started and he was more than a bit nervous. Right from the start, however, The Clown got away, and all the hopes and fears and doubts which centred round the horse were set at rest. Long before the winning-post was reached I knew The Clown had won.

'Go and collect the winnings,' I said in a laconic tone to Marsh as our horse finished first by three lengths in a hack canter.

There was now only a question of keeping Jazz in training to win another race. I decided to start him at Alexandra Park, which, in spite of its queer shape, is as good a course as there is in the country. So, on the following Monday week, he was sent to Muswell Hill. It had been raining, and the going was very heavy – circumstances which favoured the faked The Clown.

There were two circumstances which might easily have brought about the ruin of our confederacy. The first was that, in the largeness of my heart, I tipped the horse to everybody on the course I knew; and the second was, the presence in the field of a red-hot favourite in Silver Jug – and Silver Jug came from the same stable as Jazz! They were, in fact, stalled in adjoining boxes.

★ ★ ★

Now, horses are not such very intelligent animals, in spite of all that has been written about them. There isn't a half-bred mongrel pup that couldn't give the greatest racehorse that was ever foaled 21 lb; and a beating at the Brain Stakes. But they have the habit of recognition. It has been very embarrassing for me sometimes when an old fellow of mine has started to follow me about on a racecourse, at the very moment when I didn't want anybody to know that he and I were acquainted!

'Keep The Clown away from that thing of Persse's,' I told our trainer, and then learnt, to my surprise, that Atty Persse himself was present at the meeting. Persse is a shrewd natural judge of horseflesh; and our only salvation lay in the efficacy of my system of disguising horses. It was with a sigh of relief that I saw him pass the camouflaged Jazz with no more than a glance at him.

'You'll look a little bit closer when he wins, Mr. Persse,' I thought.

And win he did, much to our financial benefit, and to the vast astonishment of the Chattis Hill stable, whose hot pot was upset. I saw the keen-eyed trainer looking at The Clown with a sort of puzzled expression, and was very glad when I had got the horse boxed and on his way home.

★ ★ ★

It was over this race that I saved a family from being thrown into the street. Just as I was going on the course, I saw a poor, wretched woman leading a child by the hand, down one of the big roads which lead to the course. A miserable-looking man was following them, and I stopped and asked him what the trouble was about, for she was weeping bitterly. He said they'd been up to their landlord, who had given them notice to quit, but the landlord wanted his pound of flesh, and when he was offered £5, the amount they had managed to scrape together, he demanded £12 or nothing. They were going to be turned into the street on the Monday.

'Now come here,' said I. 'Take your fiver, go into the cheap ring at Alexandra Park, and put every penny of it on The Clown. You ought to win twenty pounds. If you lose it,' I said, seeing the look of horror on his face, 'come to me at my hotel and I will give you another fiver.'

I gave him my card and, as I never heard from him again, I presume that the landlord was paid! I know that *my* landlord was!

TURF CROOKS I'VE
TRICKED

GILBERT MARSH is in prison serving a stiff sentence for some of his many sins. He was a clever crook, one of the cleverest, in fact, I have ever met, and that is saying something, yet there was one man who could have taught him a lot.

That man was his brother D'Arcy. He could well have claimed the title 'King of Grafters'.

D'Arcy was the man who financed Billie Carleton, and it was D'Arcy who went into her room where she lay dead and collected the jewellery she wore, which belonged to him. There was no limit to his craft and cunning, and nearly all the schemes he pulled off were remarkable for the audacity and ingenuity with which they were carried into effect.

But despite this, I had the extreme satisfaction of tricking D'Arcy Marsh and his gang in as neat a fashion as it is possible to imagine.

When this happened, I was nearly broke. My possessions consisted of £40 'ready', 30s. in the bank, some smart clothes, and a nomination for a mythical horse called 'John Vance' in a race at Phœnix Park, Dublin. There wasn't such a horse. He had to materialise, and I decided that he would materialise out of D'Arcy Marsh's stable.

Now at this time I only knew Gilbert Marsh slightly, and had no idea that D'Arcy was his brother.

What I did know, and what I was interested in, was that D'Arcy was apparently a very rich man who had run through a fortune of £100,000 but still had plenty of money and a string of horses in training at Epsom.

★　★　★

In the role of Major Wilkins, racehorse owner and mug-punter, I had made the acquaintance of two steeplechase jockeys – a poor chap who was killed in France last year, and a gentleman rider whose name is today amongst the most famous cross-country riders. These men both knew D'Arcy Marsh very well, so I approached them both with the object of getting an introduction.

'I want to meet Mr. D'Arcy Marsh,' I said. 'There's a little animal of his which I'd like to strike a bargain for.'

The gentleman rider grinned.

'You won't get much of a bargain out of Marsh,' he replied. 'I know him pretty well, and if I were you I would be mighty careful in my dealings with him, Major. He's too wise for you.'

I insisted, for I had set my mind on that horse, and simply had to get him, or rather the use of him, and without parting with my £40 either.

Seeing that I was determined, the gentleman rider agreed to give me the required introduction, and on a certain night there arrived at D'Arcy's flat that man of wealth and substance, Peter Christian Barrie, *alias* Major Wilkins, of the Australians.

I dressed well – that was part of my graft. A good tailor writes the best letter of introduction. D'Arcy and his crowd took me in with one glance. They saw the easiest 'kill' in the world – a fly mug, who thought he knew it all, and so they gave me a royal welcome.

The champagne fizzed and bubbled for the 'good fellow' who had suddenly dropped from heaven, and when the 'good fellow' started boasting of how clever he was, it looked as if my money was in their pockets. I wasn't anxious to play cards, and, like the good grafters they were, they did not press me.

'The truth is,' said I, 'I wanted to meet you with the idea of buying a few horses – or at least one horse.'

'I would do anything to oblige you, Major,' said D'Arcy Marsh. 'Do you bet much?'

I shook my head.

'Not a great deal,' I said. 'I have a few bookmakers' accounts, and my limit is £400 a week, but I couldn't keep that up for more than a season.'

★ ★ ★

I could almost see their ears prick up at this. £400 a week! A man who could afford to lose that much for a season would show a fine profit if he was handled right.

'Not that I should lose that much,' I hastened to add. 'I'm not a mug.'

'I've never met anybody who looked less like a mug,' said Marsh. 'Have another drink, Major?'

'No, thank you. I like to keep my head clear. No, I know almost all that can be known about racing – they can teach me nothing in this country. I understand horses, and the fellow who tries to put one over on me has got to get up early in the morning. I can ride a bit, and it is my ambition to win the Grand National on my own horse.'

This is the kind of talk I handed out, and here let me say that it is the 'mug talk' that lands so many 'clever' men in trouble. The real grafter likes nothing better than to meet a victim who prides himself on his cunning. They are easier than young men from the country.

'If I had a few decent horses just now,' I said, 'I would soon show you the way to win races. But my present lot aren't much good.'

D'Arcy pricked his ears up at this.

'I have a horse in my stable that would win a race,' he mentioned carelessly.

'What's its name?' I asked.

'Siller,' he replied.

Now, Siller was the very horse I was after. He was, I think, a cast-off from Mr. (now Sir Edward) Hulton's stable. I always remember him because his dam was Money Down. Why I should remember that you will discover.

★ ★ ★

'What do you want for him?' I asked, and he named a price which was in the region of £400.

I told him I'd seen the animal, and thought too that she could do good if ridden properly.

'I wouldn't mind buying him,' I said. 'The only thing is that I should like to take delivery early tomorrow morning, as I'm going over to Phœnix Park, and want to try him out before I leave. You can't trust these stable-boys, and I'm a very good judge of pace.'

'That's easily fixed,' he replied. 'I can arrange that right now if you like. I'll phone the stable and give you a letter to my trainer.'

This suited me exactly. All that now remained to be done was to get the payment settled.

'That's a deal, then,' I said. 'Now how about the money?'

As I spoke, I pulled my £40 out of my pocket. It consisted of two £20 notes, wrapped round a thick roll of paper that wasn't notes at all. It looked like the wad of a millionaire.

'I haven't got much "ready" on me,' I remarked, modestly. 'I expect I'll need most of this tonight, and yet I can't very well ask you to take a cheque.'

'My dear Major, a cheque is as good as a bank-note to me,' said Marsh, and so with 30s. to my credit I wrote a cheque for £400.

★   ★   ★

After he had phoned the stable to make the necessary arrangements and given me the letter of authority to collect 'Siller', I renewed my talk about myself and my racing propensities, and they listened politely.

'I can see that you're an unusual type of sportsman,' said Marsh, 'and I'd like to see some more of you. Come up some evening.'

Of course, I said I would. Poor D'Arcy! He swallowed the pill he was gilding for me. He was a crook, and his peculiar graft was and is repugnant to me, but he had many likeable qualities.

Early in the morning I took the horse, but instead of putting him into my stable – as Marsh imagined – I hurried him off to Euston, where I had engaged a special horse-box. Before the Marshes were awake, Siller was *en route* to Holyhead.

And on the journey his colour changed, and so did the appearance of his mane and tail. He passed across to Ireland in the disguise of a hack, but it was as 'John Vance' (I am not giving the real name because somebody else is involved) that he appeared at Phœnix Park.

I only had my £40 to bet with, but I had credit from a dozen course bookmakers, and thus I was able to back my very dark horse to win me £1,800.

The race was a good one, and there was a bit of a scramble at the start, but Siller came away well, and as the field approached I could see my £1,800 coming nearer and nearer.

In the last hundred yards my little fancy stretched himself and surprised everybody except me by leaving the rest standing and winning in a canter, for the form in Ireland was two stone behind English form.

★　★　★

As soon as the horse had left the unsaddling enclosure, and was rubbed down, I whisked him back to Kingstown and on to the boat.

There was the danger that, when he found that the cheque was dishonoured, Marsh might get in touch with the police, but it was more likely that he would first look for me to get his money or horse. I was determined that it should be the horse.

On my arrival at Holyhead I sent a wire to Marsh, which ran:

'My cheque no good. Your horse very good. I am returning him.'

And back to Epsom Siller went, with all the dye on him. In fact, when he did arrive the trainer did not recognise him and refused to take delivery! However, D'Arcy Marsh had a sense of humour, and his only reproach when I met him later, was:

'Why didn't you let me into the swindle, Barrie?'

If D'Arcy had lived he would never have been caught. He was shrewd and careful; a grafter with the brain of a general. Certainly, had he lived, he would never have shielded himself behind Norman Weisz, as Gilbert did when he allowed a perfectly innocent man to go to gaol for an offence of which he knew no more than a babe unborn.

In the hope that I may yet undo something of the terrible injustice which was meted out to our poor innocent victim, Norman Weisz, I will make the fullest confession of the part he played.

THE 'MUG' WHO
WENT TO JAIL

EVEN crooks have their day-dreams, and the best of all these
is one in which there appears a mug with money. I have met
many in my life, and perhaps never so complete an innocent
as Norman Weisz.

Poor Norman Weisz! A man holding a good position, a rich man,
an innocent man, whose only offence was that he was a tool for
rascals like myself and Marsh, was sent to prison for twelve months!

I cannot quite recall my first meeting with Weisz. Marsh saw him
first, and for him he was a veritable godsend. At this time Gilbert
Marsh had run through most of his money, and was owing the
bookmakers thousands of pounds. He owned horses, it is true, but
he could not bet on them. It came to a point where he could not
even run them. In these circumstances Gilbert looked around for
somebody who would bet for him, and ill-chance brought our
unfortunate victim in his path.

Norman Weisz was a prosperous pearl merchant of Hatton Garden
and a mug-punter, as I would describe any man who bets in large
sums on horses he knows nothing about, or on the advice of people
he doesn't know.

★ ★ ★

When the Coat of Mail swindle was 'up' for discussion, I asked
Gilbert how he was going to get the money on, for I knew by now
that he was as near broke as made no difference.

'Don't worry,' he said. 'I've got a peach of a fellow in tow – a
man who will bet with both hands when I tell him.'

And then I heard for the first time about this champion innocent. I had met him, of course, and knew that he was a pigeon ready for plucking, but I thought he was 'wise' to the game. But the truth is, Weisz knew nothing! He was as innocent as you. He knew no more than that Gilbert Marsh was a great 'owner' and that I was a 'gentleman jockey'.

I could give you a hundred instances to prove this, but the little story I have already told of how Weisz came down to my stables and brought friends to see the wonderful 'Silver Badge' (which was Shining More, as you know) at a moment when the horse was piebald with dye, is proof enough.

We had to 'work' on him, of course; we gave him little sweeteners to keep him going, and it was I who prevented one of the gang from killing the goose that was laying the golden eggs. I have often thought how much better it would have been for this unhappy man if I had not interfered.

What happened was this: one day Weisz came to dinner with us. He was leaving the next morning for the Continent, and he displayed to us a bag containing £60,000 worth of pearls. We had seen the bag before, and it was easily duplicated. On such occasions Weisz put the bag between his feet whilst he was dining, and the plan put up was that, whilst we were at dinner, the bag should be hooked away from under the table and another put in its place.

To this scheme I objected. I had a sort of sneaking regard for the jeweller; and my gorge, which is not particularly delicate, rose at the idea. And so we spared him, and put upon him a greater loss – the loss of his good name and character.

★ ★ ★

Weisz was useful in many ways.

He was not always betting on faked horses. One day we got him to Sandown Park to bet for us on a perfectly straight 'un – Shining More running under his own name. And thereby hangs a tale.

We were all more or less broke, and a 'tickle' was absolutely necessary. I forget now whether we doped the horse or not – at any rate, bar accidents, we were on money to nothing.

But there was another scoundrel with a horse in the race; a well-known owner, who had been in a few of our swindles and knew just about enough to hang us, if he squeaked. Just before we went out of the paddock, he sent his secretary with a message.

'Barrie, if you win, the governor will squeak. He has got £2,000 on his horse and he's got to win.'

We were in a pretty tangle. Our money was on, and there was no escape. We knew the man well enough to know that he would keep his word. He was merciless.

'Very good,' thought I, 'if we don't win, you shan't.' And throughout the race my mind was intent on only one thing – to keep Mr.——'s horse out of the spoils. It required some doing, for I knew that the jockey would report to his master any open attempt to bump him, screw him off at the hurdles, or any other little trick which is indulged in by riders in the 'gentleman's game'.

As it was, the other scoundrel's horse was beaten a head, with my horse beaten a head for third place! But it was Weisz who lost.

When the inevitable happened, and a talkative jockey and a betting detective brought about my downfall, Weisz, who had bought in one of our ringers, was arrested as a member of the gang, whilst Marsh, by the judicious expenditure of money, was kept out of the case.

★　★　★

Morality in my mouth would seem hypocrisy, but I do not think that in the long history of crime there has ever been so flagrant a case as the shopping of Weisz. He could have been kept out of the case too, but the affair was badly managed. He believed implicity that his innocence would be so apparent at his trial that no conviction would follow. Even now I hope I may do something to help secure the free pardon that he deserves.

What secured Weisz's conviction more than anything else were the vicious attentions of Gill, the counsel of the Jockey Club. He left no stone unturned to get this unfortunate man sent down.

I declare on my oath that Weisz knew nothing of any swindle; that he was not privy to any of our roguery; that he was deliberately kept in the dark by Marsh and me; that, until the day of his arrest, he had no idea that anything was wrong.

I have nothing to gain by making this statement. I have not seen Mr. Weisz since my release from prison, and do not even know if he is in England.

Weisz was rooked by the gang of something like £10,000 – that doesn't sound like a confederate, does it? He was the banking account of every impecunious member, and when he won, he won only a little. When he lost, he lost the lot.

When we backed a 'changeling' it was our practice to go to Weisz with a story that never failed to convince him.

'Norman,' I said, when we decided on the Silver Badge ramp, 'I've found a wonder! An old Army mare that can go like the wind!'

'An old Army mare?' he said incredulously. 'But how on earth did the owner part with her?'

I told a cock-and-bull story about this horse having been requisitioned at the beginning of the war from a racing stable, and he swallowed it – bones and all!

'This one may win a Grand National,' I said. 'In fact, there is no knowing what she *can* do.'

On another occasion one of the gang, who was desperately hard up, drifted into his office with a story about a 'job' that was going to be worked at Leicester.

'Put me on a hundred, Mr. Weisz,' said the sharp, giving him the name of a horse that he had picked out of the morning newspaper. By luck it won!

That was the kind of man he was. Generous, unsuspicious, pathetically proud of knowing 'clever' people like the Marshes and having his opinion sought after.

We never let him in at all when we had the money to bet 'ready'. Over The Clown at Epsom and Alexandra Park he won nothing. At every killing, he was the burnt offering – and he paid up.

Gill is dead, and I want to say nothing harsh about him; but to my mind, all his achievements in the law do not compensate for having sent an innocent man to gaol.

★　★　★

Let me say a few words about racing in this country.

First of all, let me say that racing is cleaner in England than it is in any part of the world. That horses are doped, we know. You can hardly prevent isolated cases. That there are 'ringers' is also true. A whisper has come to me that a 'ringer' (by which I mean a horse that wasn't the horse he pretended to be) won at a small N.H. meeting on Easter Monday, and I suppose such things will continue

to happen. So far as I am concerned, I am out of any active partici-
pation in the game, though I take a very large interest in the efforts
of certain people I know. I shall sit at home and tip winners, in the
main, straight horses.

I will give one word of advice to backers. The only certain way
of winning is to back a three-year-old horse running in a two-year-
old race!

There is no other absolute certainty, though it is possible with
the right kind of information checked by a knowledge of the game
to make money by racing. I have made thousands. I shall probably
make thousands more. You never know your luck.

HORSES DIZZY WITH DOPE

ONE of the questions which are always coming to me from friends is: 'How do you dope a horse, and what effect does the dope have?' They want to know what is the dope most generally used, and how. All I will tell you is, that dope, in the hands of an amateur, is deadly – to himself. A horse requires just the right amount and no more; and the horse has to be studied, his temper, character and habits carefully noted, and he has to be tried with and without dope two or three times before the actual race, unless you want to come unstuck.

Whenever I doped a horse, I tried to get one that was already a drug fiend. And there are many! I have bought horses out of selling plates that were so dizzy with cocaine that it is a wonder how I got them home. And they belonged to quite respectable trainers, believe me!

I could generally tell from the animal's eyes and his breathing, not only what he has had, but how he has had it. A chronic dope subject you can always tell by passing your hand across his coat. If it is hard and dry, and you can't find some other reason for this condition, you may be sure that, once or twice in his recent career, he has 'had it'.

Of one thing I am certain: that horses get as much a craving for artificial stimulant as a man does; for the horse is a highly sensitive animal – a view which is not always taken about the thoroughbred, but which is one I shall never depart from.

★ ★ ★

In the early part of 1920 I was at Manchester, attending the races –
not that I had anything running or that I was riding any horse, but
I was anxious to find a nice entry. And by 'a nice entry', I mean a
horse that had an engagement in the near future. What I would do
with that engagement entirely depended upon the kind of horse I
was able to procure. If he was not much good, I might 'ring in'
another and win a small race. If, on the other hand, he was a fairly
useful performer, and ran well in a race, then I could give him a
little 'hurry-up' stuff, and we could get away with a parcel.

I stationed myself away down the course to watch the running in
the —— Stand Handicap Selling hurdle race, and I was particularly
struck by the running of the second favourite – Gainthorpe.

Gainthorpe was trained in Ireland, and he had been brought over
to Manchester with the idea of having a real gamble. He had showed
them on the training-ground that he was a fairly useful animal, but
he had been a difficult horse to train, and whenever he was betted
on, he had let his connections down.

This time he was a good second favourite at 5 to 2, and although
he ran well he didn't get nearer than fourth to Sowerby. I could see
what was the matter with this fellow: he was a faint-hearted horse,
which is a characteristic I have noticed in certain of his breed.

★   ★   ★

The winner of the race was bought in for 280 guineas, and I thought
that I would much sooner have Gainthorpe, especially as he had
been beaten by eight or nine lengths, and more especially because,
looking up my book, I saw that he had an engagement next week
at Ludlow.

Negotiations were entered into with the owner on my behalf, and
the animal was purchased. After the sale was completed I had a talk
with my trainer in a quiet corner of the Grand Hotel lounge.

'I don't think that you've bought this horse cheaply,' he said.
'He's the kind of fellow who will cost us a packet if we are not very
careful. Do you want him for a ringer, or for a straight race?'

'For a straight race,' I said at once. 'Gainthorpe is a very useful
horse. If he does it on the training-ground he can do it on the
racecourse. The horse is probably nervous of the crowd, and if once

we can take his mind off the fact that he's racing for money we ought to pack up a whole lot.'

I explained that what we would do would be to take Gainthorpe to Ludlow. Now Ludlow is a very difficult course – next to the National course at Aintree, the most difficult course in the country. And steeplechase jockeys like to give Ludlow a miss, for they are taking a little more than the ordinary risk when they put a horse at those fences.

But Gainthorpe was entered in a hurdle race, and there was no difficulty in procuring a jockey. I told the trainer my plans.

'You will take Gainthorpe to a little stable near the course. I will come down and doctor him, and he ought to win by ten lengths.'

For some reason or other I was late at the rendezvous, and the trainer, anxious not to make a mistake, waited till the last minute, put five grains of cocaine on the horse's tongue, and led him on to the racecourse. Gainthorpe was in charge of a boy when I arrived, having missed him at the stable, and I looked round to see if I could find the trainer. He was not visible, however, and time was short. So, slipping out my hypodermic needle, I pretended to be fiddling with his surcingle, and gave him five grains under the skin.

When I tell you that five grains is the most I would ever give a horse in any circumstances, you can foresee the sequel. The saddling bell rang, my jockey appeared, and took one look at Gainthorpe. Then his jaw dropped.

'What's the matter with that horse, Mr. Barrie?' he asked.

'What's the matter with him?' said I – and I must confess I was flabbergasted myself – 'there's nothing the matter with him.'

The horse was behaving like a wild and ferocious lion. He was pawing the air and snorting, and his eyes were bulging out of his head.

'Nothing the matter with him, eh?' said the jockey, whose name I will not give, for certain reasons. 'Well, allow me to tell you, Mr. Barrie, that there's enough the matter with him to stop me riding him.'

I could, of course, have taken him before the stewards; but, not being a lunatic, I did nothing of the sort.

Dashing into the jockeys' room, I changed into my riding-kit and colours, and weighed out just as the last horse had left the paddock.

★ ★ ★

I had no sooner got on Gainthorpe's back than I knew I was going to have a journey compared with which a rough night at sea was smooth sailing. However, I have a pretty good hand for a horse, and I had him down to the starting-post without mishap, and luckily we got away with no delay.

He leapt off in front, and the first hurdle we came to he hit with his head and sent it spinning. The second hurdle he jumped about fifteen feet in the air. Between the third and fourth hurdles he tried to bite the nearest horse and was with difficulty restrained. Whilst in the back stretch he did a joyous little cake-walk of his own, that nearly unseated me, and certainly upset the rest of the field.

Oh, that race! Sometimes I was in front, sometimes I was tailed off behind.

He was rolling under me like a ship in a storm, and every hurdle we approached would, I thought, be the end of Barrie. The other jockeys in the race knew that something was wrong, and they edged away to give me as clear a run as I have ever had. If the beast had only jumped straight it would have been bad enough, but he jumped sideways; in fact, one hurdle he negotiated at an angle that nearly brought him out of the field. I pulled his head straight and gave him two more to remind him that his job in life was to win races and not to waltz; but Gainthorpe was too lit up to worry his head about a little thing like a cosh.

'Keep that damned horse of yours away, Barrie!' screamed one of the jockeys, as Gainthorpe tried to bite the ear of his mount.

'I'll change places with you,' I laughed, and really I would have given a lot of money to have been on a horse that had never felt the needle.

★ ★ ★

I guessed what had happened, and between jumps I was cursing the industrious trainer who had given him the dope on his tongue. But there wasn't much time for clear thinking. Gainthorpe did everything except fall. At one part of the race I would have been glad if he had fallen, but he kept his feet and I kept my seat – two miracles which I have never been able to explain to my own satisfaction.

I think it was a two-mile race; it seemed to me like two hundred, and I wanted badly a sight of the winning-post.

In the straight I gave him a couple for himself, and, going like a steam engine, he overhauled the leaders and won in a hack canter by a length and a half.

When I got back to the paddock I was aching in every limb; my hands were raw with holding him.

'Take that horse,' said I to the trainer, 'and for heaven's sake keep him in some quiet place until he settles down.'

★ ★ ★

Whether it was the dope or not, that experience seemed to turn Gainthorpe into a fairly good horse; and when afterwards I rode him, he jumped his hurdles perfectly, and could have won, only for 'reasons of state', it happened that I did not want him to win.

The climax came in a race at Gatwick, in a selling hurdle, which I was paid a large sum to lose. I don't know how I did lose. I think at the end I fell off to stop him winning and the race was won by Submit.

After it was all over, and I had weighed in, a certain official sent for me. He was very pleasant and polite, but his parting words were ominous.

'You didn't win on Gainthorpe today, Mr. Barrie. That was a sad accident of yours. Now take my advice: don't you try to win again on that horse.'

It was advice which I took. The horse afterwards passed out of my possession, and I don't remember that it ever won races thereafter.

SUPER SWINDLERS OF THE TURF

I HAVE made Gilbert Marsh one of the principal figures in the 'arrangement' of the swindles which I have described. But Marsh in those days was perpetually broke, and the three leading conspirators, who approved of my plans and provided me with the money, were three bookmakers whose names were household words in the sporting world, who were prominent members of Tattersalls, and who are now dead.

I don't say they are dead in order to shield them. Everybody in Tattersalls knows that one of them was killed by the worry of my Old Bailey case, and the fear that his part was going to come out in court and that he would be prosecuted. Ask any regular racegoer the name of this man and he will tell you without hesitation.

The second, one of the kindest and one of the most uncouth savages I have ever met, died a short time ago.

The first time I met the leader of this little gang was when I was sent for to 'ring in' a horse at a small meeting in England, and here began an acquaintance which brought me a little money and brought him a fortune.

★   ★   ★

It was in the year 1918. The war was coming to an end, and I, who had been discharged from the Army, was rushing around, trying to make a little bit. There wasn't much money about.

Whichever way we worked we found money hard to get, and as things were not going too well with the three bookmakers, they decided to bring off a little ramp in Ireland.

I was sent for and told what was required. As soon as I learnt what the idea was, I gave them a plan.

'There's a race closing tomorrow,' I said, 'the Service Plate at the Curragh, to be ridden by officers – '

'That won't do,' interrupted the master. 'When I've got my money down, I want the best jockey I can get.'

'Never mind about what you want,' I said. 'It's what I want! If you're going to ring in a horse, let him be in a race where there will be no squeak. It's the very best race of the time, because nobody will suspect an officer of riding a dyed horse.'

In the end they let me have my way. And now we come to the question of what horse should be used for the ringing-in purpose. The entry I made immediately: there appeared a new animal in training – The Major, a brown colt by Wavelet's Pride, dam by Hackler. Now who should The Major be? There were a number of horses available, but the animal I decided upon was Chinaman; and the purchase of this horse was a delicate business, because he was the property of Douglas Stuart, a very shrewd man, and, in fact, the one man of all others in England who would smell something crooked in the air and squash any transaction he had with us.

'One of you fellows had better see Stuart and buy the horse,' I said, and named the price. 'And you'd better be very careful, because, if Duggie smells a swindle, you haven't the ghost of a chance of getting Chinaman.'

★　★　★

I don't think we ever took so much trouble in the buying of a horse as we did over Chinaman. At last we had the animal in our stable. There wasn't a better horse in England for our purpose. Chinaman was a consistent performer, who had won a good race at Newmarket, beating Viking, Blue Danube, Bridge of Marne and Haki, who afterwards won a nice race at Ascot. He had gone into Hyams' stable and had run third to a good performer like Greek Scholar, having St. Eloi behind him. He was a bay son of Santoi, a glutton for distance, and an ideal horse for an amateur to ride.

In those days it was possible to bet very heavily, not only on the course – for Ireland was full of money – but in the S.P. offices of England.

I took Chinaman to Ireland in the guise of a hack, and not a soul was wiser. Just before I left England I saw the master.

'We are going to have a lot of money on this horse, and if you shop us look out for trouble,' he said.

Why he should imagine I would shop or double-cross him I don't know, but all three seemed to be labouring under some suspicion of my 'honesty'.

★ ★ ★

Most bookmakers have business relationships with others. The big men have lists of hundreds, and sometimes thousands, of little men, amongst whom they can divide a bad wager at S.P., and these three fellows had therefore all the machinery for pulling off an enormous coup. They say that dog doesn't eat dog. Well, bookmakers eat bookmakers and grow fat on it!

The organisation at the English end was perfect. On the day of the race there would hardly be a bookmaker in England and Scotland who was not 'stuck' with a loss over The Major. Trusted agents would appear as if by magic at almost every big post office; fifty wires would be handed in and timed simultaneously; and before the telegrams could reach their destination the race would be over and the money won.

That was their end of the business and I must say they did it remarkably well. My end was to find the winner, and I thought with confidence that in Chinaman I had something which would give a stone and a beating to the best horse in the race.

★ ★ ★

I dyed Chinaman a rich deep brown, altered his mane, changed the appearance of his tail, and one morning he appeared on the Curragh training-ground and went a good gallop with a stable boy up.

The best rider available for my purpose was Mr Straker, a young officer who had shown marked ability on the flat and over jumps; and I approached him through my agent. Without knowing of our trick, of course, he readily accepted the ride.

On the morning of the race I sat down to study the entries, which included one horse which has since earned fame over the country – Gerald L. Gerald L. was then a four-year-old and a nice make of horse, and probably very few of us realised that this horse would one day win a Grand National – as I am sure he will.

* * *

My masters did not leave me entirely to my own devices. One of the three had come over with me to do the betting on the course, and to be absolutely certain that there was no jiggery-pokery, though they might have saved themselves the trouble.

However, I did not resent this, because I expect suspicion and accept it as part of the daily routine. But a curious thing happened as we were on our way to the course. As I came out of my hotel, a miserable, ragged-looking man edged up to me and whispered, in the rich Irish brogue:

'Mr. Barrie, I've got a winner for you.'

'What race is it running in?' said I, slipping him half-a-crown.

'It runs in the Service Plate.'

I didn't 'bat a lid'. I knew the winner of the Service Plate, I thought.

'What is it?' I asked.

'Kilnford. The boy that looks after him tells me he can't be beaten.'

What a precious half-a-crown's worth of information I received! But I didn't know that at the time.

Arrived on the course, I saw Mr. Straker in the paddock and took him on one side.

'This horse,' said I, 'is a natural stayer. You can wait with him, and then come away in the last half mile and win your race comfortably. Remember,' I said warningly, 'this is not a sprint, but a race over two and a half miles!'

Captain Straker had no more idea than the man in the moon that he was going up on a faked horse. To him, The Major was just a maiden horse that had never won a race, and I don't think he had very much hope that he would be successful. And he wasn't to be blamed. Owners and trainers often take an exaggerated view of the merits of their horses, and give strings of instructions which no jockey can carry out. In those circumstances, a jockey says to himself: 'I'm on a moderate horse. I'll have to ride him as I feel him. I am not going to take much notice of what owners and trainers tell me.'

* * *

The Major opened at an outside price, and it was not until the market was made that my local boss stepped in and began to back the horse steadily, going from bookmaker to bookmaker and planting it on as though there was no settling day. I warned him that, although The Major was as near a certainty as could be, it wasn't a three-year-old running in a two-year-old race, but a fairly good handicapper running against other handicappers which we hoped were moderate. And of course the distance of the race was phenomenal. The Chinaman had never run over two and a half miles in public. In fact, the only race of that distance on the flat, so far as I can recall, is a race at Ascot, two miles and six furlongs.

However, the madness of betting was on him, and he wouldn't check his speculations by a penny. The race started, and almost immediately Mr. Straker took The Major to the head of affairs. He was going so well, when they came at last into the straight, that even money was refused in Tattersalls. I, who knew something of Chinaman's temperament, knew also that the race was lost. At the distance he was tackled simultaneously by three horses, and immediately faded out of the picture.

The race was won by Kilnford – my half-a-crown tip! The Major finished nearer last than first.

★　★　★

I am a philosopher, and when a horse lets me down, I can take my medicine without squealing. But oh, what a scream came from England! I had robbed these honest gentlemen, I had double-crossed and shopped them, I was in league with the trainer of the winner, I had been got at – Heaven knows what sins I had not committed.

They were finished with me for ever! Later, they had reason to change their minds, and I was called in by one of them to nobble a Derby favourite – the story of which I will leave for a later date.

THE FAKE THAT FAILED

I N my 'profession' I had my ups and downs. Money came easily
and went with greater ease. Today a rich man, tomorrow
reduced to a balance of a few pounds – that is the history of all
men who make their living crookedly.

Marsh and I, and a certain bookmaker who financed a few of the
deals when either Marsh was unable to raise the money or no mug
was available, were one day looking through the Racing Calendar,
and our attention was principally devoted to 'Races to Close'.

* * *

'Here is a race for a ringer,' said Marsh suddenly, and read out the
conditions of the Wynn Selling Plate.

'Where's that?' I said in surprise.

'At Chester,' said Marsh, 'and it is a meeting where you can bet
like blazes and there's no squeak coming, because all sorts of funny
results happen on that course.' I shook my head.

'I don't know much about Chester,' I said. 'There are plenty of
meetings that I know where we can ring in a horse. I don't like
working on strange ground.'

All that I knew about Chester was that it was a course over which
there has been racing for the past 400 years, and that it was circular.
Even the five-furlong races start from the other side of the course
and come in a semicircle to the winning-post! The straight run in
is considerably less than two furlongs, and I saw at once that, in a
big field, if a horse happens to be drawn on the extreme outside,
he has got at least fifty yards further to run than a horse drawn in
No. 1 position.

Marsh urged again the fact that Chester was a good betting meeting, and that one could back a horse to win many thousands without disturbing the market.

I hesitated, partly because, as I say, Chester racecourse was only known to me by hearsay. I had never run a horse there, and I had no idea at the time of the difficulties that I should meet with.

I was not keen one way or the other on the Chester 'ring', but when Marsh, supported by the bookmaker, insisted, I consented to their plan, and an entry was made straightaway with a two-year-old horse called Golden Plate. There was such a two-year-old, but he could no more have won a race than I could climb the Monument. It was, in fact, as bad a horse as there was in training – that by the way.

We had a good three-year-old available, a small fellow, who had been used before for our nefarious purpose, and had also won races under his own name. In fact, he had been so often dyed that he had gone bald in places, and, so far from the dye injuring him, he seemed to enjoy his experience.

★   ★   ★

Having dyed the spurious Golden Plate, I brought him to a little village near Chester a day before the racing started, and I set off to have a look at the course. Marsh was with me, and the moment I saw the tiny track, I realised the difficulties.

'We shall win here if we are well drawn,' I said, 'and even if we aren't, our horse's speed should overcome any preliminary disadvantage.'

'It isn't a bad track,' said Marsh.

'It's a soup plate!' I said. 'But we have got three stone in hand. I don't think the draw will make a lot of difference.'

At which he was jubilant.

'That is my contention, Pat,' he said. 'We are going to put a lot of money on this horse, and, as you say, even if he's drawn outside, his superior speed and age ought to overcome that difficulty.

★   ★   ★

I had plenty of time to discover the effect of the draw, for our race was on the third and last day of the meeting. And the more I saw of the racing at Chester, the more convinced I was that the draw did not mean so much as people thought. Time after time, badly drawn horses won their races, and my misgivings vanished. Our three-year-old was a fairly good handicap performer in selling-plate class, and he was one on which I could gamble, even though (as I remembered) he had failed to get round the bends at Alexandra Park when running under his own name.

Naturally my own did not approach the enthusiasm of the other conspirators. They had engaged Tommy Weston to ride, and Weston then, as now, was a strong horseman and a capable finisher.

'If he's strong enough to lift Golden Plate from the outside to the inside, and capable of keeping him in front, he'll win,' said I. 'And even if he doesn't, I believe our little horse can beat the rags we've got up against us.'

Our conversation took place over a little dinner we had on the Wednesday.

'I've never known you to be so optimistic before, Pat,' said Marsh, all smiles.

★ ★ ★

They made very careful preparations to get the money on at the S.P. offices; in spite of the fact that they were so sure that money invested on the course would not bring the price down, they were taking no risks. All Gilbert Marsh's friends and acquaintances were put on to the good thing, and he stood to win from them alone a considerable fortune. Thousands of pounds were invested in London and in Manchester, and even Ireland was not neglected.

In the morning I had the horse out for a sharp pipe-opener, and when Weston, who rode him in his gallop, dismounted, I asked him what he thought of his mount.

'He goes more like a bad three-year-old than a good two,' he said perfectly innocently.

I got a little shock myself at that, and repeated the conversation to Marsh at breakfast.

'Never mind about what Weston says,' said the bookmaker. 'If you listen to jockeys, you'll go broke and mad on the same day.'

Now, I am one of those people who believe that jockeys can tell you a whole lot, and I knew that Weston must have 'felt' the horse's capabilities.

Ten runners went up in the frame – and we were drawn tenth,

the very worst position. I went straightaway to Marsh and told him the draw, but I was as optimistic as ever.

'Anyway,' he said, 'we can't alter the betting, because we've backed the horse "away", and I wouldn't if I could. I'm going to have another bet in the ring: you can get 10 to 1 to any amount of money.'

I had gone carefully into the form of the other horses engaged, and I had decided that the horse that had the biggest chance amongst them if it was well drawn, was First Out, a horse in Griggs' stable, at Newmarket, which I had seen run a very good race over the Rous course. He was a nippy type of animal, absolutely built for this peculiar track, and no sooner was Marsh out of sight than I went into the ring, and was not at all surprised when I discovered that Griggs' animal was favoured.

★ ★ ★

They were a fairly fractious lot at the post, which meant that Golden Plate was edged farther out to the right; and to add to his misfortunes, at the moment the gate went up, Golden Plate was sideways on. First Out went off at a rare bat, leaving his field round the first bend, with our horse almost tailed off. He got up to his field, however, but all the time he was galloping on the outside, and I have since calculated that the distance he had to go was at least 85 yards, or 28 lengths, farther than the two horses drawn on the rails.

However, he was going well within himself. Weston had not moved on him, whilst keeping the horse at full stretch. I stood by Marsh as the race was in progress, my eyes glued to my glasses.

'He'll do all right,' said Marsh confidently, and I shared his optimism because the 'ringer' was an animal which usually came with a rare burst of speed at the finish, and as they swung round into the straight, he was within striking distance of the leaders.

'Come on, ——' yelled Marsh, and in his excitement he used the real name of the 'ringer'.

I looked around. Apparently nobody had heard, and I nudged him.

'Golden Plate is the horse's name!' I whispered.

Putting up my glasses again, a horrid sight met my eyes. Weston was 'scrubbing' the horse, and in the next second up went his whip.

'We're beaten!' gasped Marsh.

Down came the whip again and again, but not a further pound could the poor beast pull out! Golden Plate finished seventh. I saw the horse unsaddled, and then hurried into the ring to draw my money. For when I saw how Golden Plate was drawn, I took the liberty of backing the winner. I do not believe in miracles, especially at Chester!

AMAZING DERBY PLOT UNMASKED

I HAVE taken part in many daring schemes in my time but amongst them one stands out, which for sheer audacity makes me almost shiver when I look back upon it.

This was the doping of The Panther, the Derby favourite of 1919. The story is an extraordinary one, but in case anyone may be sceptical of the truth of my assertions let me say at once that there are highly placed gentlemen on the Turf who can corroborate all I have said and can prove that I couldn't be in possession of one part of my information if I wasn't in possession of the other.

One day, D— X—, a well-known bookmaker, sent for me. He was an uncouth yet a big-hearted man, with the manners of an animal and the scruples of a pickpocket. I had done work for him before, and I had been well paid. It was not unusual for him to send for me, and I attached no importance to the summons. It was just before the Epsom (Derby) meeting, and I was not particularly interested in the Derby, except the interest which every lover of horses feels in that supreme test of merit.

So that, when D— X— started talking about the Derby, I listened without listening, if you understand. Naturally he did not talk from the horsey side, but entirely from the money aspect of the race, and as he rambled on, dodging from one subject to another, but always returning to the Derby, I began to smell a rat. Presently he asked in a careless way:

'Did you ever nobble a horse, Pat?'

'What do you mean by "nobble" him – "get at" him? Yes, I suppose I have – but they've always been my own horses.'

He was silent for a long while. I can see him now, sitting in an armchair in his office, a frown on his somewhat unpleasant face, drumming the chair arm with his fingers and looking out into the street.

'What about a bit of a joke with the Derby favourite?' he asked.

I thought that he was really joking, and was suggesting that I should ring one in on the horse.

'If you think that's funny you can clear out!' he growled. 'I'm serious. What about getting at The Panther?'

Hardened case as I am, I was shocked at the suggestion. 'Get at' the Derby favourite! The horse on whom all the eyes of the world rested, whose victory would decide bets to the value of millions! It hardly seemed that he could be serious.

'But why get at him?' I asked. 'Is he bad for your book?'

D— X— nodded emphatically.

'And he'll be worse,' he said.

'But can't you lay him off?' said I, and he snarled at me like a dog.

'Don't try to teach me my business,' he said. 'Will you do the job?'

I didn't think twice about it.

'No,' I said, 'I won't. You'd better find somebody else. If you do it, there will be a squeak beside which a foghorn will be a whisper.'

'I don't want any advice,' he said sharply, and there the matter ended for the moment.

On my way home I thought it over very carefully, and the more I thought the less I liked it.

★ ★ ★

The Panther was a Tracery colt, out of Countess Zia. He made his appearance during the war in the Norfolk Plate, a race which has seen the coming out of so many good horses. Starting at 14 to 1, and ridden by Donoghue, he ran a little green, but finished second to Galloper Light, and so well did he run that it was any odds against his starting at such a price again.

At the June meeting he came out and smashed up a big field,

winning the Bartlow Plate of 195 sovs. in a hack canter by eight lengths. It was a huge field that opposed him, and he treated them like hacks.

Again he was ridden by Donoghue, but on his next outing, in September, he had R. Collings up, when he won the Autumn Stakes, leaving behind him Galloper Light, that good filly Bayuda, and winning by three-quarters of a length.

Between his victories as a two-year-old and his coming out as a three-year-old he had changed stables – Collings, who had trained him before, being replaced by Mr. Manser, a capable and painstaking trainer. It cannot be said that The Panther was a great popular favourite. He was looked upon as a very good performer; a little short of classical standard; and when he came out in the Two Thousand Guineas in the first year of the peace, he was allowed to start at 10 to 1; but, ridden by Cooper, he won a great race by a neck from Buchan, Dominion and Bruff Bridge.

It was not a good-class field, with the exception of Buchan. The performance was sufficiently impressive, however, to make The Panther a strong favourite for the Derby, in a year when there was a great deal of 'mug money' in circulation, and little punters, bloated with war earnings, had had an influence on the market.

Personally, I think The Panther was not the best horse in the race, and would have been beaten in the Derby, both by Buchan and Grand Parade. He was a moderate horse in a moderate year, and I should be very much surprised if the progeny of any of the first four in the Guineas make their mark on the Turf.

It is easy enough to see all this, looking back four years. At the time the books were perfectly certain that The Panther would win and put them into an awful mess.

★ ★ ★

Knowing D— X—, I didn't expect that he would drop the subject, and sure enough the very next day he sent for me.

'I've got a man to do that job,' he said as soon as I entered his office. 'He's not as good as you, but he'll do. It's worth a thousand.'

I knew now that the matter was serious for D— X—, who wasn't the kind of man to chuck thousands about for nothing.

D— X— changed the subject, only to return again to the question of The Panther, and he was beginning to explain what he meant when the telephone bell rang, and he took down the receiver.

'Who is that?' he asked, and then, to me: 'It is a trunk call. I wonder if this is our man?'

I wondered who was on the phone. I was not left long in doubt. Presently I heard D— X— mention the name of a wealthy racing man.

He took up a pencil and scribbled a note.

'I'll lay six thousand to four thousand against The Panther.'

I wonder if this racing man will remember coming through on a trunk call to back The Panther a week or so before the race?

D— X— hung up the receiver and looked at me.

'Six thousand to four thousand,' he said very slowly, 'and that's only one bet I've got against that horse. Now, Barrie, are you game to earn a thousand?'

You must remember that this occurred in the early part of 1919, before I got properly going, and when a thousand pounds meant a lot to me.

'What do you want me to do?' I asked.

'Go down to Newmarket and tail up that horse at exercise. It ought to be easy to slip something to him that'll do him no good at all,' he said. 'You can give him an apple with a little bad stuff in it that'll do the trick.'

★ ★ ★

I am not particularly proud of the part I played, but I am not going either to justify or excuse myself. That night I left for Newmarket, put up in lodgings, and early the next morning I was up on Newmarket Heath watching the string of horses at exercise.

I had no difficulty in finding Manser's string, but after I had made my discovery I found that I should have all my work cut out. The Panther, as the Derby favourite, attracted an unusually large number of skilful horse-watchers, and I was marked down at once as a stranger, and a stranger at Newmarket on the training-ground, especially just before the Derby, has to give an account of himself.

I was very soon the subject of close questioning. The story I told was that I was an Australian who had come over to this country, and was an enthusiastic horse-lover and wanted to have a look at the Derby favourite at exercise.

Whether they believed me or not I don't know, but certainly I was seldom left alone; and when, at the end of the gallop, I strolled over to where The Panther was walking round in a circle, I was not allowed to get too close. The head lad came riding across, asked me sharply what my business was, and I had too much sense to argue the point with him. In my pocket was an apple, heavily doped, and if I could only get that between The Panther's teeth, there would be no question about his winning the Derby.

But the opportunity did not come. Morning after morning I appeared on the Heath, edging closer and closer to the horse I intended nobbling, but every time there was somebody handy to see that I didn't get too close.

Time was going on. I received frantic messages from D— X—, asking me what I was doing, and telling me that, if I hadn't something to report soon, he would send another man down.

★ ★ ★

Then for the first time I learnt that he had somebody squared in the stable and that somebody, while willing to give information about the horse, emphatically refused to do anything to stop The Panther winning.

The Newmarket detectives then began tailing me up, and I realised that the atmosphere was a little too sultry for me, and I came back to London and reported my failure to D— X—. He stormed and raved, cursed me for an incompetent fool, and finished up by saying:

'Well, if you can't get at the horse, I'll find somebody who can.'

It was no idle threat.

POWDERED GLASS FOR A DERBY FAVOURITE

THE favourite for the Derby of 1919, was The Panther and, as I have previously stated, there was a tremendous amount of money laid on him.

When I informed him that I was going to wash my hands of the affair D— X— was, of course, furious, but he had too much money at stake to allow himself to take any risks.

'I've got a man to do the job for a thousand pounds,' he said, 'and he'll get at the horse if anyone can. I'm not going to lose £17,000 without a kick. There's no horse that can't be got at and there's no man who hasn't got his price. Why couldn't you have got The Panther when they took off his sweating rug and rubbed him down after his gallop?' he asked, and I explained just why it was impossible, since the horse was so closely guarded.

'Then you ought to have got at him at night!' he said furiously. 'Manser's stable isn't a very hard one to break into.'

'There's a boy sleeps in the stable. He's been sleeping there nearly a month,' I said, 'and the head lad you can't possible get at.'

He wasn't satisfied with my explanation and sent his own man down to Newmarket with instructions to get at The Panther without delay.

★ ★ ★

Although it was some time ahead of the race, his object was to put The Panther on the easy list for a week, in which case there would be no possible chance of the horse winning.

I could see that D— X— was determined, but I really did not think he would ever succeed in accomplishing his end.

His man went to Newmarket, but he had no better success than I had had. In fact, he was known in the town, and, unfortunately for him, instantly detected; so he came back to London and reported, and D— X—'s hair looked like going white. He had a hurried consultation with his partner, the second bookmaker concerned, and they decided that they would wait till the horse was transferred to Epsom. Here, of course, they were wise, because in Derby week there is a great influx of strangers into Epsom, and it is impossible for the cleverest of detectives to keep track of the outsiders who make their mysterious appearance on the Downs.

The second of the bookmakers in this job had a friend occupying a humble position in Manser's stable, and this boy was sent for, and for the first time learnt what D— X— and his pal were trying to do. I will give the lad credit for saying that he was horrified and absolutely refused to do anything whatever to help the gang get at The Panther. He even threatened to report the matter to his boss, but I rather fancy he was too deeply in one of the bookmaker's pockets to carry that threat into execution. At any rate, Manser was not warned.

★ ★ ★

If I remember rightly, The Panther went to Epsom a few days before the race, and from that moment every man in the stable or connected with the stable was under strict observation, for D— X— was bringing all his forces to bear to carry out his plan. Mr. Manser and his visitors were 'tailed up' wherever they went, so that the man who was actually in charge of the job knew exactly were everybody was.

The thing was to get into the stable where the horse was lodged during his stay at Epsom, and on the second attempt the nobbler succeeded in evading the watchers and reaching the box where The Panther was sleeping. He could not, however, get in, and had to beat a hasty retreat as the sound of patrolling footsteps in the yard came to his ears, and he only made a getaway by the skin of his teeth. I believe he spent some hours lying on a roof.

That night he went up to London and reported his failure to D— X—, who was waiting for him anxiously.

'Have you done it?' asked D— X— eagerly, and the nobbler shook his head.

'It can't be done,' he said. 'Our only chance is to get him on the Downs in the morning, and I think that will be easier than it was at Newmarket.'

Not troubling to sleep, he went back by car to Epsom, and was on the ground early in the morning when the horses came out for their pipe-openers. But, despite all his efforts, he could not get anywhere near the horse, and D— X—'s friend has also contended that this was due to the boy in the stable, who knew what they were after, and had warned the head lad. Whether that was so or not, it looked very much as though D— X— and his confederate would have to pay out £17,000, and the idea positively frightened them!

They sent for me, after having dismissed me in disgrace, and urged me to go down to Epsom and do all I possibly could to get the horse out of action. But I had been so heartily glad to get out of this business altogether, that I did not think twice before I refused. Out of curiosity, however, I dodged about trying to find out what was happening, and the only thing I could discover was that everybody concerned was in the devil of a state of funk.

★ ★ ★

That night, however, the deed was done. The nobbler, with visions of £1,000 before his eyes, took a desperate risk, and luck was with him. He got into the stable yard and, by the greatest of good luck, found The Panther momentarily unguarded. To drop an apple into the feed-box was the work of a moment before he got out and scrambled to safety.

The dope I had been told to give The Panther was of a fairly mild nature, which would have taken days, and probably a week, to act; but they were so near to the race that D— X— had decided upon taking no risks. It is a curious fact that the poison which was put into the apple was the same as figured in the Ilford murder case – powdered glass. It was with powdered glass that The Panther was nobbled. Its action is to set up an inflammation, the minute particles of glass lacerating the delicate membrane of the stomach.

★ ★ ★

On the next day The Panther appeared at exercise, under the eyes of an admiring crowd, and apparently he went as well as ever he did in his life, though he sweated when he pulled up. I watched the gallop, and, knowing Manser by sight, I took particular notice of the trainer, to see whether he was as satisfied as the watchers. From my point of view the horse didn't go with the same heart as I had seen him gallop before, for I had come to know him as well as though he were in my own stable.

I saw Manser shake his head as he watched the horse having his cloth put on, and went back to meet the two conspirators, who stood up that day in Tattersalls and laid The Panther to lose a much larger sum than ever they had laid before. But before they went into the ring, they were by no means satisfied, for the story had come to them that The Panther had gone as well as ever, and that it was not by any means certain that the horse had eaten the apple, or that the boy hadn't come back and taken it from the box.

★ ★ ★

However, I was able to reassure them that The Panther had not gone well in his gallop. Strangely enough, no adverse criticism was heard even by the smartest of the horse-watchers; and on the morning of the race, when in his gallop he went even more sluggishly, it was difficult to get 6 to 4 about him.

There was, however, one man, I am sure, who knew that all was not well with the horse. Somebody who had watched the morning gallop on Derby Day told me that Manser had said emphatically: 'He doesn't look the same horse.'

The history of that sensational Derby is simply told. The Panther could never raise a gallop, and finished last, and there was a cheery little dinner-party at a famous restaurant in the West End to celebrate the defeat.

When I saw D— X— after the race he looked too jubilant for words, but the smile left his face when I told him what I thought of him.

'Why, you would have doped The Panther yourself,' he said, 'only you couldn't get at him.'

'Yes,' I answered, 'but when I dope horses I dope them with a fair drug. I don't give them something that will injure them for life, such as powdered glass. Horses I nobble don't suffer agonies; in fact, they generally enjoy the sensation!'

He blustered a good deal, but I could see that he felt somewhat ashamed of himself though the thought of his profits was a good salve to his conscience.

Not only did The Panther fail to win the Derby, but he never won another race, and it is probable that the effects of his nobbling did not entirely disappear.

AMAZING REVELATIONS
OF RACING ROGUERY

To those who ask me if ever I have tried to 'ring' a horse in the Derby, I reply that I haven't. And yet the Derby is the easiest race in the world in which to work a 'ringer'. He is entered two years before the day, and when you remember that only a small proportion of the entries ever see a racecourse, it isn't difficult to understand how easy it would be to make the Derby your colt's first race, and to substitute almost any horse you liked – any horse that is, of course, good enough.

But there the easiness ends; for you would have to have a smashing four-year-old to beat the average Derby field. In fact, it would have to be a horse capable of winning the Derby as a three-year-old if you wanted to bet with any confidence.

It was in 1918 that I was first approached with the object of 'ringing in' one in the following year's Derby. At that time it looked as though the war was going on for another two years, and that the substitute race would be run at Newmarket as usual. But the scheme, as it was put up to me, was so badly conceived that I turned it down promptly.

★ ★ ★

It is a race requiring too much preparation for the average ringer to trouble his head about – and when I say the average ringer, I suggest that I am not the only man who has gained a nefarious livelihood by producing horses that 'were not what they seemed'. The man who does that sort of thing is usually in a hurry for money, and certainly cannot afford to wait for two years; besides which, it is pretty difficult to buy a horse at the last moment which has been entered in the Derby and which has not paid the minor forfeit. Horses become almost public characters in this country – I am referring to the more important classic candidates – and although I know of one instance where a great handicap in England was won by a 'rung-in' horse, detection was only avoided by a fluke. What race was that you ask?

Well, think of one of the ten big handicaps in the year, and you have the race. Beyond that I cannot go without betraying, and bringing to ruin, men who today are highly respected on the English turf.

This is my biggest story, and, like most of the biggest stories of life, it cannot be told.

Whenever there is a suggestion that some horse has been run which is not all he appears to be I have a call from half a dozen interested and curious people. But with me, 'ringing' is a thing of the past. And if I 'ring', it will be done as unconsciously and as innocently as the substitution of one two-year-old for another, which is exercising the minds of the talent at this moment.

★　★　★

And here let me say about the Hypatia case, which is interesting to me at any rate, that it is the easiest thing in the world to mix two yearlings one with another. If they are both the same sex, and they are purchased in the sale yards, it stands to reason that it's a simple matter to confuse them. The purchaser hasn't seen his horses, except for the few moments when they have been walking round the sale ring, and, providing they are the same colour, it is a very simple matter to get them mixed up. The case of Stanley Wootton is, of course, a perfectly innocent one, and the person who was most deceived was Wootton himself. But there are other cases with other trainers, and please remember that I am not the only man who has rung in a horse.

It stands to reason that in 1919 and 1920, which were what I might term vintage years for turf rogues, when money was plentiful and easy to get, and you could back a selling-plater to win you a fortune, the Turf thieves lost no opportunity.

I have seen horses win for highly respectable trainers who were no more entitled to the name that appeared on the race-cards than I was. The temptation to a man with a big stable of horses, and who is going badly, to 'ring in' a certain winner is a very great one; and, though the risk in his case is enormous, yet it has been proved time and time again that it is not impossible. The danger, of course, is that somebody in the stable will squeak; and in a large stable, with scores of stable men and boys nosing into the private affairs of the trainer, it is suicidal to make the attempt. The only possible way that a dishonest trainer can 'ring' a horse is in conjunction with another stable.

When a three-year-old leaves Newmarket on the same day that a two-year-old leaves an Epsom establishment, and you can only trace the arrival of the alleged 'two-year-old' at a Midland meeting, it is any odds on a ramp being worked, and a thousand to one against either of those two horses returning to their stables.

★　★　★

'Ringing in' in this country, however, is not general, and racing in England is the cleanest and straightest in the world. As one who has broken the laws, written and unwritten, of the Turf, so often that I almost forget when I kept them, may I be permitted to make this acknowledgment to all concerned.

The real difficulty which confronts the authorities is in absolutely identifying, or having the means to identify, every horse that runs. A few years ago a well-known Indian, who races in this country, sent two second-class horses to India. One was a sprinter and the other was a stayer, and by some mischance on the boat, these horses got mixed up and arrived in their Indian stable with their identities changed. For a year the owner and his trainer tried to make the sprinter win distance races, and he entered unsuccessfully the real stayer in sprints. It was only the arrival by chance of a well-known English trainer, who recognised the two horses, that caused the mistake to be discovered. Thereafter, I believe, each horse won for his owner pretty considerable stakes.

When you consider the character of the men who are engaged in the business of owning and training horses; when you realise how easily money is obtained, and how quickly bets are settled and money is transferred, it is a standing wonder to me that there can be anything straight in racing.

Within half an hour a fortune can be staked on a horse whom not one man in ten thousand would recognise by sight; the fortune is won, and the horse vanishes from the course almost as soon as the winnings are paid over. A number goes in the frame; So-and-so has won; the blue flag waves 'all right' or 'weighed in', and the racing public settles down to the discussion of the next race and the chances of the horses engaged.

In no other walk of life are settlements so quickly made. In no other branch of commerce is a man's bona fides and honesty accepted with such little proof. Is it remarkable that the racecourse thief should find his opportunity in this haphazard method of 'business'?

★   ★   ★

In my reminiscences I have told enough to show that the very best laid plans of the horse-faker are liable to go badly astray. There are no certainties in racing; even faked certainties go wrong sometimes, as I know to my sorrow. The case of Chinaman and Golden Plate are two in point. I have seen other unbeatable horses (the reader will remember the Mexican Belle swindle) which have come unstuck through causes over which the swindler had no control.

On the other hand, we have had enormous coups, as in the case of The Clown, Coat of Mail, and Silver Badge; but where is the money we made? It disappeared like water in sand, leaving us to take a new risk in order to secure enough money to waste again!

It has never been my policy, in conducting racing swindles, to dabble in trivial affairs. When I have made up my mind to try to bring off a coup I have always made sure that it would be a real coup, one which would line the pockets of myself and my fellow-swindlers with substantial profits. That is why I have specialised in 'ringing in' horses. The more ordinary form of racing swindle, such as doping favourites, never appeared to me to be worth the candle. But, indeed, that could not be said of all Turf crookedness.

Honesty pays but the dividends are small. Dishonesty pays big bonuses, and sometimes rewards you with a bleak outlook from Dartmoor.

My revelations have, I think, shown that even the most insignificant Turf swindle involves an amount of risk not only of discovery, disgrace and imprisonment, but of losing large sums of money in a few minutes, which is in no way compensated by successes achieved. The anxiety which I have experienced, even though I am not of a nervous disposition, while preparations for a big coup were in process would turn an ordinary person's hair white.

My mind is made up. Never again!

THE EDUCATED EVANS STORIES

THE BROTHERHOOD

INSPECTOR Pine was something more than an inspector of police. He was what is known in certain circles as a Christian man. He was a lay preacher, a temperance orator; a social reformer. And if any man had worked hard to bring Educated Evans to a sense of his errors, that man was Inspector Pine. He had wrestled with the devil in Mr. Evans' spiritual make-up, he had prayed for Mr. Evans; and once, when things were going very badly, he had induced Mr. Evans to attend what was described as 'a meeting of song and praise'.

Educated Evans respected the sincerity of one whom he regarded as his natural enemy, but discovering, as he did, that a 'meeting of praise and song' brought him no financial advancement, he declined any further invitations and devoted his energies and excursions to picking up information about a certain horse that was running in a steeplechase at Kempton Park on Boxing Day.

Nevertheless, Inspector Pine did not despair. He believed in restoring a man's self-respect and in re-establishing his confidence; but here he might have saved himself a lot of trouble, for the self-respect of Educated Evans was enormous, and he was never so confident as when, after joining in a hymn, two lines of which ran:

> The powers of darkness put to flight,
> The day's dawn triumphs over night.

he accepted the omen and sent out to all his punters, 'Daydawn – inspired information – help yourself.' For, amongst other occupations, Educated Evans was a tipster, and had a clientèle that included many publicans and the personnel of the Midland Region Goods Yard.

One day in April, Educated Evans leant moodily over the broad parapet and examined the river with a vague interest. His melancholy face wore an expression of pain and disappointment, his under-lip was out-thrust in a pout, his round eyes stared with a certain urgent agony, as though he had given them the last chance of seeing what he wanted to see, and if they failed him now they would never again serve him.

So intent was he that one who – although a worker in another and, to Evans, a hateful sphere – bore many affectionate nicknames, was able to come alongside of him and share his contemplation without the sad man observing the fact.

Fussing little tugs, lethargic strings of barges, a police-boat slick and fast – all these came under the purview of Educated Evans, but apparently he saw nothing of what he wanted to see, and drew back with an impatient sigh.

Then it was that he saw his companion and realized that here, on the drab Embankment, was one whom he had imagined to be many miles away.

The newcomer was a tall man of thirty, broad-shouldered power in every line of him. He was dressed in black, and a broad-rimmed felt hat was pulled over his eyes. He was chewing a straw, and even if Mr. Evans had failed to identify him by another means, he would have known The Miller – whose other name was William Arbuthnot Challoner – by this sign.

'Why, Miller, I thought you was dead! And here was I speculatin' upon the one hundred and ninety million cubic yards of water that passes under that bridge every day, and meditatin' upon the remarkable changes that have happened since dear old Christopher Columbus sailed from that very pier, him and the Pilgrim Fathers that discovered America in fifteen seventy-nine.'

The Miller listened and yet did not listen. The straw twirled between his strong teeth; his long, saturnine face was turned to the river; his thoughts were far away.

'A lovely scene,' said Mr. Evans, ecstatically, indicating the smoky skyline; 'the same as dear old Turner used to paint, and Fluter – '

'Whistler,' said his companion absently.

'Whistler, of course – dear me, where's my education!' Mr. Evans rolled his head in self-impatience. 'Whistler. What an artist. Miller

– if you'll excuse the familiarity. I'll call you Challoner if you're in any way offended. What – an – artist! There's a bit of painting of his in the National Gall'ry. And another one in the – the Prado in Madrid. Art's a perfect weakness with me – always has been since a boy. Do you know Sergeant? Great American painter. One of the greatest artists in the world. An' do you know the celebrated French artist, Carrot?'

'Do you know,' began The Miller, speaking deliberately and looking at the river all the time, 'do you know where you were between seven-thirty and nine-fifteen on the night of the eighth of this month?'

'I do,' said Educated Evans promptly.

'Does anybody else know – anybody whose word would be accepted by a police magistrate gifted with imagination and a profound distrust of the criminal classes?'

'My friend, Mr. Harry Sefferal,' began Evans, and The Miller laughed hollowly and with an appearance of pain.

'You have only to put your friend in the witness-box,' he said, 'you have only to let the magistrate see his sinister countenance to be instantly remitted to Dartmoor for the remainder of your life. Harry Sefferal could only save you from imprisonment if you happened to be charged with murder. Reading his evidence, the hangman would pack his bag without waiting for the verdict. Harry Sefferal!'

Mr. Evans shrugged.

'On the evening in question it so happened that I was playing a quiet game of solo in the company of a well-known and respected tradesman, Mr. Julius Levy – '

'You're a dead man!' groaned Miller. 'Julius Levy is the man who put the "u" into "guilty". Know Karbolt Manor?'

Mr. Evans considered.

'I can't say that I do,' he said at last.

'Near Sevenoaks – the big house that Binny Lester burgled five years ago and got away with it.'

Educated Evans nodded.

'Now that you mention the baronial 'all, Miller, it flashes across my mind – like a dream, as it were, or a memory of happier days.'

'Is there a ladder in your dream? A ladder put up to Lady Cardington's bedroom window when the family was at dinner? Dream carefully, Evans.'

Mr. Evans wrinkled a forehead usually smooth and unlined.

'No,' he said; 'I know the place, but I haven't been near there. I can take the most sacred oath – '

'Don't,' begged The Miller. 'I'd rather have your word of honour. It means more.'

'On my word of honour as a gentleman,' said Evans solemnly. 'I have not been to, frequented, been in the vicinity of, or otherwise approached this here manor. And if I am not telling the truth may Heaven smite me to the earth this very minute!'

He struck an attitude, and The Miller waited, looking up at the skies.

'Heaven didn't hear you,' he said, and took the arm of Evans. 'Pine wants to see you.'

Educated Evans shrugged his resignation.

'You are taking an innocent man,' he said with dignity. The Miller bore the blow bravely.

The Miller was always The Miller to a certain class. He was taxed in the style and title of Detective-Sergeant W. Arbuthnot Challoner, Criminal Investigation Department. He was an authority on ladder larceny, safe-blowing, murder, gangery, artfulness, and horses. Round Camden Town, where many of his most ardent admirers had their dwelling-places, he was called The Miller because of this odd straw-nibbling practice of his.

He was respected; he was not liked, not even by Educated Evans, that large-minded and tolerant man. Evans was both liked and respected. In North London, as distinct from South London, erudition has a value. Men less favoured look up to those proficient in the gentle arts of learning. Educated Evans was one of whom the most violent and the least amiable spoke with respect.

Apart from his erudition – he had written more speeches for the defence than any other amateur lawyer – he was undoubtedly in the confidence of owners, trainers, jockeys and head lads. He admitted it. He was the man who gave Braxted for the Stewards' Cup and Eton Boy for the Royal Hunt Cup. There are men holding affluent positions in Camden Town who might trace their prosperity to the advice of Educated Evans. It was said, by the jealous and the evil-minded, that the Workhouse never was so full as it was after that educated man had had a bad season.

'It was a matter of regret to me,' said Evans as he shuffled along by his captor's side, 'that the law, invented by Moses and Lord What's-his-name, should be employed to crush, so to speak, the weak. And on the eve, as it were, of the Newbury Spring Handicap, when I *did* hope to pack a parcel over Solway.'

The Miller stopped and surveyed his prisoner with curiosity and disapproval.

'Solway,' he said deliberately, 'is not on the map. St. Albyn could give Solway two stone and lose him!'

The lip of Educated Evans curled in a sneer.

'Solway could fall dead and get up and *then* win,' he said extravagantly. 'St. Albyn ain't a horse, he's a hair trunk. The man who backs St. Albyn – '

'I've backed St. Albyn,' said The Miller coldly. 'I've had it from the owner's cousin, who is Lord Herprest, that, barring accidents, St. Albyn is a stone certainty.'

Educated Evans laughed; it was the laugh of a man who watches his enemy perish.

'And they *hanged* poor old Crippen!' he said.

There was this bond of sympathy between The Miller and his lawful prey – that they were passionate devotees of the sport of kings. When The Miller was not engaged in the pursuit of social pests – amongst whom he awarded Educated Evans very nearly top weight – he was as earnestly pursuing his studies into the vagarious running of the thoroughbred racehorse.

'What about Blue Chuck?' he asked. 'There's been a sort of tip about for him.'

Evans pulled at his long nose.

'That's one that might do it,' he admitted. 'Canfyn's told his pals that it won't be ready till Goodwood, but that feller would shop his own doctor. I wouldn't believe Canfyn if he was standin' on the scaffold and took an oath on Foxe's *Book of Martyrs*.'

Passers-by seeing them, the shabby man in the long untidy coat and the tall man in black, would never have dreamt that they were overlooking a respected officer of Scotland Yard and his proper prey.

'What makes you think that St. Albyn hasn't a chance, Evans?' asked The Miller anxiously.

'Because he ain't trying,' said Evans with emphasis. 'I've got it straight from the boy who does him. He's not having a go till Ascot, an' they think they can get him in the Hunt Cup with 7 to 5.'

The Miller blew heavily. That very morning Teddie Isaacheim, a street bookmaker who possessed great wealth and singular immunity from police interference, had laid him fifty pounds to five and a half – ready – about this same St. Albyn. And five and a half pounds was a lot of money to lose.

'If you'd asked me I'd have told you,' said Educated Evans gently. 'If you'd come to me as man to man an' as a sportsman to a sportsman, instead of all this ridiculous an' childish nonsense about me actin' in a thievous and illegal manner, I'd have given to you the strength of St. Albyn. *And* I'd have put you on to the winner of the one o'clock race tomorrow – saved specially . . . not a yard at Kempton . . . not busy at Birmingham – havin' a look on at Manchester, but *loose* tomorrer!'

'What's that, Evans?'

The Miller's voice was mild, seductive, but Evans shook his head, and they marched on.

'Never,' said the educated man with great bitterness, 'never since old Cardinal Wolsey was pinched for giving lip to King Charles has a man been more disgustin'ly arrested than me. If I don't get ten thousand out of the police for false imprisonment . . . if I don't show up old Pine for this – '

'Is it Clarok Lass, old man?' asked Miller, as they came in sight of the police station.

'No, it ain't Clarok Lass,' said Evans savagely. 'And if you think you're going to get my five-pound special for a ha'p'orth of soft soap, you've got another guess coming. I'm finished with you, Miller, I am. Didn't I give you King Solomon an' Flake at Ascot last year? Didn't I run all over the town to put you on to that good thing of Jordan's?'

'You've certainly done your best, Evans,' agreed his captor soothingly, 'and if I can put in a word for you – what did you say was going to win that one o'clock race?'

Educated Evans pressed his lips tightly and a few seconds later The Miller was his business-like self.

'Here is Evans, sir; he says he knows nothing of the Sevenoaks job, and he can produce two witnesses to swear that he was in town at the time of the robbery. Maybe he can produce forty-two – '

Inspector Pine came in while Evans was being searched by the goaler, and shook his head grievously.

'Oh, Evans, Evans!' he sighed. 'And you promised me faithfully that you'd never come again!'

Educated Evans sniffed.

'If you think I came here on my own, sir, you're wrong.'

Again the white-haired inspector shook his head.

'There's good in every human heart,' he said. 'I will not lose hope in you, Evans. What is the charge?'

'No charge, sir, detention. We want him in connection with the Sevenoaks affair, but there are a few alibis to be tested,' said The Miller.

So they put Educated Evans into No. 7, which was his favourite cell, and Evans wondered what horse in the Newbury Cup was numbered 7 on the card.

That night certain heated words passed between the Honourable George Canfyn and the usually amiable attendants at the Hippoleum Theatre. George, who had dined, retaliated violently.

George Canfyn was a man of property and substance, an owner of racehorses, and a gentleman by law. His father was Lord Llanwattock. His other name was Snook, and he made soap in a very large way. And in addition to soap he made margarine, money and political friends. They in turn made him a Baron of the United Kingdom. The law made him a gentleman. God was not even consulted.

George was the type of man who liked money for money's sake. Most people tell you that money means nothing to them, only the things you can buy with it. George liked money plain. He wanted all the money there was, and it hurt him to see the extraordinary amount that had failed to come his way. He lived cheaply, he ate meanly, and he changed his trainer every year.

If a horse of his failed to win when he had his packet down, he did everything except complain to the Stewards. He never had the same jockey more than three times, because he believed that jockeys cut up races and arranged the winner to suit their own pockets. He believed all trainers were incompetent, and all the jockeys who weren't riding his horse to be engaged in a conspiracy to 'take care' of it.

When he won – as he did very often – he told his friends before the race that his horse just had a chance, and advised them not to bet heavily. George hated to see the price come down, because he invariably had his bets with the S.P. offices. And when it won, he appeared surprised, and told everybody how he nearly had a fiver on, but thinking the matter over in a quiet place, he had decided that, with the income tax what it was, it was criminal to waste money. And some people believed him.

George was in a fairly happy state of mind when he went out to the Hippoleum, for that morning he had come up from Wiltshire after witnessing the trial of Blue Chuck, his Newbury Cup horse. Blue Chuck had slammed the horses in the trial and had won on a tight rein by many lengths. And not a single writing person had tipped Blue Chuck. It was certain to start amongst the '100 to 6 others' and George was already practising the appearance of amazement which he would display when he faced his acquaintances.

In the cheerful contemplation of Wednesday Mr. Canfyn sallied forth, his complacency fortified by three old brandies, which had cost him nothing, a sample bottle having been sent to him by a misguided wine merchant. And then came the disaster.

Three policemen brought him into Hallam Street Station, and here the matter might have been satisfactorily arranged if the third of the three old brandies had not started to put in some fine work.

'I'll have your coats off your backs for this, you scoundrels!' he screamed, as they searched him scientifically. 'I'm the Honourable George Canfyn, the son of Lord Llanwattock – '

'What's the charge?' asked the weary station-sergeant, who was not unused to such scenes of agitation.

'Drunk and disorderly and assault,' said the policeman who had brought in this scion of nobility.

'I'm not drunk!' roared George. 'Don't take those things away from me, they're my private papers! And count that money – if there's a penny missing, I'll have you kicked out of the police force – '

'Number 8,' said the man on the desk, and they led George below.

'Oh, that a man should put an enemy into his mouth to steal away his brains,' murmured the inspector, standing in the open doorway of his room. 'Drink is a terrible thing, Sergeant!'

'Yes, sir,' said the sergeant, and looked up at the clock. It was perilously near ten.

The inspector went back to his room with a sigh. The big table was covered with cards and addressed envelopes, and the inspector was an elderly man and very tired. He looked for a long time at the accumulation of work that had to be finished before the midnight post went out.

Inspector Pine was, amongst other things, Secretary of the Racecourse Elevation Brotherhood for the Suppression of Gambling. And the cards were to announce a special meeting of the Brotherhood to consider next year's programme. And, as yet, not one of the thousand cards had been stamped with the announcement that, owing to a regrettable prior engagement, the Bishop of Chelsea would not be able to attend.

He was so contemplating the unfinished work when there was a tap at his door and The Miller came in.

'A miracle has happened, sir,' he said. 'I've found three decent people who can swear that Evans was practically under their eyes when the larceny was committed. Mr. Isaacheim, the well-known and highly respected commission agent – '

'A bookmaker,' murmured Inspector Pine, reproachfully.

'Still, he's a taxpayer, and a rate-payer,' said The Miller loyally. 'And though to me gambling is a form of criminal lunacy, we must take his word. And Mr. Corgan, of the "Blue Hart" – '

'A publican,' said the old man Pine in distress.

'And a sinner. But he's a well-known town councillor. Can I tell the gaoler to let Evans go?'

Inspector Pine nodded, and his eyes returned to the unfinished work.

'You don't know anybody who could help me to put these cards into envelopes, I suppose, Sergeant?'

It was an S.O.S.: an appeal directed to The Miller himself.

'No, sir,' replied Miller promptly; and then, as a thought occurred to him: 'Why don't you ask Evans? He's a man of education, and he'd be glad to stop for a few hours.'

Educated Evans had spent a sleepless five hours in a large and sanitary cell, meditating alternately upon man's injustice to man and the depleted state of his exchequer. For his possessions consisted of the exact amount to cover the return fare to Newbury, and the price of admission.

For purposes of investment he had not so much as a tosser. It was the beginning of the season, and his clientele had been dissipated by mistaken efforts on his part to carry on business through the winter. It would take him to the Jubilee meeting before he could re-establish their confidence.

He heard the sound of an angry voice and, peering through the ventilator of the cell, saw and recognised the Honourable George Canfyn being led to confinement. When the gaoler had gone:

'Excuse me, Mr. Canfyn!' said Educated Evans, in a hoarse whisper, his mouth to the ventilator. He was all a-twitter with excitement.

'What do you want?' growled the voice of the Honourable George from the next cell.

'I'm Johnny Evans, sir, better known as Educated Evans, the well-known Turf Adviser. What about your horse, Blue Chuck, for tomorrow?'

'Go to hell!' boomed the voice of his fellow-prisoner.

'I can do you a bit of good,' urged Evans. 'I've got a stone pinch – '

'Go to blazes, you – '

In his annoyance he described Educated Evans libellously.

Educated Evans was meditating upon the strangeness of fate that had brought the son of a millionaire into No. 8, when the lock of his cell snapped back.

'You can go, Evans,' said The Miller genially. 'I've gone to no end of trouble to get you out – as I said I would. What's that horse in the one o'clock?'

'Clarok Lass,' said Evans; and The Miller swore softly.

'If I'd known that, I'd have left you to die,' he said. 'You said it wasn't Clarok Lass – here, come on, the inspector's got a job for you.'

Wonderingly, Educated Evans followed the detective to the inspector's room, and in a few gentle words the nature of the job was explained.

'I will give you ten shillings out of my own pocket, Evans,' said

Inspector Pine, 'and at the same time I feel that I am perhaps an instrument to bring you to the light.'

Educated Evans surveyed the table with a professional eye. He was not unused to the task of filling envelopes, for there was a time when he had a thousand clients on his books.

Miller, glad to escape, left them as soon as he could find an excuse, and the inspector proceeded to enlighten his helper in the use of the stamp.

'When the stencil is worn out you can write another. Fix it over the inking pad so, and go ahead.'

It was a curious stamp, one unlike any that Evans had ever used. It consisted of an oblong stencil paper, fixed in a stiff paper frame and a metal ink-holder. The inspector showed him how the stencil was written with a sharp-pointed stylus on a stiff board, how it had to be damped before and blotted after, and Evans, who had never stopped learning, watched.

'It will be something for you to reflect upon that every one of these dear people is an opponent to the pernicious sport of horse-racing. For once in your life, Evans, you are doing something to crush the hydra-headed monster of gambling.'

'Where's that ten shillings, sir?' said Evans, and the officer parted.

He was on the point of leaving Evans to his task when the station-sergeant came in.

'Here's the money and papers of that drunk, sir,' he said, and deposited a small package on the desk. 'Perhaps you'd better put them in the safe. He's sent for his solicitor, so he'll probably be bailed out. But he made such a fuss about his being robbed that it might be better to keep them until he comes before the magistrates in a sober mind.'

Mr. Pine nodded and opened the big safe that stood in one corner of the room as the sergeant went out. First he put the money, the watch and gold cigarette-case in a drawer. Then he took up the little pocket-book and turned the leaves with professional deftness.

'Another gambler,' he said sadly.

'Who's that, sir?'

'A man – a gentleman who is unfortunately with us tonight,' said Inspector Pine, and paused. 'What is a trial, Evans?'

'A trial, sir?'

'It is evidently something to do with horse-racing,' said the inspector, and read, half to himself: ' "Blue Chuck 8 to 7; Golders Green 7 to 7; Miliken 7 to 0. Won four lengths. Time 1.39." That has to do with racing, Evans?'

Educated Evans nodded, not trusting himself to speak.

'You have your ten shillings, Evans. I will leave you now. Give the letters to the sergeant; he will post them. Goodnight.'

From time to time that night the sergeant glanced through the open door of the inspector's room, and apparently Educated Evans was a busy man. At midnight, just as the Hon. George Canfyn's solicitor arrived, he carried his work to the station-sergeant's desk, and after the sergeant had made a quick scrutiny of the private office to see that nothing was missing, Evans was allowed to depart.

At ten o'clock next morning Inspector Pine was shaving when his crony and fellow-labourer in the social field (Mr. Scott, the retired grocer) arrived in great haste. And there was on Mr. Stott's face a look of bewilderment and annoyance.

'Good morning, Brother Stott,' said the inspector. 'I got all those cards out last night – at least, I hope I did.'

Mr. Stott breathed heavily.

'I got my card, Brother Pine,' he said, 'and I'd like to know the meaning of it.'

He thrust a piece of cardboard into the lathered face of the inspector. There was nothing extraordinary in the card. It was an invitation to a meeting of the Brotherhood for Suppressing Gambling.

'Well?'

'Look on the other side,' hissed Mr. Stott.

The inspector turned the card and read the stencilled inscription:

If any brother wants the winner of the Newbury Handicap, send P.O. for 20s. to the old reliable Educated Evans, 92 Bayham Mews. This is the biggest pinch of the year! Defeat ignored! Roll up, Brothers. Help yourself, and make P.O. payable to J. Evans.

'Of course, nobody will reply to the foolish and evil man,' said the inspector, as he was giving instructions to The Miller. 'Every member of the Brotherhood will treat it with contempt; still, you had better see Evans.'

When The Miller arrived at 92 Bayham Mews – it was the upper part of a stable – he found that melancholy man opening telegrams at the rate of twenty a minute.

'And more's coming,' said Educated Evans. 'There's no punter like a Brother.'

'What's the name of the horse?' asked The Miller in a fever.

'Blue Chuck – help yourself,' said Educated Evans. 'And don't forget you owe me a pound.'

The Miller hurried off to interview Mr. Isaacheim, the eminent and respectable Turf accountant.

MR. HOMASTER'S
DAUGHTER

M R. HOMASTER's daughter was undoubtedly the belle of
Camden Town, and when she retired from public life
there is less doubt that Mr. Homaster's trade suffered in
consequence.

But Mr. Homaster very rightly said that even the saloon-bar was
no place for a young lady, and although, as a result of her with-
drawal, many clients who had with difficulty sustained themselves
at saloon prices returned in a body to the public portion of the Rose
and Hart, where beer is the staple of commerce, Mr. Homaster –
formerly Hochmeister – bore his loss with philosophy, and his
reputation, both as a gentleman and a father, stood higher than ever.

Miss Belle Homaster was the most beautiful woman that Educated
Evans had ever seen. She was tall, with golden hair and blue eyes,
and a fine figure. Across her black, tightly-fitting and well-occupied
blouse she invariably wore the word 'Baby' in diamonds, that being
her pet name to her father and her closer relatives.

Evans used to go into the saloon-bar every night for the happiness
of seeing her smile, as she raised her delicately pencilled eyebrows
at him. She never asked unnecessary questions. A lift of those arched
brows, a gracious nod from Evans, the up-ending of a bottle, a
gurgle of soda water, and Evans laid two half-crowns on the counter
and received the change with a genteel 'Thenks.'

Sometimes she said it was a very nice day for this time of year.
Sometimes, when it wasn't a very nice day, she asked, with a note
of gentle despair: 'What else can you expect?'

It was generally understood that Evans was her favourite.

Certainly he alone of all customers was the recipient of her confidences. It was to Evans that she confessed her partiality for asparagus, and it was Evans who heard from her own lips that she had once, as a small girl, travelled in the same bus as a well-known murderer.

A friend of his, at his earnest request, spoke about him glowingly, told her of his education and his ability to settle bets on the most obtuse questions without reference to a book. The way thus prepared by his friendly barker, Evans seized the first opportunity of producing samples of his deep knowledge and learning.

'It's curious, miss, me and you standing here, with the world revolving on its own axle once in twenty-four hours, thereby causing night and day. Few of us realise so to speak, the myst'ries of nature, such as the moon and the stars, which are other worlds like ours. They say there's life on Mars owing to the canals, which have been observed by telescopic observation. Which brings us to the question: Is Mars inhabited?'

She listened, dazed.

'The evolution of humanity,' Evans went on enjoyably, 'was invented by Darwin, which brings us to the question of prehistoric days.'

'What a lot you know!' said the young lady. 'Would you like a little more soda? The weather's very seasonable, isn't it?'

'The seasons are created or caused by the revolutions of the world – ' began Evans.

But she was called away to tend the needs of an uneducated man who needed a chaser.

Everybody knew Miss Homaster. Even The Miller. When that light and ornament of the Criminal Investigation Department desired an interview with any of his criminal acquaintances, he was certain of finding them hovering like obese moths about the flame of her charm and beauty.

At eight, or thereabouts, Sergeant William Arbuthnot Challoner would push open the swing doors of the saloon-bar and glance carelessly round, nod to such of his old friends as he saw, raise his hat to Miss Homaster and retire.

The news of her engagement was announced two days before she left the bar for good. It was to the unhappy Evans that she made the revelation.

'I'm being married to a gentleman friend of mine,' she said, as

Educated Evans clutched the edge of the counter for support. 'I
believe in marrying young and being true. A wife should be a friend
to her husband and help him. She ought to be interested in his
business. Don't you agree, Mr. Evans?'

'Yes, miss,' said Evans with an effort. 'For richer and poorer, in
sickness and in woe, ashes to ashes.'

The Miller learnt of the engagement from Educated Evans.

'I believe in marriage,' he said. 'It keeps the divorce court busy.'

A heartless, cynical man, in whom the wells of human kindness
had run dry.

There is a legend that once upon a time The Miller had a fortune
in his hand, or within reach of that member. The Miller never
discussed the matter, even with his intimates. Even Educated Evans,
who counted himself something more than an ordinary acquaintance, with rare delicacy never referred to that tremendous lost
opportunity.

Yet, there it was: Fortune, with a row of houses under each arm,
had kicked at the door, and The Miller had hesitated with his hand
on the latch.

Rows of houses, a fast car, Tatts every day of his life if he so
desired, and his ambition moved to such a lofty end – and lost
because The Miller refused to credit the evidence of his own ears,
or to accept the dictum of the ancients, *in vino veritas*.

Mr. Sandy Leman was certainly *in vino* when The Miller pinched
him for (1) drunk, (2) creating a disturbance, (3) conduct calculated
to bring about a breach of the peace, (4) insulting behaviour. ('He
was,' to quote the expressive language of Educated Evans, 'so soused
that he tried to play a coffee stall under the impression it was a grand
pianner.') As to the *'veritas'*, was The Miller justified in believing that
there was only one trier in the Clumberfield Nursery, and that trier
Curly Eyes? Mr. Sandy Leman proclaimed the fact to the world on
the way to the station, insisted on seeing the divisional surgeon to
tell him, and made pathetic enquiries for Mr. Winston Churchill's
telephone number in order to pass the good news along to one about
whom – in moments of extreme intoxication – he was wont to shed
bitter tears.

The Miller had the market to himself, so to speak, and after much
hesitation had five shillings each way. And that, after having decided
overnight to take a risk and have fifty to win! Curly Eyes won at

100 to 6. The Miller read the news, cast the paper to the earth and jumped on it. That is the story.

Along the platform of Paddington Station came Educated Evans at a slow and not unstately pace. His head was held proudly, his eyes half-closed, as though the sight of so many common racing people en route for Newbury was more than he dared see, and in his mouth a ragged cigar. Race glasses, massive and imposing, were suspended from one shoulder, an evening newspaper protruded from each of the pockets of his overcoat.

Educated Evans halted before the locked door of an empty first-class carriage and surveyed the approaching guard soberly.

'Member,' he said simply.

'Member of Parliament or Member of Tattersalls?' asked the sardonic guard.

'Press,' said Evans, even more gravely. 'I'm the editor of *The Times*.'

The guard made a gesture.

'Where's your ticket?' he asked, and with a sigh Educated Evans produced it.

'Third class – *and* yesterday's,' said the guard bitterly. 'Love-a-duck, some of you fellows *never* lose hope, do you?'

'I shall take your number, my friend,' said Evans, stung to speech. 'The Railway Act of eighteen seventy-four specifically specifies that tickets issued under the Act are transferable and interchangeable – '

The guard passed on. Evans saw the door of a corridor car open and the guard's back turned. He stepped in and, sinking into a corner seat, blotted out his identity with an evening newspaper.

'I always say, sir,' said Evans, as the train began to move and it was safe to appear in public, 'that to start cheap is to start well. Not that I'm not in a position to pay my way like a gentleman and a sportsman.'

His solitary companion was also hidden behind an extended newspaper.

'It stands to reason,' Mr. Evans went on, 'that a man like myself, who is, so to speak, in the confidence of most of the Berkshire and Wiltshire stables, and have my own co-respondents at Lambourn, Manton, Stockbridge, et cetera, it only stands to reason that, owning my own horses as I do – hum!'

The Miller regarded him coldly over the edge of his newspaper.

'Don't let me interrupt you, Evans,' he said, politely. 'Let me hear about these horses of yours, I beg! Tell-a-Tale, by Swank out of Gullibility, own brother to Jailbird, and a winner of races; Tipster, by Annanias out of Writer's Cramp, by What-Did-I-Give-Yer.'

'Don't let us have any unpleasantness, Mr. Miller,' said Evans, mildly. 'I'm naturally an affable and talkative person, like the famous Cardinal Rishloo, who, bein' took to task by Napoleon for his garolisty, replied, "There's many a good tune played on an old fiddle".'

'Not satisfied,' continued The Miller, 'with defrauding the Railway by travelling first on a dud third-class ticket, you must endeavour, by misrepresentation of a degrading character, to obtain money by false pretences.'

The Miller shook his head, and the straw between his teeth twirled ominously.

'What are you backing in the two-thirty?' asked Evans pleasantly. 'I've got something that could lay down and go to sleep and then get up and win so far that the judge'd have to paint a new distance board. This thing can't be beat, Mr. Miller. If the jockey was to fall off this here horse would stop, pick him up, and win with him in his mouth! He's that intelligent. I've had it from the boy that does him.'

'If he does him as well as you've done me,' said The Miller, 'he ought to glitter! I'm doing nothing but your unbeaten gem in the Handicap. Isaacheim wouldn't lay me the money I wanted, so I thought I'd come down. Not that the horse will win.'

The melancholy face of Educated Evans twisted in a sneer.

'It will win,' he said with calm confidence. 'If this horse was left at the post and started running the wrong way he could turn round and *then* win! I know what I'm talking about. I can't give you the strength of it without, in a manner of speakin', betrayin' a sacred confidence. But this horse will *win*! I've sent it out to three thousand clients – '

'That's a lie,' said The Miller, resuming his perusal of the *Sporting Life*.

'Well, three hundred – an' not far short.'

Mr. Evans fingered the crisp notes in his pocket, and the crackle of them made music beside which the lute of Orpheus would have sounded as cheerful as a church bell on a foggy morning. He had certainly received inspired information. If Blue Chuck was not a certainty for the Newbury Handicap, then there were no such things as certainties. He had seen the owner's description of the trial in the owner's own pocket-book.

All that morning Mr. Evans had been engaged in despatching to his clients – for he was a tipster not without fame in Camden Town – the glorious and profitable news. For an hour he had carried the tidings of great joy to an old and tried clientèle. Some had been so well and truly tried that they publicly insulted him. Others to whom, leaning across the zinc-covered counter of the public bar, he had whispered the hectic intelligence, had drawn a pint, mechanically, and said: 'Is this another one of your so-and-so dreams?'

Educated Evans had time to catch the 12.38. Mr. Evans could have afforded a first-class ticket, but he held firmly to the faith that there were three states that it was the duty of every citizen to best. First came the Government; then, in order of merit, came the railways; thirdly, and at times even firstly, appeared the bookmaking class.

He had secured his ticket from a fellow sojourner at the Rose and Hart. Its owner valued it at two bob. Evans beat him down to eightpence.

'Making money out of Blue Chuck is easier than drawing the dole,' said Evans, 'as I know. Mr. Miller, you understand these things. What would you put eighteen hundred pounds into if you was me?'

'Eh?' said the startled Miller. 'You've got eighteen hundred pounds?'

'Not at the moment,' admitted Evans modestly. 'But that is the amount I'll have when I come back. It's a lot of money to carry about. House property is not what it was,' he added, 'nor Government Bonds, after what this Capital Levy is trying to do to us. Who *is* this feller Levy, Mr. Miller? It's Jewish, but I don't seem to remember the Christian name?'

As the train was passing through Reading, Educated Evans delivered himself of a piece of philosophy.

'Bookmakers get fat on what I might term the indecision of the racin' public,' he said. 'The punter who follows the advice of his Turf Adviser blindly and fearlessly is the feller who packs the parcel.

But does he follow the advice of his Turf Adviser blindly and
fearlessly, Mr. Miller? No, he doesn't.'

'And he's wise,' said The Miller without looking up from his
paper, 'if you happen to be the Turf Adviser.'

'That may be or may not be,' said Educated Evans firmly. 'I'm
merely telling you what I've learnt from years an' years of experience
– and mind you, my recollection goes back to the old days. It's
hearin' things, it's bein' put off, it's bein' told this, that and the
other by nosey busybodies that enables Sir Douglas Stuart – ain't
he? well, he ought to be – to spend his declining days on the
Rivyera.'

'The trouble with you, Evans,' said The Miller, folding his paper
as the train slowed for Newbury, 'is that you talk too much.'

'The trouble with me,' said Educated Evans, with dignity, 'is that
I *think* too much!'

He parted from the detective on the platform, and was making
his way towards the entrance of the Silver Ring when he stopped
dead. A lady was crossing the roadway to the pay gate, and the
heart of Educated Evans leapt within him. He knew that tightly
belted black coat, that fur hat and, beneath it, that golden hair. For
a second the economist and the lover struggled one with the other,
and the lover won. Educated Evans followed hot on her trail, winc-
ing with pain as he counted out the notes and followed the lady to
the paddock.

She turned at the sound of her name, and it must be said of Miss
Homaster that her attitude towards Evans was not only extremely
cordial but amazingly condescending.

'Why, Mr. Evans, whoever expected to see you?' she said. 'What
extraordinary weather it is for this time of the year!'

'It is indeed, Miss Homaster,' said Evans. 'Is your respected father
with you?'

'No, I've come alone,' said Miss Homaster, with a saucy toss of
her head, 'and I'm going to back all the winners.'

Here was the chance that Educated Evans had been praying for,
the opportunity which he never dreamt would come. He had pictured himself rescuing her from burning houses, or diving into the
seething waters of the canal and bringing her back to safety, perhaps
breathing his last in her arms; but he had never imagined that the
opportunity would arise of giving her 'the goods'.

'Miss Homaster,' he said in a hoarse whisper, 'I'm going to do you a bit of good. I've got the winner of the Handicap. It's Blue Chuck; he's a stone certainty. He could fall down and get up and then win.'

'Really?' She was genuinely interested as he told her the strength of it.

He left her soon after – he knew his place – and strolled into the ring. He had been in Tattersalls once before, but the experience was not as exciting as it might have been. An acquaintance saw him and came boisterously towards him.

'Hallo, Educated!' he said. 'I've got something good for you, old cock; I've got the winner of the Handicap up me sleeve. Bing Boy!'

He looked round to see that he was not overheard, and in his interest he failed to see the cold sneer that was growing on the face of Mr. Evans.

'This horse,' said his acquaintance, 'has been tried good enough to win the Derby even if it was run over hurdles! This horse could fall down – '

'And I should say he would fall down,' said Evans, his exasperation getting the better of his politeness. 'You couldn't make me back Bing Boy with bad money. You couldn't make me back it with bookmakers who had twilight sleep and forgot all that happened a few minutes later. Bing Boy!' he said, with withering contempt.

Nevertheless, Bing Boy was favourite, and the horse that Educated Evans had come to back was at any price. Evans was disconcerted, alarmed. He went into the paddock and saw the scowling owner of his great certainty. He did not look happy. Perhaps it was because he had spent the greater part of the previous evening in an uncomfortable police cell.

Evans went in search of the man who gave him Bing Boy to get a little further information.

And they were backing Smocker. He was a strong second favourite, and it was difficult to get 7 to 2 about him. A man Evans knew drew him aside to a place where he could not be overheard by the common crowd and told him all about Smocker.

'This horse,' he said impressively, as he poked his finger in Evans' waistcoat to emphasise the seriousness of the communication, 'has been tried twenty-one pounds better than Glasshouse. He won the trial on a tight rein, and if what I hear is true – and the man that told me is the boy that does him – Smocker could fall down – '

'There'll be a few falls in this race,' said Educated Evans hollowly.

The first few events were cleared from the card, betting started in earnest over the Handicap, and yet Educated Evans delayed his commission. To nearly three hundred clients he had wired 'Blue Chuck. Help yourself. Can't be beaten.' And here was Blue Chuck sliding down the market like a pat of butter on the Cresta Run! Tens, a hundred to eight, a hundred to seven in places.

'Phew!' said Educated Evans.

The notes in his pocket were damp from handling. He made another frantic dive into the paddock in the hope of finding somebody who would give him the least word of encouragement about Blue Chuck. Again he saw the owner of Blue Chuck, scowling like a fiend.

And then somebody spoke to him, and he turned quickly, hat in hand.

'Why, I've been looking everywhere for you, Mr. Evans,' said Miss Homaster. 'I've got such a wonderful tip for you. Your horse – Blue Chuck, wasn't it? – isn't fancied in the least bit. The owner told a friend of mine that he didn't expect he'd finish in the first three.'

The heart of Educated Evans sank, but it was not with sorrow for his deluded clients.

'Smocker will win.' She lowered her voice. 'It's a certainty. I've just been offered five to one, and I've backed it.'

'Five to one?' said Educated Evans, his trading instincts aroused. 'You can't get more than four to one.'

'*I* can,' said the girl in triumph. 'I'll show you.'

Proud to be seen in such delightful company, Educated Evans followed her, through the press of Tattersalls, down the rails, until near the end he saw a tall, florid young man – no less a person than Barney Gibbet!

'Mr. Gibbet, this is a friend of mine who wants to back Smocker. You'll give him five to one?'

Gibbet looked sorrowfully at Educated Evans.

'Five to one, Miss Homaster?' he said, shaking his head. 'No, it's above the market price.'

'But you promised me,' she said reproachfully.

'Very well. How much do you want on it, sir?'

The lips of Educated Evans opened, but he could not pronounce the words. Presently they came.

'Three hundred,' he said in broken tones.

'Ready?' asked Mr. Gibbet, with pardonable suspicion.

'Ready,' said Educated Evans.

It proved, on examination, that he only had £240. He had conjured up the other £60, for he was ever an optimist. In the end he was laid £1,100 to £220.

'You won't mind if I give you a cheque for your winnings?' asked Mr. Gibbet. 'I don't carry a large sum of money around with me; it's not quite safe amongst these disreputable characters you meet on racecourses.'

'I quite agree,' said Educated Evans heartily and went up to the stand to see the race.

It was a race that can easily be described, calling for none of those complicated and intricate calculations which form a feature of every race description.

Blue Chuck jumped off in front, made the whole of the running, and won hard held by five lengths. Two horses of whose existence Educated Evans was profoundly ignorant were second and third. Smocker was pulled up half-way down the straight.

Educated Evans staggered down from the stand and into the paddock. His only chance, and it seemed a feeble one, was that the twelve horses that finished in front of Smocker would be disqualified. But the flag went up and a stentorian voice sang musically, 'Weighed in.'

Educated Evans dragged his weary feet to the train.

'It doesn't leave for an hour yet,' said an official.

'I can wait,' said Educated Evans gently.

Just after the last race The Miller came along the platform looking immensely pleased with himself. He saw Evans and turned into the carriage.

'Had a good race, my boy?' he asked. 'I did, and thank you for the tip.'

'Not at all,' murmured Evans in the tone of one greatly suffering.

'They tried to lumber me on to Smocker, but no bookmakers' horses for me!'

'Is he a bookmakers' horse?' asked Evans with a flicker of mild interest.

'Yes, he belongs to that fellow Gibbet – the man who's engaged to Miss Homaster.'

Educated Evans tried to smile.

'If you feel ill,' said the alarmed Miller, 'you'd better open the window.'

THE COOP

SOMETIMES they referred to Mr. Yardley in the newspapers as 'the Wizard of Stotford', sometimes his credit was diffused as the 'Yardley Confederation'; occasionally he was spoken of as plain 'Bert Yardley' but invariably his entries for any important handicaps were described as 'The Stotford Mystery'. For nobody quite knew what Mr Yardley's intentions were until the day of the race. Usually after the race, for it is a distressing fact that the favourite from his stable was usually unplaced, and the winner – also from his stable – started amongst the '100 to 7 others'.

After the event was all over and the 'weighed in' had been called, people used to gather in the paddock in little groups and ask one another what this horse was doing at Nottingham, and where were the Stewards, and why Mr. Yardley was not jolly well warned off. And they didn't say 'jolly' either.

For it is an understood thing in racing that, if an outsider wins its trainer ought to be warned off. Yet neither Bert Yardley, nor Colonel Rogersman, nor Mr. Lewis Feltham – the two principal owners for whom he trained – were so much as asked by the Stewards to explain the running of their horses. Thus proving that the Turf needed reform, and that the stipendiary steward was an absolute necessity.

Mr Bert Yardley was a youngish man of thirty-five, who spoke very little and did his betting by telegram. He had a suite at the Midland Hotel, and was a member of a sedate and respectable club in Pall Mall. He read extensively, mostly such classics as *Races to Come*, and the umpteenth volume of the Stud Book, and he leavened his studies with such lighter reading as the training reports from the daily sporting newspapers – he liked a good laugh.

His worst enemy could not complain of him that he refused information to anybody.

'I think mine have some sort of chance, and I'm backing them both. Tinpot? Well, of course, he may win; miracles happen, and I shouldn't be surprised if he made a good show. But I've had to ease him in his work and when I galloped him on Monday he simply wouldn't have it – couldn't get him to take hold of his bit. Possibly he runs better when he's a little above himself, but he's a horse of moods. If he'd only give his running, he'd trot in! Lampholder, on the other hand, is as game a horse as ever looked through a bridle. A battler! He'll be there or thereabouts.'

What would you back on that perfectly candid, perfectly honest information straight, as it were, from the horse's mouth?

Lampholder, of course, and Tinpot would win. Even stipendiary stewards couldn't make Lampholder win, not if they got behind and shoved him. And that, of course, is no part of a stipendiary steward's duties.

Mr. Bert Yardley was dressing for dinner one March evening when he discovered that a gold watch had disappeared. He called his valet, who could offer no other information than that it had been there when they left Stotford for Sandown Park.

'Send for the police,' said Mr. Yardley, and there came to him Detective-Sergeant Challoner.

Mr. Challoner listened, made a few notes, asked a few, a very few, questions of the valet and closed his book.

'I think I know the person,' he said, and to the valet: 'A big nose, you're sure of the big nose?'

The valet was emphatic.

'Very good,' said The Miller. 'I'll do my best, Mr. Yardley. I hope I shall be as successful as Amboy will be in the Lincoln Handicap.'

Mr Yardley smiled faintly.

'We'll talk about that later,' he said.

The Miller made one or two enquiries and that night pulled in Nosey Boldin, whose hobby it was to pose as an inspector of telephones and who, in this capacity, had made many successful experiments. On the way to the station, Nosey, so-called because of a certain abnormality in that organ, delivered himself with great force and venom.

'This comes of betting on horse-races and follering Educated Evans' perishin' five-pound specials! Let this be a warning to you. Miller!'

'Not so much lip,' said The Miller.

'He gave me one winner in ten shots, and *that* started at 11 to 10 on,' ruminated Nosey. 'Men like that drive men to crime. There ought to be a law so's to make the fifth loser a *felony*! And after the eighth loser he ought to 'ang! That'd stop 'em.'

The Miller saw his friend charged and lodged for the night and went home to bed. And in the morning, when he left his rooms to go to breakfast, the first person he saw was Educated Evans, and there was on that learned man's unhappy face a look of pain and anxiety.

'Good morning, Mr. Challoner. Excuse me if I'm taking a liberty, but I understand that a client of mine is in trouble?'

'If you mean Nosey, he is,' agreed The Miller. 'And what's more, he attributes his shame and downfall to following your tips. I sympathise with him.'

Educated Evans made an impatient clicking sound, raised his eyebrows and spread out his hand.

'Bolsho,' he said simply.

'Eh?' The Miller frowned suspiciously. 'You didn't give Bolsho?'

'Every guaranteed client received "Bolsho: fear nothing".' said Evans even more simply: 'following Mothegg (ten to one, beaten a neck, hard lines), Toffeetown (third, hundred to eight, very unlucky), Onesided (won, seven to two, what a beauty!), followin' Curds and Whey (won, eleven to ten – can't help the price). Is that fair?'

'The question is,' said The Miller deliberately, 'did Nosey subscribe to your guarantee wire, your five-pound special, or your overnight nap?'

'That,' said Educated Evans diplomatically, 'I can't tell till I've seen me books. The point is this: if Nosey wants bail, am I all right? I don't want any scandal, and you know Nosey. He ought to have been in advertisin'.'

The advertising propensities of Nosey were, indeed, well known to The Miller. He had the knack of introducing some startling feature into the very simplest case, and attracting to himself the amount of newspaper space usually given to scenes in the House and important murders.

It was Nosey who, by his startling statement that pickles were a greater incentive to crime than beer, initiated a press correspondence which lasted for months. It was Nosey who, when charged with hotel larceny – his favourite aberration – made the pronouncement that buses were a cause of insanity. Upon the peg of his frequent misfortunes, it was his practice to hang a showing-up for somebody.

The case of Nosey was dealt with summarily. Long before the prosecutor had completed his evidence he realised that his doom was sealed.

'Anything known about this man?' asked the magistrate.

A jailer stepped briskly into the box and gave a brief sketch of Nosey's life, and Nosey, who knew it all before, looked bored.

'Anything to say?' asked the magistrate.

Nosey cleared his throat.

'I can only say, Your Worship, that I've fell into thieving ways owing to falling in the hands of unscrupulous racing tipsters. I'm ruined by tips, and if the law was just, there's a certain party who ought to be standing here by my side.'

Educated Evans, standing at the back of the court, squirmed.

'I've got a wife, as true a woman as ever drew the breath of life,' Nosey went on. 'I've got two dear little children, and I ask Your Worship to consider me temptation owing to horse-racing, and betting and this here tipster.'

'Six months,' said the magistrate, without looking up.

Outside the court Mr. Evans waited patiently for the appearance of The Miller.

'Nosey never had more than a shilling on a horse in his life,' he said bitterly, 'and he *owes*! Here's the bread being took out of my mouth by slander and misrepresentation; do you think they'll put it in the papers, Mr. Challoner?'

'Certain,' said The Miller cheerfully, and Educated Evans groaned.

'That man's worse than Lucreature Burgia, the celebrated poisoner,' he said, 'that Shakespeare wrote a play about. He's a snake in the grass and viper in the bosom. And to think I gave him Penwiper for the Manchester November, and he never so much as asked me if I was thirsty! Mr. Challoner.'

Challoner, turning away, stopped.

'Was that Yardley? I mean the trainer?'

The Miller looked at him reproachfully.

'Maybe I'm getting old and my memory is becoming defective,' he said, 'but I seem to remember that when you gave me Tellmark the other day, you said that you were a personal friend of Mr. Yardley's and that the way he insisted on your coming down to spend the weekends was getting to be a public nuisance.'

Educated Evans did not 'bat a lid'.

'That was his brother,' he said.

'He must have lied when he told me he had no brothers,' said The Miller.

'They've quarrelled,' replied Educated Evans frankly. 'In fact, they never mention one another's names. It's tragic when brothers quarrel, Mr. Challoner. I've done my best to reconcile 'em – but what's the use? He didn't say anything about Amboy, did he?'

'He said nothing that I can tell you,' was his unsatisfactory reply, and he left Mr. Evans to consider means and methods by which he might bring himself into closer contact with the Wizard of Stotford.

All that he feared in the matters of publicity was realised to the full. One evening paper said:

RUINED BY TIPSTERS

Once-prosperous merchant goes to prison for theft.

And in the morning press one newspaper may be quoted as typical of the rest:

TIPSTER TO BLAME

Pest of the Turf wrecks a home.

Detective-Sergeant Challoner called by appointment at the Midland Hotel, and Mr. Yardley saw him.

'No, thank you, sir,' The Miller was firm.

Mr. Yardley put back the fiver he had taken from his pocket.

'I'll put you a tenner on anything I fancy,' he said. 'Who's this tipster, by the way? – the man who was referred to by the prisoner?'

The Miller smiled.

'Educated Evans,' he said, and when he had finished describing him Mr. Yardley nodded.

He was staying overnight in London *en route* for Lincoln and he was inclined to be bored. He had read the *Racing Calendar* from the list of the year's races to the last description of the last selling hurdle race on the back page. He had digested the surprising qualities of stallions and he could have almost recited the forfeit list from Aaron to Znosberg. And he was aching for diversion when the bell-boy brought a card.

It was a large card, tastefully bordered with pink and green roses: its edge was golden and in the centre were the words:

J. T. EVANS
(better known as 'Educated Evans'!!)
The World's Foremost and Leading Turf
Adviser and Racing Cricit
c/o Jockey Club, Newmarket or direct:
92 Bayham Mews, N.W.1
'The Man Who Gave Braxted!!
What a beauty!' – *vide* Press.

Mr. Yardley read, lingering over the printer's errors.

'Show this gentleman up, page,' he said.

Into his presence came Educated Evans, a solemn purposeful man.

'I hope the intrusion will be amply excused by the important nature or character of my business,' he said. This was the opening he had planned.

'Sit down, Mr. Evans,' said Yardley, and Educated Evans put his hat under the chair and sat.

'I've been thinking matters over in the privacy of my den – ' began Evans, after a preliminary cough.

'You're a lion tamer as well?' asked the Wizard of Stotford, interested.

'By "den" I mean "study",' said Evans, gravely. 'To come to the point without beating about the bush – to use a well-known expression – I've heard of a coop.'

'A what?'

'A coop,' said Evans.

'A chicken coop?' asked the puzzled Wizard.

'It's a French word, meaning "ramp",' said Evans.

'Oh yes, I see. "Coup" – it's pronounced "coo", Mr Evans.'

Educated Evans frowned.

'It's years since I was in Paris,' he said; 'and I suppose they've altered it. It used to be "coop" but these French people are always messing and mucking about with words.'

'And who is working this coop?' asked the trainer, politely adopting the old French version.

'Higgson.'

Educated Evans pronounced the word with great emphasis. Higgson was another mystery trainer. His horses also won when least expected. And after they won, little knots of men gathered in the paddock and asked one another if the Stewards had eyes, and why wasn't Higgson warned off?

'You interest me,' said the trainer of Amboy. 'Do you mean that he's winning with St. Kats?'

Evans nodded more gravely still.

'I think it's me duty to tell you,' he said. 'My information' – he lowered his voice and glanced round to the door to be sure that it was shut – 'comes from the boy who does this horse!'

'Dear me!' said Mr. Yardley.

'I've got correspondents everywhere,' said Educated Evans mysteriously. 'My man at Stockbridge sent me a letter this morning – I daren't show it to you – about a horse in that two-year-old race that will win with his ears pricked.'

Mr. Yardley was looking at him through half-closed eyes.

'With his ears pricked?' he repeated, impressed. 'Have they trained his ears too? Extraordinary! But why have you come to tell me about Mr. Higgson's horse?'

Educated Evans bent forward confidently.

'Because you've done me many a turn, sir,' he said; 'and I'd like to do you one. I've got the information. I could shut my mouth an' make millions. I've got nine thousand clients who'd pay me the odds to a pound – but what's money?'

'True,' murmured Mr. Yardley, nodding. 'Thank you, Mr. Evans. St. Kats, I think you said? Now, in return for your kindness, I'll give you a tip.'

Educated Evans held his breath. His amazingly bold plan had succeeded.

'Change your printer,' said Mr. Yardley, rising. 'He can't spell. Good night.'

Evans went forth with his heart turned to stone and his soul seared with bitter animosity.

Mr. Yardley came down after him and watched the shabby figure as it turned the corner, and his heart was touched. In two minutes he had overtaken the educated man.

'You're a bluff and a fake,' he said, good-humouredly, 'but you can have a little, a very little, on Amboy.'

Before Educated Evans could prostrate himself at the benefactor's feet Mr. Yardley was gone.

The next day was a busy one for Educated Evans. All day Miss Higgs, the famous typist of Great College Street, turned her duplicator, and every revolution of the cylinder threw forth, with a rustle and a click, the passionate appeal which Educated Evans addressed to all clients, old and new. He was not above borrowing the terminology of other advertisement writers.

> You want the best winners – I've got them.
> Bet in Evans' way! Eventually, why not now?
> I've got the winner of the Lincoln!
>   What a beauty!
>   What a beauty!
>   What a beauty!
> Confidentially! From the trainer! This is the coop
> of the season! Help yourself! Defeat ignored!

To eight hundred and forty clients this moving appeal went forth.

On the afternoon of the race Educated Evans strolled with confidence to the end of the Tottenham Court Road to wait for the *Star*. And when it came he opened the paper with a quiet smile. He was still smiling, when he read:

> Tenpenny, 1
> St Kats, 2
> Ella Glass, 3
> All probables ran.

'Tenpenny? – never heard of it,' he repeated, dazed, and produced his noon edition. Tenpenny was starred as a doubtful runner.

It was trained by – Yardley.

For a moment his emotions almost mastered him.

'That man ought to be warned off,' he said hollowly, and dragged his weary feet back to the stable-yard.

In the morning came a letter dated from Lincoln.

Dear Mr. Evans, – What do you think of my coop?–
Yours, H. YARDLEY

There was a P.S. which ran:

I put a fiver on for you. Your enterprise deserved it.

Evans opened the cheque tenderly and shook his head.

'After all,' he said subsequently to the quietly jubilant Miller, 'clients can't expect to win *every* time – a Turf Adviser is entitled to his own coops.'

Tenpenny started at 25 to 1.

THE SNOUT

SATURDAY night in High Street, Camden Town, and the lights were blazing. About each stall a group of melancholy sceptics, for the late shopper is not ready to believe all that loud-voiced stallholders claim for their wares.

At one corner a dense, hypnotised crowd of men listening to a diminutive spellbinder who wore a crimson and purple racing jacket over a pair of voluminous tight-gartered breeches.

'. . . did I tell yer people that Benny Eyes was no good for the City an' Suburban 'Andicap? Did I tell yer *not* to back Sommerband for the Metropolitan? Did I tell yer on this very spot last week, an' I'm willing to pay a thousan' poun' to the Temperance 'Ospital if I didn't, that Proud Alec could fall down an' get up and then win the Great Surrey 'Andicap? Did I . . .'

One of the audience edged himself free from the crowd with a sigh and, so doing, edged himself into a quiet-looking, broad-shouldered man, who was chewing a straw and listening intently.

'Good evening, Mr. Challoner,' said Educated Evans.

'Evening, Evans,' said The Miller. 'Picking up a few tips?'

A contemptuous yet pitying smile illuminated the face of the learned Evans.

'From *him*?' he said. 'Do you buy detective stories such as is published in the common press in order to learn policery? No, Mr. Challoner – I was a-standing there as an impartial observer an' a student of the lower classes, their cupidity and credulity bringin' tears to my eyes. I won't knock Holley – I know the man; he takes my tips and goes and sells 'em to the common people. I don't complain, so long as he don't use my name. But the next time he professes to be sellin' Educated Evans' five-pound specials for fourpence I shall take action!'

The Miller half turned and, after a second's hesitation, Educated Evans fell in at his side.

'You don't mind, Mr. Challoner?'

'Not a bit, Evans. If I meet anybody I know I can tell them afterwards I was taking you to the station.'

Evans winced.

'Doesn't it do your heart good to see all these people out and about, and every one got his money honestly by working for it?'

Evans sniffed.

'You know your own business best,' he said cryptically.

'Perhaps they're not *all* horny-handed sons of toil,' admitted The Miller as a familiar face came into his line of vision. 'If my eyes aren't getting wonky, that was old Solly Risk I saw – how long has he been out?'

Educated Evans did not know.

'The habits of the criminal classes,' he said, 'are Greek to me, as Socrates said to Julius Caesar, the well-known Italian. They go in and they come out, and no man knoweth. Solly is as wide as that famous African river, the Amazon, discovered by Stanley in the year seventeen forty-three. But you can be too wide, and snouts being what they are – '

'Snouts?' said The Miller, elaborately puzzled. 'What is a "snout"?'

'It's a phrase used by low people, an' I can well understand you've never heard it,' said Evans politely.

'If by that vulgar expression you mean a man who keeps the police informed on criminal activities,' said The Miller, who knew much better than Evans the title and functions of a police informer, 'let me tell you that Solly was arrested on clear evidence. That's a bad cold of yours, Evans.'

For Educated Evans had sniffed again.

'As a Turf Adviser and England's premier sportin' authority,' said Evans, 'I've me time fully occupied without pryin' into other people's business. I've nothing to say against Ginger Vennett – '

The Miller stopped and regarded his companion oddly.

'Get it out of your mind that Ginger is a snout,' he said. 'He's a hard-working young man – more hard-working than his landlord.'

'Or his landlady,' suggested Evans, and this time his sniff was a terrific one.

'I know nothing about his landlady except that she's good-looking, hard-working and too good for Lee,' said The Miller, and Educated Evans laughed hollowly.

'So was Cleopatra, whose famous needle we all admire, he said. 'So was Lewd-creature Burgia, the celebrated wife of Henry VIII, who tried to poison him by pourin' boilin' lead in his earhole. So was B. Mary, who murdered the innercent little princes in the far-famed Tower of London in . . .'

'Don't let's rake up the past,' pleaded The Miller. 'Have you seen anything of Lee lately? They tell me he's gone into the clock business again?'

It was a deadly insult he was offering to Educated Evans, and nobody knew this better than The Miller. He was actually inviting Evans to turn Nose!

'I'm surprised at you, Mr. Challoner,' said Evans, genuinely hurt, and The Miller laughed and went on.

Everybody liked Lee. He was a good friend, a quiet, unassuming citizen, and more than a faithful husband and father to the pretty shrew he had married in a moment of mental aberration.

His one weakness was clocks. The sight of a clock – particularly an ornate clock – set his blood on fire and provoked him to unlawful doings. He had taken other things but clocks were his speciality.

'It's a hobby,' he told his lodger, a tall, good-looking and fiery-headed young man, who did nothing for a living except back a few up and downers and run for a bookmaker. He had previously represented a West End firm of commission agents, until unprofitable papers appeared in the bunch and they discovered he was getting quick results over the tape at the Italian Club.

The lodger had been a client of Educated Evans; but, following a dispute as to whether he had or had not received a certain winner (odds to 10s.), Educated Evans had struck his name from the list. And this was a source of great distress to Ginger, for he reposed an unnatural faith in the prescience of the educated man.

'I know more about clocks,' said Lee with pride, 'than any other man in the business. I can price every one I see to within a few shillings.'

One night the premises of Halloway's clocks and jewellery shop was broken into, and a silver clock was missing. Two nights later came an urgent call from Lifton House. A valuable ormolu clock, the property of Lord Lifton himself, had vanished . . .

The Miller made a few independent enquiries, met – by appointment and in a dark little street – a Certain Man, and made a midnight call at 930 Little Stibbington Street.

The Miller did not call at Little Stibbington Street to enquire after Lee's health, nor was it a friendly call in the strictest sense of the word. Mrs. Lee was in bed, and answered the door in a skirt, a cardigan, an apron and a look of startled wonder. Later, in the language of the psalmist, she clothed herself with curses as with a garment – for she was, ostensibly, a true wife.

'If I never move from this doorstep, Mr. Miller, and I'm a Gawd-fearing woman that's been attendin' the Presbyterian Church in Stibbington Street off an' on for years, if I die this very minute, my old man hasn't been out of this house for three days with rheumatics antrypus. Without the word of a lie, he can't move from his bed, and you know, Mr. Miller, I've never told you a lie – 'ave I? Answer me, yes or no?'

'Let me talk to your husband,' said the patient Miller.

'He's that ill he wouldn't know you, Mr. Miller,' she urged, agitatedly – if the listening neighbourhood had not heard the agitation appropriate to the moment, she would have been condemned. 'I haven't been able to get his shoes on for days. He's delirious, as Gawd's my judge! He don't know anybody and, what's more, it's catching – measles or something – and you with a wife and family too.'

'I've caught measles before, but I've never caught a wife or family,' said The Miller good-naturedly.

'He won't know you.' The reluctant door opened a little wider. 'Mind how you go – the pram's in the passage and the young man lodger upstairs always leaves his bit of washing to dry . . .'

Wet and semi-dry shirts flapped in the detective's face as he made his way to the back room, illuminated by a low-powered bulb.

Entering, he heard a deep groan. And there was Lee in bed, and on his face a wild and vacant look.

'He won't know you,' said Mrs. Lee, wiping her eye with the corner of her apron. In support of her statement Lee opened his mouth and spoke faintly.

'Is that dear mother?' he quavered. 'Or is it the angels?'

'That's how he's been goin' on for days,' said Mrs. Lee with great satisfaction.

'I 'ear such lovely music,' he went on. 'It sounds like an 'arp!'

'The Welsh Harp,' said Miller. 'Now come out of your trance, Lee, and step round with me to the station – the inspector wants to talk with you.'

Mrs. Lee quivered.

'Are you goin' to take a dyin' man from his bed?' she asked, bitterly. 'Do you want to see yourself showed up in *John Bull*?'

'God forbid!' said Miller and with a dexterous twist of his hand pulled the bedclothes back from the invalid. He was fully dressed, even to his shoes, and between his shoes was an ormolu clock.

'It's a cop,' said Lee, and got up without assistance. 'There's a snout somewhere in this neighbourhood,' he said, without heat. 'If I ever find him, I'll tear his liver out. And his lights,' he added as he remembered those important organs.

It was his ninth offence and Lee, as he knew, was booked for that country house in Devonshire near the River Dart and adjacent to the golf links of Tavistock.

Having vindicated her position as a true wife and faithful help-mate, Mrs. Lee returned to her honorary status of Respectable Woman. The Miller saw her coming out of a cinema with the red-haired lodger, and she tripped up to him coyly – a smile upon her undoubtedly attractive features. The Miller always said that if she had had the sense to keep her mouth shut she might have been mistaken for a French lady. He specified the kind of French lady, but the description cannot be given in a book that is read by young people.

'Oh, Mr. Challoner, I *do* owe you an apology for all the unkind things I said,' she said in her genteel voice; 'but a wife must stick up for her husband, or where would the world be, in a manner of speaking?'

'That's all right, Mrs. Lee,' smiled The Miller, and glanced at her escort. 'I see Vennett is looking after you.'

Mrs. Lee launched forth into a rhapsody of praise.

'He's been so good to me and the children,' she said. 'He's got a bit of money, and he doesn't mind spending it either – you've no idea how kind he's been to me, Mr. Challoner!'

'I can guess,' said the Miller.

The Miller was a philosopher. He accepted, in his professional capacity, a situation which sickened him as a man. One morning he met Educated Evans at the corner of Bayham Street, and that learned man had on his face a look of peace and content which did not accord with his record as the World's Premier Turf Adviser. For Educated Evans had sent out three horses to his clients, of which two had finished fourth and fifth, and the third absolutely last, as The Miller knew.

'It's no good talking to me, Mr. Challoner,' said Educated Evans firmly. 'My information was that Rhineland could have run backwards and won. He was badly rode, according to the sportin' descriptions, and my own idea is that the jockey wasn't trying a yard.'

'If Statesman doesn't win – ' began The Miller threateningly, and Evans' face changed.

'You ain't backing Statesman, are you?' he asked.

'I've backed him,' said The Miller and Educated Evans groaned.

'Then you've lost your money,' he said, with resignation.

The Miller frowned.

'I saw Ginger Vennett, and he told me you'd given it to him as the best of the century, that you'd had this from the owner, and that you told him to put every farthing he had in the world on it. What's the idea, Evans?'

'The idea is,' said Mr. Evans, speaking under the stress of great emotion, 'that I want to put that snout where he belongs – in the gutter!'

The Miller gasped.

'Do you mean to tell me that you twisted him?'

'I do,' said Evans savagely. 'He's got all his savings on Statesman, who hasn't done a gallop for a month. If you've been hoisted with his peter, to use a naval expression, I'm sorry, Mr. Challoner; but I've got one for you on Saturday that can't lose unless they put a rope across the course to trip him up.'

The Miller hurried away to the nearest telephone and called up Mr. Isaacsheim.

'It's Challoner speaking, Isaacsheim,' he said. 'That bet you took about Statesman – I think you'd better call it off.'

'All right, Mr. Challoner,' said the obliging Isaacsheim. 'I don't think much of it myself: the horse hasn't done a gallop for a month and Educated Evans told me – '

'I know what Educated Evans told you,' said The Miller, 'but it's certainly understood that that bet's off.'

In the afternoon The Miller bought an evening newspaper and turned to the stop press, and the first thing he saw was that Statesman had won!

When, in the evening, he discovered that the price was 25 to 1 he went in search of Educated Evans, and found that sad man on the verge of tears.

'I did my best. It's no good arguing the point with me, Mr. Challoner,' he said. 'I've had Ginger round here congratulating me, but telling me that he'd forgotten to have the bet, and that's about as much as I can stand. The only thing I can tell you is *don't back Blazing Heavens* in the two-thirty race tomorrow, because I've given it to Ginger and I've asked him, as a man and a sportsman, not to tell anybody and to put his shirt on it. Revenge,' he went on, 'is repugnant to my nature. But the snout's a snout, and if I don't settle Ginger, then I'm an uneducated man – which, of course, I'm not,' he added modestly.

Obedient to his instructions, The Miller refrained from backing Blazing Heavens and under any circumstances would not have invested a penny on a horse that had 21lb. the worse of the weights with Lazy Loo. And Blazing Heavens won. Its price was 100 to 6. Ginger sent a boy with a ten-shilling note to Educated Evans and asked for his five-pound special for the day.

Educated Evans sat up far into the night examining and analysing the programme for the following day, and at last discovered a certain runner, that not only had 14lb. the worse of the weights, but enjoyed this distinction, that the training reporters of the sporting Press, who usually have something kind to say about every horse, dismissed him with a line: 'Ours has no chance in the Tilbury Selling Handicap.'

He saw also a paragraph in the following morning's newspaper that Star of Sachem – such was the elegant nomenclature of this equine hair-trunk – was being walked to the meeting because his owner did not think that he was worth the railway fare.

Ginger came round to see Evans at his den; and Ginger was wearing a new gold watch and two classy, nearly-diamond rings, a new hat and a tie of brilliant colours.

'Morning, Evans,' he said briskly as he came in. 'Thought I'd come and see you. Me and my young lady are going away to the seaside for our good old annual.'

'Ha, ha!' said Evans politely.

'You've done me a bit of good, old boy.' The snout laid a large, soft hand on Evans' shoulder. 'But I want something better. Give me a stone certainty, and I'll put every bean I've got in the world on it, Evans, and you're on a fiver. Is that fair?'

'That's fair,' said Educated Evans, his hopes rising.

'If we win, I'm buying a little public-house in Kennington,' said Ginger. 'My young lady's going to get a divorce from her husband for cruelty and desertion, and carrying on with the girl at the sweet shop; we'll put the two kids in a home, and there you are. So you see, Evans, it's a bit of a responsibility for you.'

'It is,' said Evans bravely; 'and, speaking as one with a wide and vast experience, I appreciate same, and in the language of Lord Wellington at the battle of Waterloo, I shall only do my duty – Star of Sachem,' he said slowly, deliberately, and with proper emphasis, 'can't be beat in the Tilbury Handicap this afternoon.

'If that horse were poleaxed he could crawl faster than any of the others can run. I've had it from the boy that does him. They've tried him on the time test to be twenty-one pounds better than Ormonde. He's a little faster than The Tetrarch in the first five furlongs, and he stays. If you don't mind, I'll have the five pounds in advance, because I know a reliable bookmaker, and you mightn't get paid.'

Mr. Vennett compromised with three pounds ten; and, miraculous as it may appear, Star of Sachem won by three lengths pulling up, and started at 20 to 1.

Educated Evans had his fiver on the third, which had been given to him by a man who knew the proprietor of a public-house where the owner called for his midday lunch, which was invariably served in a tankard.

It was drawing near to the end of the week when Mrs. Lee called at the police station and had the good fortune to meet The Miller as he was coming out. Her eyes were red, and she was quivering with natural indignation.

'That fellow, Ginger Vennett,' she began without preliminary, 'has run away with the girl at the sweet shop, and I want him pinched for taking my wedding ring for the purpose. Of all the dirty, lying, falsifying, perjurous hounds in the world, he's the worst! He's a snout, Miller, and you know it! Didn't he tell me that he gave away my husband? And to think that I've been nourishing a viper, so to speak, in my bosom – if you'll excuse the language; but this is not the time to be mock-modest.

'To think of all I've done for that man, and how I turned out of my own room for him, and given him the best of food to eat when he was broke, and my poor, dear husband on the moor worrying his heart out about his poor, dear wife and dear innocent children . . .'

When The Miller could get a few words in, those few words were of a nature which left Mrs. Lee in a condition bordering upon hysteria. Educated Evans was not in much better case when The Miller called on him.

'They say he got twenty-two hundred pounds out of Isaacsheim,' said Educated Evans in a voice that trembled. 'Twenty-two hundred – lovaduck! And I give it to him! And all I got was four pounds, and ten bob of that was snide! I had a telegram from him from Margate today and he wants to know what'll win the Brighton Cup.

'And I dare not send it, Mr. Challoner,' he said earnestly; 'I simply dare not send it for fear of the damned thing winning! There's one in the race that will die of heart disease if they go too fast, but if I sent it to Ginger it'd walk home alone!'

'Try it,' said The Miller urgently. 'That woman says he's got such faith in you now that he'll do anything you tell him.'

So Evans wrote a telegram which ran:

Little Sambo in Brighton Cup absolutely unbeatable. Take no notice of the market. Fear nothing; go for a fortune, and don't forget your old pal, Educated Evans.

At three o'clock, when the runners came up with the result, Miller and Evans stood side by side at the corner of Tottenham Court Road – the extent of The Miller's jurisdiction. Two boys came at once, and Evans snatched at the nearest and opened the paper with feverish haste – Little Sambo was unplaced!

'Gotcher!' chortled Evans in triumph.

The Miller was looking at his newspaper. He was reading *The Evening News*, Evans had *The Standard*.

'What do you mean – gotcher?' snarled The Miller and read: 'All probables ran except Little Sambo!'

MR KIRZ BUYS A FIVE-POUND SPECIAL

IN an inner waistcoat pocket, buttoned and rebuttoned, Mr. Jan Kirz kept a five-pound note. Later he grew careless and carried it folded in the top right-hand pocket of that same waistcoat. He would have been wise to have burnt it, as some of the Scottish bookmakers burn their clients' money when the horses they back win at a long price. But he was mean, and the sight of a fiver blazing in the grate would have broken his heart.

Mr. Jan Kirz had, in his time, been American, Dutch, Swiss and Russian. His birthplace was unknown, but it is a fact that he had at one time been detained whilst the authorities were disentangling the mystery of his origin. In the end he was released and ordered to report at the nearest police station at regular intervals.

About every other week during that period of detention it was reported that he had been shot in the Tower – or hanged at Pentonville. So that when Mr. Kirz came back to Camden Town, bearing no signs of having been executed, there was a great deal of disappointment.

Always a wealthy man, the owner of a fine house in Mornington Gardens, he grew in prosperity with the years, and was one of the most consistent, as well as one of the most unsatisfactory, of Educated Evans' clients.

For such was the perversity of fate that he only backed the losers that the learned man sent forth.

'Ah, my poor Effens,' said Mr. Kirz sorrowfully, meeting the educated one – Evans had taken up a position at the corner of Mornington Gardens so that he couldn't be missed – 'and to t'ink dat you gafe me Colly Eyes und I did not pack it! I t'ought of it fife minutes before der race and den I vergot! Ach! it is terriple hard luck. Und after packing two of your losers!'

Evans was not unnaturally annoyed, for he had an arrangement with Mr. Kirz whereby he drew the odds to a pound on every horse which his patron backed.

'I won't go so far as to say that it's capable negligence – to use a legal expression – on your part, Mr. Kirz,' he said, 'but I've got a mouth. And my information costs money. I got this horse from the boy that does him, an' *that* cost me a pony. I've got me office to keep up an' advertising, and one thing and another – '

'My poor Effens!' sympathised Mr. Kirz – he was a stout man with close-cropped hair, and was subject to asthma – 'dis is derrible! But der nex' time you git me one, dare is der odds to *two* bound!'

So Evans had to be content.

Mr. Kirz was by profession a printer and stationer. His premises were known as the Old England Cheap Printing Company and he did a considerable sporting business, though it was rare to find his imprint on the printing he sent forth. Continental philanthropists, anxious to benefit the British public to an incredible extent, found in Mr. Kirz a willing assistant. He specialised in lottery announcements, snide sweepstakes, and other documents of an illicit nature.

Everybody in Camden Town knew this; the police knew it as well as anybody, and had paid surprise visits to the Old England Printing Works. But by the side of the two machines engaged in this practice was a square opening in the wall, for all the world like a service lift. And at the first hint of trouble, every printed sheet and the forme from which it was struck was cast into the hole and fell to the cellar. And in the cellar was a large furnace which was kept going winter and summer, to maintain the hot-water supply.

And that is what the police did not know – in fact, nobody knew it except three compositors whose names ended in 'ski' – Mr. Kirz printed a Russian newspaper – and three machinemen whose names, curiously enough, concluded with 'heim'. And so Mr. Kirz grew wealthy, for in addition to these he had a valuable side line.

One morning The Miller called on Mr. Kirz at his handsome and palatial residence in Mornington Gardens and, being a plain man, he came to the point at once.

'Mr. Kirz, you are in touch with all the wrong 'uns in London; who is working all this slush?'

'Bad money is derrible.' Mr. Kirz shook his head gravely. 'Dat is one of der most derrible dings dat a mans can do. It striges at der root of gommercial gonfidence – '

'Don't let us discuss high finance,' pleaded The Miller. 'Where does it come from? You ought to know; you do more snide printing than any two men, and all the dirt of the town comes through your hands. The Danish Lottery prospectus was your last. Now come across, Kirz, who is the gentleman who is turning out fivers numbered B. 70 992533?'

'Gott knows,' said Mr. Kirz. 'I haf offen tought dat Education Evans did somet'ing of dat – he had a quiet blace in Bayham Mews, hein? He goes to der race-gourse where it is bossible to change – '

'Educated Evans is not that kind of man,' said The Miller quietly; 'it's one of the West End crowd. Is it Podulski?' He named, one after another, certain of Mr. Kirz's acquaintances, and at each mention the stout gentleman shook his head.

'If I know, I tell,' he said. 'I would not soil my hands wit' such wickness. Und as to der Copenhagen Lottery, dat is not my business. I ask you to gome and see my plant – any tay, any night. It is a scandoulness dat I am evil spoken of.'

The Miller had not hoped for any great success in this quarter, though he was certain that Kirz, who knew the foreign-speaking underworld, could have given him a hint. Most discreetly, he did not tell Educated Evans that suspicion had been attached to his fair name.

The Miller was not alone in his distress. His unhappiness was shared by an Assistant-Commissioner of Police, several superintendents, and the disorder even spread to the sacred precincts of Whitehall. There never were better forgeries than this batch of five-pound notes which had come into circulation and, had it not been for the fact that they all bore the same number, detection would have been impossible.

The paper was perfect, the watermark, with its secret gradations, was copied exactly. The notes felt good and looked good; and they had been unloaded, not only on the Continent but in London itself. There was not a bookmaker who did not take two or three in the course of a week. They had been changed at banks, at railway stations, at cinemas and shops.

In such moments of crisis the Home Secretary sends for the Chief Commissioner of Police and says: 'This is very serious', and hints that the responsibility rests with the Chief Commissioner. And that worthy passes the kick down until it reaches quite unimportant detective-constables.

The kick came to Sergeant Challoner with direct force, for the forgeries had appeared more frequently in Camden Town than elsewhere.

That evening he went in search of 'The World's Premier Turf Adviser'.

The western skies were streaked with pale turquoise and the softest pink, and Educated Evans lounged, with his arms folded on the stone parapet, his chin resting on his elbow, absorbing the glory of the sunset. The Thames or the Albert Embankment drew him as a magnet attracts steel filings. The vague unease which disturbs the soul of genius was soothed to a dreamy languor, the dark and sinister thoughts that assail men of imagination were dissipated by the serenity of the scene.

Day after day, when business was slack or fortune turned a broad back upon his wooings, and the inexplicable failure of his selections had warped and soured his gentle nature, this man of learning turned his steps instinctively to the solace of the steel-grey river and the dun-coloured horizons of London. And here he would stand and dream and watch with eyes that were comforted, yet did not see the ceaseless traffic that passed to Thames River through the Pool.

When his professional duties allowed, Sergeant Challoner would detach himself from his proper sphere and enjoy a two-fold pleasure. For here he could satisfy his aesthetic yearnings and enjoy the society of one who, by reason of his erudition and intimate acquaintance with the thoroughbred horses, was respected from Holloway Road to Albany Street. Sometimes the knowledge that he could find Evans in a certain place at a given time was of the greatest value.

Glancing sideways, Educated Evans saw the broad-shouldered figure approaching, but did not move.

'Making up a poem, Evans?' said The Miller, leaning on the parapet by his side.

'No, Mr. Challoner; poetry was never in my line – do you believe in divine guidance, if you'll pardon the expression?'

The Miller was startled.

'Yes, I believe in divine guidance. Why?'

'For three nights in succession,' said Educated Evans dreamily, 'there's been a tip in the sky. Look at it! Pink an' green stripes – Solly Joel's got two in the Jubilee an' the question is, which? Last month, when I was standing on this very spot, I see a black cloud and a white cloud on top of it, an' Lord Derby won the Liverpool Cup. Another time there was nothing but yeller and pink, and up popped Lord Rosebery's horse at Warwick. If that ain't fate, what is?'

The Miller was more than startled – he was staggered.

'I can't think of anything more unlikely,' he protested, 'than that Providence arranges the sunset for the benefit of your dirty-necked punters.'

Evans shook his head.

'You never know,' he said. 'There's things undreamt of in your theosophy, as Horatio Bottomley said. Don't it make you feel solemn, Miller, watchin' the river goin' down, so to speak, to the sea? Flowin' straight away to Russia an' Arabia, an' other foreign places until it forms the famous Gulf Stream that causes the seasons, summer an' winter. Carryin' the ships that go here and there – '

'Have you been drinking?' said The Miller suspiciously.

'If I met a glass of beer in the street I shouldn't reckernise it,' said Educated Evans, 'it's so long since I saw one. No, I'm dealin' with hypo-thesis an' conjectures. What won the three-thirty, Mr. Challoner?'

'Coleborn,' replied The Miller and Evans heaved a deep and happy sigh.

'That's the second I've given this week,' he said almost cheerfully. 'I simply didn't dare to wait for the paper. Any price?'

'Five to two,' said The Miller. 'I backed it.'

A look of peace and calm lay upon the melancholy face of Educated Evans.

'What a beauty!' he murmured. 'There'll be sore hearts in the synagogue tomorrer! Five to two. An' sent out on my five-pound Job Wire to a hundred and forty-three clients!'

'How many?'

'Forty-three – an' *all* payers! I'm certain of ten, anyway. Nine, not counting Kirz, an' if he twists me again he's off my list for *good*!'

'Do you know anything about Kirz?' asked The Miller, regarding a passing tug with such a fixed stare that nobody would have guessed that he had any interest in the answer. 'What is he?'

Evans sniffed.

'It depends whether he acts honourable,' he said cautiously, 'as to whether he's an educated Foreign Gentleman or a dirty 'Un – if you'll forgive the vulgarity.'

'Does a bit of funny printing on the quiet, doesn't he?' asked The Miller, still absorbed in the tug.

'I don't know anybody's business but me own,' said Educated Evans, with emphasis. 'As Looy the Fifteenth said to the Black Prince, so called because, bein' a lord, he swore he wouldn't wash his neck till Gibraltar was taken, "Honny swar," he says, "key mally pence" – meanin' that if you don't stick your nose where it's not wanted, you won't get it pinched. After which, accordin' to statements in the Press, he never smiled again. That's history.'

'Sounds like *Comic Cuts* to me,' said The Miller. 'And it doesn't answer my question. What do you think about him?'

'I'll tell you tonight,' said Educated Evans significantly.

In the evening he took his best tie out of the shoe box – wherein were stored his most precious possessions, such as a cigarette-end that Lord Derby had thrown away and a racing plate worn by the mighty Bart Snowball, Prince of Platers – and hied him to Mornington Gardens. Mr. Kirz was not at home. Nobody knew when he would be home. Nobody knew where he was. Slam! The door closed in his face.

'Common slavery!' said Educated Evans, and proceeded to search the town. Mr. Kirz was not at the Arts and Graces Club, and he wasn't in the resplendent private saloon of the White Hart, nor yet in the Blue Boar lounge. The dogged searcher turned westward and by great good fortune overtook Mr. Kirz as he was coming out of the Empire. Mr. Kirz was wearing the garments of festivity.

'Ah! My poor Effens!' he began.

'Not so much of that "poor Evans",' snarled the exasperated man. 'You phoned the bet when I was with you, an' unless Isaacsheim's dead, you're *on*!'

Mr. Kirz was embarrassed; there were with him two other gentlemen, and in the background hovered a lady who flashed and sparkled to such an extent that it appeared that she had been rolling down a diamond heap and most of them had stuck.

'Tomorrow, tomorrow, my Effens,' said Mr. Kirz in a whisper. 'I cannot dalk pusiness now.'

'You owe me five pounds,' said Evans loudly. 'You've keep me messing and mucking about for weeks, an' you're off my list! Pay me what you owe me, you perishin' 'Un, or I won't leave you!'

'My dear goot man – ' began Mr. Kirz, holding up his hands in horror at this unsought publicity.

'An' don't start "camaradin" me, because it's no good. You're worse than Shylock Holmes, you are. Pay – me – what – chew – owe – me!'

Mr. Kirz, his face purple, his hands trembling, searched his pocket.

'Dake it!' he hissed. 'An' neffer led me see your ugly face again! As for your dips, dey are rodden!'

Evans retorted long after his client was out of hearing, and would have continued retorting if it had not been for the arrival of a policeman.

'Hop it,' said the man in blue.

Evans hopped it.

He was a happy man, and strode with a free step, his head held high, when he came back to his own land. So proud and haughty was he that he would have passed The Miller without noticing him.

'Come to earth – you!' said The Miller. 'What's the matter?'

Evans turned back.

'I've got my dues out of that low alien,' he said.

'And what were your dues, Evans?'

'Five of the best.' Evans produced a crumpled note. 'It's gettin' a bit thick when you've got to go down on your knees to ask for your own!' he said.

The Miller laughed.

'Let me see that fiver,' he asked suddenly, and after a second's hesitation Evans passed it to him.

'There's no other policeman in the world that I'd trust with money,' he said offensively.

The Miller looked at the note and whistled.

'Dud!' he said, and a cold shiver ran down the spine of Educated Evans.

'You don't mean it?' he quavered.

'I do mean it – look at the number, B. 70 992533 – it's the number of all the dud notes on the market. Let me keep this – '

'Let you keep it!' snorted Evans. 'Am I sufferin' from lack of education and self-respect? I'm going to see this hero Kirz, an' I'm going to tear his pleadin' heart from his pleadin' body!'

'Language, language!' murmured The Miller.

'I'm goin' to get reparations from Germany,' said Evans more calmly, 'even if I have to search his pockets, the same as the celebrated Lloyd George said. I'm goin' – '

'You're going to do nothing. Give me that note. You shall have it back.'

'I don't *want* it back,' wailed Evans. 'I want money!'

It took a great deal of persuasion to induce him to part. He went home eventually, his outlook warped and blackened by the misfortune which had come to him.

Educated Evans lived in two rooms over a stable. The apartment was approached by a flight of stairs from the mews below, and the railed landing produced a slight balcony effect and added a touch of the romantic, which was very pleasing to Evans in his more sentimental moods.

He went in, slammed the door, and went to bed without troubling to turn on the light. There was no need, for he invariably hung his clothes on the floor. He fell into a troubled sleep and dreamt.

It was about an august personage whom it would be improper to mention. He dreamt that he had been sent for to Buckingham Palace, and had travelled there in a coach of state, throwing his cards out of the window to the cheering throng. At the Palace he had been arrayed in a long robe of pink and green stripes by a bearded gentleman, who had shaken him by the hand and insisted upon Evans calling him Solly, and then he had been ushered into a crimson and purple chamber with a black ceiling and gold-braided carpet, and the august person had bid him kneel. Evans sank gracefully onto one knee and the august person had said:

'Arise, Sir Educated Evans, England's Premier Turf Adviser and Sporting Authority! And don't forget that Daydawn is a pinch for the Friary Nursery.'

There was a thunder of applause. All the little princes were knocking their heels against the sideboard. So insistent was the noise that Sir Educated awoke and asked mediaevally:

'Who knocks?'

'Open the toor, Mr. Effens. It is Mr. Kirz – it is of der gr-reatest importance.'

Evans rose and put on his trousers and shoes and turned on the light.

'Come in,' he said, wide awake. 'I suppose you've come to act honourable about that dud fiver?'

'Indeet I haf!' replied Mr. Kirz. He was pale and damp, and in his shaking hand he already held a five-pound note. Evans took it.

'It was a gread mistake,' said Mr. Kirz, holding out his hand expectantly. 'I knew I had dat bad one. And when I missed him I say, "Oh, my Gott! I give it to Edugated Effens!" Where is it?'

Evans shook his head.

'The police have got it,' he said.

Mr. Kirz went yellow and staggered against the wall.

'Mind that wash basin,' warned Evans, 'it's new. Yes, my friend The Miller's got it – Mr. Challoner, that is to say, and a nicer man never drew the breath of life.'

For The Miller was standing in the open doorway and, following the direction of Evans' gaze, Mr. Kirz turned.

'I want you, Kirz,' said The Miller. 'Will you step round to the station and have a talk with our inspector?'

'I dit not know dat note was forged,' said Mr. Kirz, quivering.

'It wasn't,' said The Miller tersely. 'It was a good one – the one you've been making plates from – I found the plant in your cellar at Mornington Gardens.'

One of the principal witnesses for the Crown stepped into the witness-box and clasped the Book affectionately.

'What is your name and profession?' asked the clerk.

'My name's Educated Evans, and I'm commonly known as England's Premier Turf Adviser and the Wizard of North-West One. I gave Braxted, Eton Boy – what a beauty! – Irish Elegance, Music Hall, Granely and Sangrail . . .'

'You nearly got yourself *hanged*!' said The Miller after the proceedings were adjourned. 'And, by the way, I'd better give you another fiver for this one we've got – we shall want it as an exhibit. Kirz didn't give you another one, did he?'

'If he did,' said the diplomatic Evans, 'he owed me another – *and more!*'

MICKY THE SHOPPER

EDUCATED Evans was sitting in Regent's Park one morning, watching the ducks and waiting for inspiration. It was a day in late May, and the hawthorn bushes were frothy with blossoms, pink and white. There was sunshine on the yellow paths and a tang in the air, for the summer was late in coming, and the world was young and fresh and smelt clean. And the entries for the Royal Hunt Cup were public knowledge.

Educated Evans was pondering the inexplicable workings of fate that had brought to favouritism for the Derby a horse that he was reserving for his five-pound outsider, when he heard the steady pacing feet and, looking up, saw a broad-shouldered man with a straw between his teeth.

'Good morning, Mr. Challoner,' he said politely, and Detective-Sergeant Challoner sat down by his side.

'I was wondering whether Amboya can give St. Morden ten pound,' said Educated Evans.

'I thought you were turning over some crime,' said The Miller. 'Amboya is a dog-horse anyway, and if you think you can forestall Yardley you're booked for a jar.'

Educated Evans pursed his lips thoughtfully.

'Mysteries are repugnant to me,' he said, 'though I've nothing to say against Yardley. The question is: IS this Amboya's journey? There's a lot of betting on the event – the foolish public dashes in without the advice of experts, and prognosticators, with the result that Amboya is 6 to 1. But will he or she win? I've got news about a Thing that will come home alone if he runs up to his trial – come – home alone.'

'In a false start?' suggested The Miller.

'In a true start,' corrected Evans gravely. 'This Thing could get left twenty lengths and stop to bite the starter and *then* win. It's the pinch of the century. Some of the widest men who go racing have been backin' this Thing for weeks – before the weights come – before the entries was published.'

'I'll buy it,' said the interested Miller.

'That's the only way anybody will get it,' stated Evans determinedly. 'It's cost me many a sleepless night. I've been toutin' the stable an' watching this Thing at exercise, and the way he goes – with his head on his chest!'

'Forgive my ignorance,' said The Miller, 'but wouldn't he go as well if his head was at the end of his neck?'

'I'm speakin' metaphor or figure of speech,' said Evans, lighting his cigar. It had the appearance of having been picked up after being severely trodden on. 'It's Catskin.'

The Miller made a scoffing noise.

'You've been listening to the newspaper boys,' he said scathingly. 'Catskin's been a street-corner tip for weeks. And it doesn't run.'

Educated Evans raised his eyebrows.

'Indeed!' he asked politely. 'And who might have told you that?'

'The owner,' said The Miller. 'I'll admit that he shouldn't know as much about it as you, but possibly he's had information about Catskin from the boy who does him. And he's under the impression that Catskin has picked up a nail at exercise and is lame.'

'He's wrong,' said Evans, with great calmness. 'That horse will run and win. He's the kind of horse that a nail or two wouldn't worry.'

'The trainer told Mr. Oliver,' said The Miller, 'that Catskin wouldn't run again this year; and the boy that does him says so too,' he added ingeniously.

This was indeed convincing. The owner might not know, the trainer could be honestly mistaken; but the boy who did Catskin was evidence beyond question.

'That Mulcay is *hot*!' said Evans, harking back to the trainer. And here he spoke so incontrovertible a truth that The Miller could not contradict him. Micky Mulcay came from Ireland, a country which has given us so many fine, sporting, open-hearted and honest trainers.

By this description Micky would not have been known to his

intimate friends. If he had trained for the 'clever division', or for dubious owners, he would not have lasted on the Turf for ten minutes. But he had the intelligence to accept in his little stable of Parlhampton only the horses of men of the greatest integrity, men whose names were synonymous with honour and straight dealing.

They made an excellent frieze about the wall of the Stewards' room when he was called to explain the running of Cabbage Rose one hectic day at Kempton. The Stewards accepted his explanation ('They ought to have given him somethin' from the poor box,' said Educated Evans sardonically) and thereafter none questioned his doings. Micky was a philosopher, who realized that life was short and money hard to come by. Over his desk was hung the motto, 'Make hay while the sun shines.' And he made it – even when it was raining.

Owners who do not bet heavily like to see their horses win whenever they can. Micky liked to see them win when his wife, his brothers-in-law and a couple of trusted friends had slipped in as many wires to S.P. merchants as the Post Office could deal with. No wise man ever backed a horse from Micky's stable if Micky, his wife, his brothers-in-law and his trusty friends were on the course.

Micky was the man who invented the phrase: 'Horses are not machines.' It was Educated Evans who furnished the historic reply: 'It's a good job for all concerned that they're not talking machines.'

'That Mulcay is that hot,' said Evans again, 'he'd keep a room warm. Catskin could doddle it! But is Micky's money down?'

The Miller shook his head.

'I saw Lord Claverley at the Midland – I went down on duty though why I give you intimate information, I don't know,' he said. 'And Micky wouldn't shop his Lordship.'

The lips of Educated Evans curled in a sneer.

'Micky would shop his own young lady Sunday-school teacher,' he said. 'Every time he passes the Zoo the snakes stand up and touch their hats to him. That feller's so underhanded that he can steal with his toes. There's only one man he wouldn't shop, an' that's Micky Mulcay, bless him!'

Educated Evans did not say 'bless him'.

'I don't like your expressions of hate,' said The Miller, rising to go. 'Anyway, Evans, you can count out Catskin.'

'If the boy that does him says so, I suppose it's right,' said Evans and, left alone to his own reflections, gave his mind up to the problem of the Derby Stakes.

A few days after the Derby was won, Catskin ran at a Midland Meeting and was beaten by a moderate horse. He started at 6 to 4 on. His Hunt Cup price had been 100 to 6. It drifted to 25 to 1.

Evans observed the change with no great interest, until one afternoon, when he was strolling down Regent Street in order to be near the Piccadilly Underground when a Lingfield result came up, he saw Mr. Micky Mulcay and his brother-in-law. They were walking at a slow pace past the Piccadilly Hotel, and Evans, who never lost an opportunity of acquiring information, crossed the road and came very slowly past them, his eyes fixed on the ground, his mind apparently occupied with weighty matters.

And as he passed, he heard Micky say in his inimitable brogue:

'Sure; try Hereford, but be certain, Denis, that the Post Office is open on Wednesday. Some of these country offices – '

That is all Evans heard, and his heart beat thumpingly. Hereford . . . post office . . . Wednesday!

Instinctively he filled in the gaps. They were backing Catskin S.P.! His soul grew jubilant at the thought of all that this knowledge meant to him.

And then Evans was seized with a sudden resolve to do something he had never done before in his life. That evening he left for Steynebridge, five miles from which historic market town was situated the training quarters of Mr. Micky Mulcay.

It is sad to relate that Educated Evans had never before seen a training ground, if we except Newmarket and Epsom. And the ways of stables were as much of a mystery to him as the breakfast tastes of Tut-ankh-Amen. Fortunately he secured a bed at the inn which was nearest the stable; more fortunately still, Catskin was the one horse in all the wide world that Educated Evans could have recognized without colours and number-cloth. It was a bay with three white legs. But for this fact Evans might never have made the journey.

He was up at daybreak, and tramped across the downs to where, if local report be accurate, Mr. Mulcay exercised his string. And sure enough, soon after five, there appeared in the distance a long train of sheeted horses, moving at a hard canter.

When they had gone past him there came, at a terrific pace, three horses, the first of whom was undoubtedly Catskin. The little boy who rode the horse was trying to pull him up, and after he had passed Evans by a hundred yards, he succeeded, and turned back to meet Mr. Mulcay himself, very red in the face, and galloping at full speed on his hack.

'What the hell do you mean by galloping the horse when I told you to canter?' he demanded furiously, and his ready whip fell on the small boy's shoulder.

Evans watched interested, for the boy was the stable apprentice, Lakes, who usually rode Mr. Mulcay's horses when they were not trying as hard as they ought. He was still interested when Mulcay turned round and came trotting towards him.

'Who are ye?' he said violently. 'And what are ye doing here? Get off my ground.'

'If you'll allow me to argue the matter with you,' said Educated Evans with dignity, 'I – '

Smack!

The whip fell on Educated Evans' shoulders, and for a moment he was paralysed with wrath and astonishment. And then, with a roar, he leapt at his attacker. Mr. Mulcay might be a very dishonest man, but he was an excellent horseman and the whip fell again, this time on a more tender portion of Mr. Evans' anatomy.

'I'll get you warned off for this!' snorted Evans. 'I'll learn you, you – '

It would be unwise to record faithfully all that Educated Evans said on the spur of the moment and in the heat of his annoyance.

'I don't allow anybody to come touting my horses,' said Mr. Mulcay with that sublime air of majesty which sits so easily upon an Irish trainer, and is even more appropriate in an Australian. 'You get off and stay off!'

Evans very wisely obeyed. All the way back to town he was engaged in the humiliation of Micky Mulcay. In his imagination he saw the tyrant begging his bread on the street and himself passing by without so much as a tip for the next day's seller. But he carried with him another memory than his own embarrassment. He remembered the malignity on the face of Master Lakes, and the wild fury of that small boy struck a sympathic chord in Educated Evans' nature.

He took the earliest opportunity of seeking out The Miller.

'That horse is going to win, Mr. Challoner,' he said, 'and it's up to me to spoil the blighter's market! When he saw me he nearly dropped dead! I'm sorry he didn't. He'd got that horse all ready, and he's going to shop his pals for the Royal Hunt Cup as sure as my name is Educated Evans, the World's Premier Turf Adviser!'

'You should have kept away from Steynebridge,' said The Miller wisely. 'None of these trainers like to have their horses touted.'

'I'll tout him all right,' hissed Educated Evans, and when he was really annoyed, which was seldom, he was very annoyed. He would spend money – what was a pound here or there? – to bring his enemy to his knees.

He had – not so much a friend as a dependent – a man who had seen better days, an elderly, crimson-faced man, known as Old Joe. As he had not been convicted it never transpired what his other name might be. He smoked shag in a well-used pipe, helped the barmen and lived on beer. Nobody had ever seen him eat anything else.

Educated Evans sent for Joe, and he came uneasily from his self-imposed task of supporting the walls of the White Hart.

'Me go down to Hereford!' he gasped, shocked. 'Why I've never been out of London in my life, Mr. Evans.'

'You'll go out now,' said Evans firmly, 'and you'll do what I tell you.'

He explained.

'Send me a telegram to the paddock at Ascot the moment you see the number of telegrams put in by that perisher's brother-in-law. They won't be handed in till a quarter of an hour before the race. If you're in the Post Office then, you can't miss spottin' 'em. All I want you to do is to wire to me the number of telegrams this here Mulcay's brother-in-law sends away.'

Old Joe took a great deal of convincing but, on learning that there were several public-houses in Hereford, and that West Country beer was of surprisingly good quality, he left. The journey was going to cost Educated Evans over four pounds, but what was money?

The principal patron of Mulcay's stable was Lord Claverley. He was a man who plunged very occasionally and he plunged only on the advice of his trainer. If there was one thing of which Lord Claverley was certain before the Royal Hunt Cup, it was that Catskin would not win. He not only told his friends, he told his staff, he told his chauffeur, he whispered the words in the ears of illustrious princes and potentates. Catskin gradually drifted out in the preliminary market until it was either 40 to 1 or 33 to 1, according to the temperament and honesty of the layer.

Educated Evans very seldom went to Ascot. When he did, he invariably gave the paddock a miss; but on this occasion he decided that the circumstances warranted an extra outlay and, with a groan, he paid the terrific sum demanded by the Ascot executive and gained for himself a small chocolate shield which, pinned to the lapel of his coat, admitted him either to Tattersalls or the paddock.

The Miller, in a top hat and morning coat, saw the unhappy figure leaning against the rails, and approached him.

'You're not in the Royal Enclosure this year, Evans?' he said.

'No, Mr. Challoner,' said Evans, without annoyance. 'My invitation didn't come. I wouldn't have known you,' he added with respectful admiration. 'You look like a gentleman.'

'If I didn't think that insult was wholly unintentional,' said The Miller good-humouredly, 'I should be offended. Well, have you backed your Catskin?'

'For every penny in the wide, wide world,' said Evans emphatically. 'I've sent it out to three thousand two hundred and forty clients, and I've been sittin' up two nights doing it. This Catskin is not only a pinch, it's a squinch! It's the greatest certainty there's been since that hurdle race at Hurst Park – three runners and one trying. You know the one I mean.'

The Miller shook his head.

'None of the stable are backing him,' he said.

'The stable!' sneered Educated Evans. 'I could tell you something that'd make your hair stand up. I could make your eyeballs roll! Mr. Miller, I'm going to see Lord Claverley.'

The Miller stared at him.

'You'll get yourself pinched,' he warned; but this threat had no effect on Evans.

He knew Lord Claverley by sight, having seen his portrait in the illustrated newspapers, and when the saddling bell was ringing for the Hunt Cup he saw his Lordship walking alone, and seized the opportunity.

'I beg your pardon, m'Lord,' he said, touching his hat. 'You've probably heard of me. I'm Educated Evans, the World's Prime Minister of Tippery.'

Lord Claverley looked at him, and his eyes twinkled. 'Oh, you are, are you?' he said. 'I'm afraid I can give you no tips, my man.'

'I don't want any, m'Lord.' Evans' voice was solemn and convincing. 'I want to give you one. Back Catskin!'

For a moment Lord Claverley looked at him as though he were undecided as to whether he should call a policeman and have him thrown on or across the spikes to the course, or whether he should be greatly amused.

'You're wrong, my friend,' he said quietly. 'Catskin isn't fancied. That's all I can tell you.'

He was turning away when Evans urgently caught his arm.

'Me lord,' he said, agitatedly, 'don't you take any notice of what they say about Catskin; it'll win! Mulcay would double-cross the ghost of his grandmother! I tell you it'll win, and it will win!'

Even Lord Claverley was impressed.

'You're altogether wrong, Mr. – er – Evans,' he said. 'But I'm afraid I can't discuss the matter with you.'

Evans wormed a way through the elegantly dressed ladies at the rails to watch the field parade. Amboya was a hot favourite; Catskin, with the stable apprentice, Lakes, in the saddle, was at any price. The mere presence of an apprentice up, instead of the well-known jockey who usually rode for the stable, was sufficient to put off nine hundred and ninety-nine out of every thousand punters. But Evans was not put off. That stalwart man invested his last farthing at the longest price he could wring from the perspiring magnates of Tattersall's.

It was from the reserved lawn that he saw the race, and no very detailed description is necessary. Catskin was the first to appear above the crest of the hill; he stayed in front throughout, and he won in a hack canter by six lengths. Amboya was second.

Educated Evans trod on air as he rushed back to the paddock to see the winner led in. Three faces he saw. Mulcay's was green; he walked like a man in a dream. Lord Claverley's face was like thunder. Only on the cherubic countenance of the jockey was there a look of happiness amounting almost to ecstasy.

It was not a popular victory. That it was one of Mulcay's famous 'shops' no man on the course doubted. Lord Claverley did not speak to Mulcay, but a look passed between them which made the trainer squirm. And then his lordship caught sight of Evans.

'You're the man I want,' he said, and led the shabby figure away from the crowd. 'Now tell me all you know about this. Why were you so certain this horse would win?' he asked.

He had to listen, with such patience as he could command, whilst Educated Evans recited his own virtues and the record of his past successes, and then he heard all that that tipster had to tell.

'You say he's backed this horse "away" – from Hereford? Are you sure?'

'I can tell you in half an hour, me lord,' said Evans, importantly. 'My agent at Hereford – I've got agents all over the shop and touts in every stable – '

'Well, what about him?' asked Lord Claverley, impatiently, for he was a very angry man.

Half an hour later a bewildered Evans placed in the hands of his lordship a telegram he had received, and it ran:

Three hundred telegrams handed in, all backing Amboya . . .

'Of course, it may be as you say, Mr. Challoner,' said Educated Evans, philosophically, 'and it's very possible that Lakes *did* shop the stable by winning when he oughtn't to have been trying. I won't say it was from Lakes that I had my information; if I did, you wouldn't believe me.'

'I wouldn't,' said The Miller, 'because you'd be lying.'

'It's very likely,' admitted Educated Evans. 'Perhaps Lakes was gettin' even with him, the same as I was. And to think that that perishing horse-sweater was backing another one all the time! That's dishonesty if you like. Downright thievery, I call it! But fifty to one. What a beauty! And all out of my own deductions. From information seen with my own eyes.'

'Micky Mulcay has lost a lot of money,' said The Miller, who also had sources of information, a little more reliable, however, than those which were tapped by his companion.

'I wish he'd lost it all,' said Educated Evans, viciously. 'All except eighteen pence – you can get a couple of yards of good rope for eighteen pence anywhere.'

THE DREAMER

IT is a popular delusion that certain clubs in London have a monopoly of Turf transactions. 'There will be a "call over" at the Omph Club,' says a sporting paper; 'Tonight the Cambridgeshire card will be called over at the Zimph Club,' says another. There is no mention of the Cheese Club in Camden Town, and you might imagine from the character of its membership that if there was any betting there it was so insignificant as to be negligible.

Yet, this is hardly the case, for the Cheese was quite an important factor in the sporting world. There were certain big layers in the north whose agents never went south of the Euston Road; other layers of fame who made the Cheese their headquarters and kept their agents at the more pretentious clubs.

For the Cheese had come to be a vital clearing house, and even those great bookmakers, Notting and Elgin, did not disdain the Cheese when they had something particularly hot to lay off. You could get a 'monkey' on a horse up to the 'off' at the Cheese, and on big race days find men in the club who would take 4,000 to 500 in one bet.

And yet the membership was as mixed as any club in the world. Educated Evans was a member; Billy Labock, who laid £20,000 to £20 the back-end double, was a member; the Hon. Claud Messinger was a member – as hot a member as ever drew the breath of life.

'It seems to me,' said Educated Evans despondently, 'that such an article as domestic happiness and felicitous connubiality belongs to the Greek Calendar – in other words, *non est*, if you understand the language, Mr. Challoner? And yet Camden Town is full of happy couples.'

Detective-Sergeant Challoner nibbled his straw thoughtfully.

'To be happily married, I admit,' continued the educated man, 'you've not only got to be as broad-minded as a parson at a raffle, but you've also got to have the patience of Job – an' talking of jobs, they're workin' one at Gatwick this afternoon – the boy that does the horse says he could fall down an' get up an' *then* win.'

'Not Toofick?' The Miller was instantly alert.

'It *is* Toofick – he's the biggest certainty we've had in racin' since Tishy was beat. Help yourself, an' don't forget that I've got a mouth.'

'You were using it to discuss matrimony – who are you thinking of?'

Educated Evans fished the stump of a cigar from his overcoat pocket and lit a match on the leg of his ill-fitting pants.

'Women may have the vote, but they'll never do that,' he said. 'It's a gift.'

'If you know anybody in Camden Town who is happily married,' said The Miller deliberately, 'I should like to know his or her name.'

'I could name hundreds,' said Evans, and his melancholy face grew more dismal at the thought, 'thousands even. I'm not talking about lovey-dovey happiness. When I see a couple goin' on as if they're not married, they usually ain't. I'm talking from the depths of my experience and education about people that the poets write about. Two minds with but a single horse, two hearts that bet as one – Tennyson or Kiplin', I'm not sure which. I haven't much time for poetry, what with interviewin' owners an' jockeys – '

'Let's keep to the facts,' interrupted The Miller. 'Who is happily married amongst your extensive circle of victims, past and present?'

Educated Evans uttered a note of impatience.

'Would you say Mr. Joe Bean is happily married?' he challenged.

The Miller considered.

'His wife never strikes me as being hilariously pleased with life,' he said.

'I don't know whether she drinks or whether she doesn't,' said Educated Evans, 'and it's not my business whether she gets hilarious – which every educated man knows means "soused". But she's happy. She told me the other day, when Joe was ill, that if he popped off she'd never lift her head again.'

'Because she'd forgotten to pay Joe's insurance money,' said the practical Miller, chewing thoughtfully at the straw in his mouth.

'She told *me* that! Said she'd never forgive herself, and that she hadn't been so careless since her first. Who else?'

'Mr. and Mrs. Hallam Corbin.' Educated Evans pronounced the name with self-conscious emphasis. 'You wouldn't know 'em, Mr. Challoner, they're out of our class, got a house in Ampthill Square. I know 'em because they're reliable clients of mine. Keep their own servant an' thinkin' of buying a car. Class.'

The Miller looked at his companion with a speculative eye.

'I know them too,' he said shortly. 'Happily married, are they? Well, well.'

Mr. and Mrs. Hallam Corbin had swum into the ken of Educated Evans as a result of a publicity campaign undertaken by him. This consisted of a four-line foot-of-column announcement in all the leading sporting dailies.

> Well-known Commissioner, in touch with leading stables, would like to hear from a few reliable sportsmen of unimpeachable integrity. Only educated people need reply.

In consequence he had heard from very unexpected persons, amongst whom was Mr. Hallam Corbin. Miraculously enough, the horse which that well-known Commissioner, Educated Evans, despatched to such reliable sportsmen of unimpeachable integrity won in a trot at 6 to 1, and as the odds were promised to 10s. by some two hundred 'unimpeachables' he made a profit of £60. He ought to have made £600, but punters aren't honest – not even as honest as tipsters.

Amongst those who acted honourable – Mr. Evans' own expression – were the Hallam Corbins. They sent him a fiver, which was more than his due, and asked him to lunch at 375 Ampthill Square, which was a distinction to Evans beyond his wildest dreams. For Ampthill Square is more than respectable – it is class. People who live in Ampthill Square are Rich, have Areas, and have their groceries delivered. Some – indeed many – have cars, and the women wear pretty dresses even when they are in their own houses and are not expecting visitors.

Educated Evans had known Ampthill Square from his childhood. He had walked through it on summer Sunday evenings with and without a young lady – little did he think that he'd ever be asked in by the front door – and to dinner! Even though the dinner was called lunch.

Mr. Corbin was of stout build and had livid pouches under his eyes. Mrs. Hallam Corbin was stoutish and girlish. She was the sort of lady who was all good spirits and go. You would never imagine she was more than fifty-four; at the same time – and here Mrs. Corbin would have been profoundly annoyed had she known – you would not have thought she was any less.

Educated Evans dressed himself with unusual care. For this occasion he removed the sheaf of newspapers which permanently occupied his overcoat pocket; he wore his pink and grey tie and a stiff collar which cut his throat every time he turned his head.

A trim and good-looking maid opened the door to him and he was ushered into a drawing-room of surprising splendour. A mirror which must have been worth several pounds, a carpet of surpassing luxury, gilt arm-chairs and settees, large and valuable plants standing on pedestals that could not have been bought out of a five-pound note, rich velvet curtains, and on the mantelpiece, a confusing gold clock, the hands of which pointed to half-past six – morning or evening, Evans did not know – and surmounted by two reclining ladies, who evidently had just come straight from the bath and had mislaid their clothes.

All these things Educated Evans took in with a glance.

Then Mr. Corbin came in, both hands outstretched.

'My dear Evans,' he said, 'I'm glad you've come. My dear wife will be glad.'

'It's very kind of you,' said Evans, coughing, self-conscious of the pink and grey tie on which the dazed eyes of Mr. Corbin were resting. 'I must say I'm not much of a society man, though naturally, mixin' as I do with high-class trainers an' jockeys an' owners an' what not, I've seen a bit of life. I always say,' said the learned man, 'that class is all right in its way, but give me education an' understandin'. A lot of people that go about wearin' stiff collars and top hats haven't got the slightest idea about physical geography, etymology, syntax, or prosody, whilst if you get 'em on the subject of history their mind's a blank, if you'll pardon the expression.'

'Yes, yes,' said Mr. Corbin, who evidently took no interest in the precious gift of education. 'Here is my dear wife.'

His 'dear wife' floated in at that moment and fell upon Educated Evans to an alarming extent.

Contrary to the statements that had been made about the fabulous wealth of the Corbins, the lunch was not served on gold plates, nor were there twelve courses. Mr. Corbin ate a chop; Mrs. Corbin toyed with a cutlet; Evans, who did not feel that it was polite to eat in public, nibbled an occasional pea.

When lunch was over the mystery of the invitation was solved.

'We've been discussing you,' said Mr. Corbin soberly, as he pushed back his plate and handed his cigar-case to Evans. 'As you probably know, Mr. Evans, my dear wife is clairvoyant.'

Evans nodded politely.

'Though I'm not a family man,' he said, 'I'm glad. I think everybody ought to have one or two children – '

'By "clairvoyant",' explained Mr. Corbin hastily, 'I mean she is gifted with second sight – she has visions of the unseen world.'

'Goodness gracious!' said Evans, impressed.

'She has the power,' said Mr. Hallam Corbin gravely, 'of projecting her spirit to the infinite and of roaming at will upon the planes of ethereal nothingness!'

'Good Gawd!' said Evans, and shifted his chair a little farther away from this alarming lady.

'She is in daily communication with Napoleon, Julius Caesar, Alexander the Great – you have heard of these famous people?'

A faint smile lighted the gloom of Educated Evans.

'History is my weakness,' he admitted. 'Give me a history book an' I'll read for hours. Solly Joel had a horse called Napoleon, but naturally I'm too educated to make any mistake about your meaning. You're referrin' to the celebrated French King that said "Up, guards, and at 'em!" in the days of the far-famed French Revolution – '

'Exactly,' replied Mr. Corbin, a little dazed. 'Exactly. Now, my love' – he turned to his wife – 'perhaps you will tell our friend?'

He excused himself and went out of the room. Mrs. Hallam Corbin's smile was sweet, her manner most gracious.

'I'm sure you'll think we're very mercenary, dear Mr. Evans,' she said, and before Educated Evans could decide in his mind what was the correct thing to say, she went on, 'but my dear husband thinks that he ought to make money out of my dreams.'

'Your dreams, ma'am?'

She nodded.

'I dream winners,' she said simply. 'Twice, often three times a week, I dream winners. I see numbers hoisted in the frame: I see colours flash majestically past the post: I hear voices saying "So-and-so has won." '

'Dear, dear!' said Evans, wondering why, in these circumstances, Mr. Corbin subscribed to his five-pound special. As though she read his thoughts, she continued:

'I suppose you are asking yourself why we seek your clever advice? Mr. Evans, it's because we could not believe our good fortune and we simply *had* to have our dreams confirmed by the cleverest Turf Adviser of the day!'

Evans coughed.

At this point Mr. Corbin returned to take up the narrative and became severely practical and friendly.

'Now, Evans, my boy, what's the best way of exploiting my dear wife's gift? She had an extraordinary dream last night – saw a horse win at Gatwick. A horse called Too Thick. We've searched the programme, but no such horse is entered.'

'Toofick!' said Educated Evans, trembling with excitement. 'And he's a certainty! That horse could fall down and get up and *then* win!'

'Indeed!' said Mr. Corbin. 'How stupid of me! And she dreamt that Lazy Loo was second and Mugpoint was third. That's the amazing thing about her dreams. Now the point is, Mr. Evans, my dear wife doesn't wish to go into the tipping business at all. In a woman it would be unseemly.'

'Exactly,' said Evans. 'I quite understan'.'

In truth he understood nothing.

'What I have been considering is whether one could not *back* the horses that my dear wife dreams about – back for large and – er – generous sums. The question is, where?'

'The Cheese,' said Evans, promptly.

Mr. Corbin knit his brows, puzzled.

'The Cheese – you don't mean the Cheshire Cheese?' he asked.

'Never heard of the Cheese?' demanded Evans, almost shocked. 'Why, you can see it from your back winder!'

Whereupon Mr. Corbin insisted on taking him to a classy room at the back of the house and here, through a gap between two other houses, the decorously red-curtained 'library' of the Cheese was plainly visible. It was called 'the library' because it contained four ticker-tape machines, a bulletin board and a nearly complete set of Ruff's *Guide to the Turf.*

'Well, well!' said the astonished Hallam Corbin. 'I had no idea that that was a betting club. Well, well! Is your eyesight good, Mr. Evans?'

For a moment Evans was taken aback.

'My eyes,' he said emphatically, 'could see two jockeys winkin' at one another at the seven-furlong post, I'm that keen-sighted.'

'Splendid,' murmured the other, and led the way back to the dining-room. Mrs. Hallam Corbin had disappeared.

'My wife always lies down after lunch. It is then that her best dreams occur. Which is very awkward, Mr. Evans, because she seldom dreams a winner until within a few minutes of the race. It must be the transmission of thought – a psychic phenomenon which has puzzled the greatest experts of the day. Now if I only had a friend at the – what did you call the club?'

'The Cheese,' said Evans.

'If I only had a friend there to whom I could *signal* the horse of her dream! Why, we could make a fortune!'

Evans thought.

'It could be done,' he said; 'but how?'

'Let me consider,' said Mr. Corbin; and Evans remained silent whilst the mighty brain of Mr. Hallam Corbin revolved. 'I have it,' he said at last. 'I will have a number of large cards painted in numbers. I'll give you every morning a programme, and against each horse I'll place a number. If we can see the club, the club can see us – though, of course, my dear Mr. Evans, nobody but you must know the secret of my dear wife's clairvoyance. When you have seen the number you will back the horse and you shall have ten per cent of the winnings.'

Educated Evans left Ampthill Square with a thick roll of twenty-pound notes and a feeling that he also was walking on those ethereal planes which were to Mrs. Corbin as familiar as High Street, Camden Town.

His first act was to get a newspaper and, reading the result of the 'job' race, he gasped. Toofick won, Lazy Loo was second, Mugpoint third! Exactly as the smiling lady had dreamt! And she couldn't have known, because she had been with him all the time.

Even bookmakers who knew Educated Evans and respected him as a source of profit, hesitated to lay him £200 to £80 Lamma a couple of days later until Evans produced the money. The bet was hardly laid before the tape clicked the 'off'. And Lamma won. The next day he had £300 to £90 Pinky. It won.

On the following Tuesday, after making a few insignificant losses – 'You'd better not back winners every day,' said the practical Mr. Corbin, 'or they won't lay you' – he took £200 to £50 Kellerman in a seller at Hurst, and there was time for the layer to phone away part of his bet before the 'off' was signalled.

'They tell me you're backing them for yourself, Evans,' said The Miller, meeting him that afternoon after racing, 'and that you're making a lot of money.'

'Not a lot,' said Evans complacently. 'Just enough to keep the celebrated wolf from the fold. Money means nothing to me,' he said. 'I never forget the famous King Morpheous. Everything he laid his mitts on turned into gold and silver, owin' to which he got filled teeth and everybody thought he was American.'

Detective-Sergeant Challoner pulled meditatively at his pipe.

'Where are you getting your information, Evans?' he asked softly. 'From the angels?'

'From the boy that does 'em,' said Evans soberly.

He had an interview with Mr. Hallam Corbin that evening to pay over some money, and Mr. Corbin's manner was short and not especially sweet. Nor was his manner towards Mrs. Corbin exactly in accordance with Evans' idea of domestic serenity.

'I told you to put fifty pounds on the horse Mrs. Corbin dreamt,' he said, 'and you say you only put a pound on. And I've information that you took two hundred to fifty from Bill Oxford – don't you start twisting *me*, Evans!'

'Twist you?' said the outraged Evans. 'However can you think such a thing! Why, if I went misbehavin' towards Mrs. Corbin's dreams I should expect to be struck by one of them Clara's Voyages – '

'It's like this, Mr. Evans,' began Mrs. Corbin sharply; 'our expenses are very heavy – '

'You shut up!' snarled her husband; and it began to dawn on Educated Evans that they were not as happily married as they might be.

'Don't do that again, Evans,' said Mr. Corbin, paying over the ten pounds which represented the agent's commission.

The next day when Evans offered to take £150 to £30 Hazam Pasha in the three o'clock race, his bet was refused.

'I don't know how you beat the tape, Evans,' said the principal layer not unkindly, 'but you do. And I can't afford to lay you.'

Evans left the club soon after and found The Miller waiting on the doorstep.

'What is Number Six on your list?' asked The Miller.

Evans professed astonishment.

'Now take the advice of an old soldier,' said The Miller. 'Leave the Corbins to stew in their own juice. I've been watching the back of their house, and I saw the number put up at the window – six. And you saw it too. It isn't the tape, because they beat the tape.'

He shaded his eyes and looked up at the roof, and saw what he had not seen before – a strand of wire between two chimney-pots. Behind the Corbins' house – which they rented furnished – was a mews, and in Mr. Corbin's garage stood a large and antiquated car, the blinds of which were invariably drawn when it passed through the gates of any racecourse that was honoured by its presence. And on the top was something that looked like a wire hanger.

Sergeant Challoner inspected the car that night with the aid of a key that opened the garage. The interior was still warm from the heat which valves create. The seat had been removed and certain instruments and batteries completely filled the interior.

Mr. Corbin had finished dinner when The Miller called.

'I'm summoning you for being in possession of a radio transmission set without a licence from the G.P.O.' said The Miller. 'I could pinch you for conspiracy to defraud, but I won't. You and your gang have been sending radio results from the course, and you've made a fortune.'

Mr. Corbin glared at the officer.

'I'd have made a fortune if that rat-faced tipster hadn't twisted me!' he snapped.

'There's no honesty in this world,' sighed Evans when he heard the news. 'Fancy him a-making me a party to a low-down swindle! It's disgusting!'

'You can ease your conscience by sending your ill-gotten gains to the Temperance Hospital,' suggested The Miller.

'I wouldn't be such a hypocrite,' said Educated Evans.

THE GIFT HORSE

MEN may acquire fame in a night, but reputation is a thing of slower growth. Mr. Evans did not earn the coveted prefix of 'Educated' in a day, or a week, or yet a year. The sum of his learning totalled through the years, and behind his title lay a whole mine of information delved by him and distributed gratis to the world.

Once there had appeared on the stage of a London music-hall a human encyclopaedia who answered instantly and accurately any question that was flung at him by members of the audience. Thus, if you had any doubt as to the exact date of the Great Fire of London or the name of the horse that won the Derby in 1875, you secured admission to the music-hall at which this oracle appeared and squeaked or roared your question, to have whatever doubts you might possess immediately dissipated.

Educated Evans had never appeared in the glare of the footlights, but standing in a graceful attitude at the bar of the White Hart, his legs crossed easily, one elbow resting on the zinc-covered counter, he had from time to time settled bets, delivered historical orations and corrected misapprehensions.

Furthermore, he had framed letters to obdurate creditors, indicated warning epistles to offensive neighbours – not his neighbours, but the neighbours of those who had sought his services – and had prepared defences to be read from the dock. These latter invariably began: 'My Lord and gentlemen of the jury, I stand before you a poor and hard-working man who has been led astray by evil companions.'

These defences often brought tears to Evans' eyes as he wrote them, a sob to the throat of the unfortunate prisoner who read them, though the effect upon judge and jury was, alas, of a negligible character.

It was the day after such defence had been read in the dock of the Old Bailey by one Simmy Joiner that Evans, wandering disconsolately along the Hampstead Road, his mind entirely occupied by the contemplation of his affluence, came face to face with Inspector Pine.

'Good morning, Evans,' said the old inspector gently, and Mr. Evans woke from his reverie with a start.

'Good morning, sir,' he said rapidly. 'I was just thinking whether I would come down to the Brotherhood meeting tonight. I'm beginnin' to feel the need, if I might use that expression, of a little religion.'

Inspector Pine shook his head sadly. He was, as has already been explained, a Christian man, and took a leading part in certain social movements designed to bring spirituality into the lives and souls of small punters.

'I fear we shall not see you, Evans,' he said; 'tomorrow is our gift meeting.'

The predatory instincts of Evans were awakened.

'I'll come, sir,' he said respectfully, 'though it won't be for the gift. I'm willin' to take anything you give me, because it's in a good cause – '

'You are mistaken Evans,' said the inspector gently. 'At tomorrow's meeting we will *receive* gifts. Money or articles that can be sold for the good of our great racecourse mission. We will accept even a portion of your ill-gotten gains.'

The light of interest died out of the learned man's eyes.

'I'll have a look round, sir,' he said; 'bein' hard up, I can't subscribe as I'd like to.'

The inspector frowned.

'A liar is worse than a thief!' he said sternly. 'I happen to know that you have made a great deal of money from your disgusting tipping business!'

Educated Evans hastened to explain.

'It's like this, Mr. Pine – ' he began; but the old man interrupted him.

'Evans,' he said sombrely, 'there are two things that will bring a man to ruin – bad company and horses! The time will come, Evans, when you'll hate the sight of a horse.'

'Personally I prefer cars, Mr. Pine,' said Evans, anxious to propitiate.

'The sight of a horse will drive you to despair. You'll shudder when you see one. Today you wallow in your ill-gotten gains, but the pinch will come!'

'It's come, Mr. Pine,' said Educated Evans eagerly; 'Light Bella for the two o'clock race tomorrow – help yourself! It's been kept for this – not a yard at Birmingham! Get your winter's keep, Mr. Pine!'

But he spoke to the winds. Inspector Pine had stalked majestically on his way.

Sergeant Challoner, C.I.D., heard from his superior's own lips and with every evidence of sympathy the story of Evans' obduracy.

'Disgusting, sir,' he agreed, shaking his head. 'What did you say was the name of the horse that was winning tomorrow?'

'I didn't trouble to remember,' said the inspector suspiciously. 'Who do you ask, Sergeant?'

'Curiosity, sir,' said the sergeant.

Mr. Pine scratched his chin reflectively.

'What a splendid thing it would be,' he mused, 'if one could fight this gambling curse with money wrung from the very people who encourage and thrive upon it, eh, Sergeant?'

The Miller thought so too.

'What a – er – *tour de force* – I'm not quite sure whether or not that is the phrase – it would be if one could act on the information of this rascal and – er – '

'Exactly, sir.' The Miller's face was blank. It was exceedingly difficult not to laugh.

Just as soon as he could get away, he went in search of Educated Evans, and ran him to earth on the doorstep of the White Hart's saloon bar.

'Not only have you demoralised the proletariat of Camden Town,' complained The Miller, 'but you have corrupted the police service – the inspector wants your next five-pound special.'

Educated Evans beamed.

'But I think it is only fair to warn you that if your snip doesn't come off he'll get you ten years,' said The Miller, and Mr. Evans was not unnaturally annoyed.

'That's against the lore,' he said testily; 'it's laid down in Magnum Charta that you cannot lose if you can't win. There's historical instances, such as Oliver Cromwell – '

'Never mind about Oliver Cromwell,' said The Miller; 'what is this snip of yours for tomorrow?'

'Light Bella,' answered Evans promptly: 'this is the squinch of the season. Don't back it till the last minute, or you'll spoil the price. This is the biggest racin' certainty since Eager beat Royal Flash. This horse could fall on his back an' wag himself home with his tail! He's been tried twenty-one pound better than Captain Cuttle – help yourself!'

'Is it a he or a she?' asked the puzzled Miller.

'I'm indifferent,' said Evans.

Racing was at Hurst Park on the following day, and Educated Evans was a passenger by a comparatively early train. He invariably travelled first class, for Mr. Evans was partial to 'toney' society. And, anyway, nobody worries about examining tickets on busy race-days, though of late the inspectors have shown a marked aversion to allowing passengers through the barriers on the strength of an ante-dated platform ticket.

The carriage filled up quickly and Evans, ensconced in a corner seat – as usual – with an early evening paper widely opened to hide him from the view of passing officials, found himself in goodly company. There was Lecti, the jockey, and Gorf, the trainer, and a couple of men whom he took to be Stewards of the Jockey Club; they spoke so definitely and so authoritatively – they were, in fact, racing journalists, but Evans could not be expected to know this.

Seated opposite Evans was a stout, military-looking gentleman, who fixed the tipster with a cold and unfriendly stare.

'Nice morning, sir,' said Evans briskly. He had a happy knack of making people feel at home.

'Is it?' said the other icily.

'Very interesting race that two o'clock selling,' said Evans, 'and to anybody without information an inscrutable problem. 'Appily I know the boy that does a certain candidate – '

'If you talk to me I shall hand you over to the police!' said the cold, military-looking man in his chilliest military manner.

Educated Evans shrugged his shoulders. Even education is no protection against vulgar abuse.

The day was in many ways a memorable one. He had brought with him forty-eight pound ten, and it was his intention to take 500 to 40 about Light Bella. Two sets of circumstances prevented his carrying his plan into execution. The first was the fact that Light Bella opened at 7 to 4; the second was his tardy arrival in Tattersall's owing to a heavy shower of rain that drove him into cover. Light Bella was 5 to 4 when he plunged into the human whirlpool that surrounded the only bookmaker who was willing to lay that price, and he had taken £50 to £40 when the bell signalled the start.

He climbed to the stand and had the mortification of seeing Light Bella beaten a head for third place.

'Not a yard!' hissed Evans, and all within range of his voice agreed with him – except a few who had backed the winner.

There was one miserable satisfaction, and that, in his own inimitable language, was that he had not 'blued the parcel'.

He strolled, oblivious to the falling rain, toward the paddock and came to the sale ring just as the steaming winner was knocked down to its owner.

'I will now sell Fairy Feet, by Gnome out of Pedometer,' said the big auctioneer in the rostrum, and Evans recognised the voice. It was the military-looking gentleman who had treated him with such discourtesy. Evans edged into the crowd with a sneer on his expressive face.

'Who'll start me at a hundred?' demanded the auctioneer. 'Fifty? Well, ten – '

'Ten,' said a voice, and the bidding for the weedy-looking animal that had entered the ring rose slowly to 25 guineas.

'Twenty-five?' said the auctioneer, looking straight at Evans; and then to the surprise of that learned man he nodded.

Evans, who was nothing if he was not a gentleman, nodded back.

'Thirty,' said the auctioneer. Somebody bid thirty-five, and the man in the rostrum nodded to Evans.

'I saw you the first time,' said Evans, and nodded back.

'Forty,' said the auctioneer, and a few seconds later the hammer fell. 'What's your name, sir?'

Evans nearly dropped. The auctioneer was speaking to him.

'Educated Evans,' he answered, and heard like a man in a dream.
'Sold to Mr. Ted K. Evans.'

Evans often debated to himself at a later date what he should have done. He might have run away. He might have disclaimed any responsibility; he might have done so many of the things that were afterwards suggested to him.

Instead, numbly, like a man under the influence of an anaesthetic, he paid £42. And the worst was to come. He had scarcely paid when his elbow was nudged by a small boy. Attached to the small boy by a leading rein was Fairy Feet.

'Who's your trainer, sir?'

Evans' jaw dropped. Only for an instant did he lose his self-possession, and then took the rein.

'Don't ask questions,' he said, and led the leggy animal away.

The paddock was emptying, for the rain was pelting down.

Evans looked round wildly, and then moved towards the gate.

'Excuse me, sir,' said the new owner to the gateman, 'do you happen to know where I can leave this horse?'

The staggered gateman shook his head.

'Where do you train?' he asked.

'Camden Town,' said Evans vaguely.

'Why don't you take him home?' suggested the gatekeeper; and it seemed a very good idea.

The glow of ownership descended on Evans as he trudged up the muddy road towards Hampton Court Station. It wasn't such a bad idea after all. In his minds' eye he cast new advertisements.

EDUCATED EVANS!
Racehorse Owner and the World's Premier
Sporting Prophet.
Owner of Fairy Feet, Winner of the Stewards' Cup.

He stopped dead in the middle of the road and, turning, surveyed his purchase. There was a look of infinite sadness in the eyes of Fairy Feet. It almost seemed as if the intelligent animal realised the amazing absurdity of Evans supposing that it could win anything.

'Come on,' said Evans, and the docile creature followed him to the railway station. There was no need for the lead rein. Fairy Feet would have followed Evans anywhere except to a racecourse, for

Fairy Feet hated racecourses and was as firm an opponent to the practice of horse-racing as Inspector Pine.

'I want to get this horse to Camden Town,' said Evans. The station-master looked dubious.

'We haven't a spare horse-box, but we'll get one down tomorrow,' he said. 'Why don't you walk him home?'

The idea had occurred to Evans and, as if to encourage him, the rain had ceased to fall. He was passing over Kingston Bridge when the rain began again. He was footsore, weary, sick at heart. Searching the examples of human suffering which his education presented, he could recall no more horrible experience.

At eight o'clock that night a bent and weary figure shuffled into Bayham Mews, followed in a sprightly fashion by a light-hearted thoroughbred racehorse.

Fortunately he found Harry Tilder at home. Harry had recently come from the country and was known to love horses – and he had a yard. Evans fell upon his neck.

'Got a racehorse, Harry,' he gasped. 'Paid a thousan' pounds for him! Can you put him up an' give him a bit of meat or something till the morning?'

Young Harry looked at Fairy Feet in the waning light, then he looked at Evans.

'Can't do it, Mr. Evans,' he said. 'I don't want to be mixed up in this.'

'But he's mine!' wailed Evans. 'I bought him for a thou – for forty guineas.'

'You said a thousand just now,' said Young Harry. 'It can't be done. Take him round to Bellamy's.'

But Mr. Bellamy, the corn merchant, would have none of it.

'I've kept honest all my life,' he said, 'and I'm not going to change my plans. I don't want to say anything against you, Evans, but I know that you've been in trouble before.'

Inspector Pine had often attempted to persuade The Miller to attend the meetings of the Brotherhood, but hitherto his efforts had failed. Sergeant Challoner had a sense of humour, and a sense of humour is an effective bar to hypocrisy. But he had evaded his obligations so often that he decided on this occasion to keep a promise – often made and as often broken.

The Brotherhood held their meeting in a little tin hall in a turning off Great College Street. Here were planned the programmes for the various great race-meetings. Here pale and long-haired young men laboriously painted banners with holy words and bore them forth amidst the unnoticing throng, and very proud were the bearers of banners that they were not as other men.

Inspector Pine was in the chair and, after the meeting had been solemnly opened, he presented the accounts of the year.

'There is, my dear friends,' he said, 'a heavy deficit. Perhaps some friends who are outside our fold will come to contribute their mite' – he looked down at The Miller, and that uncomfortable man went red and felt in his pocket – 'but in the main we must depend upon our own efforts. It may not be gold or silver nor precious stones that our brethren will care to offer. But whatever you contribute will be welcome.'

The gifts in cash were few; in kind, many. A red-faced brother brought to the platform a steel fender amidst loud applause. Another member of the Brotherhood carried up a sack of potatoes. One fell at The Miller's feet, and he picked it up. It was not of the finest quality. Yet another member of the audience brought a pot of jam – almost everyone brought something.

The Miller, remembering a spasmodic gramophone that he had and which only went when it felt so inclined, regretted that he had not brought it with him. At last the final gift had been brought up, and Inspector Pine rose and beamed on the congregation.

'I am glad to say – ' he began when the door at the end of the hall was flung open violently and a man staggered in.

He was drenched from head to foot, and one lock of hair fell saucily over his long nose. Behind him, wet and shining and surveying the hall and its occupants with interested and intelligent eyes, was a lank quadruped.

'Ladies and gents,' said the bedraggled stranger, 'I'm well known to most of you, bein' Educated Evans, the famous and celebrated Turf Adviser, an' I've brought a little gift.'

A profound silence met this remarkable announcement.

'There's them that say you can get tired of horses,' said Educated Evans, pushing back his lock, 'and they're right! This here horse is the celebrated and far-famed Fairy Feet, sired by The Tetrarch and dam'd by everybody that's ever had anything to do with him – he's yours!'

So saying, he dropped the leading rein and slipped from the room, slamming the door behind him.

Fairy Feet looked round, and then with a neigh of anguish as she realised the base desertion, lifted her hind legs and kicked the frail door to splinters.

Running out into the street The Miller saw Educated Evans running down the street with a dark horse hot in pursuit. Probably Fairy Feet had never run quite so fast as she did that night.

STRAIGHT FROM
THE HORSE'S MOUTH

IT is generally believed in Somers Town that a policeman would shop his own aunt for the sake of getting his name before the magistrate, but this is not the case. A policeman, being intensely human, has what the Portuguese call a *repugnancio* to certain jobs.

Sergeant Challoner, C.I.D., was called into the office of his superior and entrusted with a piece of work which revolted his soul – namely the raiding of Issy Bodd's flourishing ready-money starting-price business, which he carried on at his house off Ossulton Street.

Complaints had been made by a virtuous neighbour.

'Tibby Cole,' said The Miller. 'He's annoyed because Issy caught him trying to work a ramp on him, and one of Issy's minders gave him a thick ear.'

'My dear Sergeant!' said the shocked Inspector Pine. 'There is really no reason why you should employ the language of Somers Town.'

The Miller went forth to his work in no great heart. He was too good a servant of the law to send a warning, and he came upon the defenceless Issy at a most compromising moment.

'I'm very sorry, Bodd,' he said, as he effected the arrest. 'I'll take all the slips you've got – you can get bail, I suppose?'

'You couldn't have come on a better day,' said the philosophical Mr. Bodd. 'All Camden Town's gone mad over Sanaband, and as I never lay off a penny, it looked as if I was going through it.'

Sanaband, as all the world knows, started a hot favourite for the

Northumberland Plate and finished last but one, and everybody said: 'Where are the Stewards?'

Thousands of people, who had had sums varying from a shilling to a hundred pounds on the favourite, gnashed their teeth and tore their hair, and said things about Mr. Yardley, the owner and trainer of Sanaband, which were both libellous and uncharitable.

Bert Yardley himself saw the finish with a whimsical smile and, going down to meet the disgraced animal, patted his neck and called him gentle names, and people who saw this exhibition of humanity nodded significantly.

'Not a yard,' they said, and wondered why he was not warned off.

Yardley, in truth, had backed Sanaband to win a fortune, but he had spent his life amongst horses and backing them. He knew that if Sanaband had been human, that intelligent animal would have said:

'I'm extremely sorry, Mr. Yardley but I've not been feeling up to the mark this past day or two – you probably noticed that I didn't eat as well as usual this morning. I've a bit of a headache and a pain in my tummy, but I shall be all right in a day or two.'

And knowing this, Yardley neither kicked the horse in the stomach nor did he tell his friends that Sanaband was an incorrigible rogue. He casually mentioned that he had fifteen hundred pounds on the horse, and nobody believed him. Nobody ever believes trainers.

'What's the matter with you, you old devil?' asked Mr. Yardley as he rubbed the horse's nose, and that was the beginning and end of his recriminations.

In far-off Camden Town the news of Sanaband's downfall brought sorrow and wrath to the heart of the World's Premier Turf Adviser and prophet, and the situation was in no sense eased by the gentle irony of Detective-Sergeant Challoner.

'I don't expect miracles,' said The Miller, 'and I admit that it was an act of lunacy on my part to imagine that you could give me two winners in a month.'

'Rub it in, Mr. Challoner,' said Educated Evans bitterly. 'How was I to know that the trainer was thievin'? Am I like the celebrated Mejusa, got eyes all over my head?'

'Medusa is the lady you are groping after,' said The Miller, 'and she had snakes.'

'Ain't snakes got eyes?' demanded Educated Evans. 'No, Mr. Challoner, I got this information about Sanaband from the boy that does him. This horse was tried to give two stone an' ten lengths to Elbow Grease. My information was that he could fall down – '

'*And* get up, *and* win,' finished the patient Mr. Challoner. 'Well, he *didn't* fall down! The only thing that fell down was your reputation as a tipster!'

Educated Evans closed his eyes with an expression of pain.

'Turf Adviser,' he murmured.

The whole subject was painful to Evans. Just as he had re-established confidence in the minds and hearts of his clientèle, at the very moment when the sceptics of the Midland Goods Yard at Somers Town were again on friendly terms with him, this set-back had come. And it had come at a moment when the finances of Educated Evans were not at their best.

'It's a long worm that's got no turning,' said Educated Evans despondently, 'an' there's no doubt whatever that my amazing and remarkable run of electrifyin' successes is for the moment eclipsed.'

The Miller sniffed.

'They never electrified me,' he said. 'Two winners in ten shots – '

'*And* five seconds that would have won if they'd had jockeys up,' reproached Evans. 'No, Mr. Challoner, my education has taught me not to start kicking against the bricks, as the saying goes. I'm due now for a long batch of losers. If Sanaband had won – but it didn't. And I ought to have known it. That there thieving Yardley's keepin' the horse for Gatwick.'

The sneers that come the way of an unsuccessful Turf Adviser are many. There is an ingratitude about the racing public which both sickened and annoyed him. Men who had fawned on him now addressed him with bitterness. Hackett, the greengrocer, who only a short week ago had acclaimed him great amongst the prophets, reviled him as he passed.

'You put me off the winner,' he said sourly. 'I'd have backed Oil Cake – made up my mind to back it, and you lumbered me on to a rotten 5 to 4 chance that finished down the course! It's people like you that ruin racing. The Stewards ought to warn you off.'

'I'm sorry to hear you say that, Mr. Hackett,' said Educated Evans mildly. 'I've got a beauty for you on Saturday – '

Mr. Hackett's cynical laughter followed him.

A few yards farther on he met Bill Gold, an occasional client and a bus conductor.

'I wouldn't mind, Evans,' he said, sadly, 'only I've got a wife and eight children, and this was my biggest bet of the year. How I'm going to pay the rent this week Gawd knows! You ought to be more careful, you really ought!'

It was a curious circumstance, frequently observed by Educated Evans, that his clients invariably had their maximum wager on his failures, and either forgot to back his winners or had ventured the merest trifle on them. In this they unconsciously imitated their betters, for it is one of the phenomena of racing that few ever confess to their winnings, but wail their losses to the high heavens.

Misfortune, however, has its compensations, and as he was passing through Stebbington Street he met a fellow sufferer.

'Good morning, Mr. Bodd,' said Evans respectfully – he was invariably respectful to the bookmaking class. 'I suppose you had a good race yesterday – that Sanaband wasn't trying.'

Mr. Issy Bodd curled up his lip.

'Oh, yes, I had a good day,' he said sardonically. 'Three hours at the station before my bail came, and a fine of fifty and costs – and six hundred slips destroyed and every one of 'em backing Sanaband. I've had a crowd round the house all the morning getting their money back on the grounds that if you can't win you can't lose. The public knows too much about the rules to suit me. It's this popular education, Evans, and novel reading that does it. If I hadn't paid out, I'd have lost my trade, though how I'm going on now, heavens only knows.'

He looked at Evans with a speculative eye, listening in silence as the educated man recited his own tale of woe.

'That's right,' he said, as Educated Evans paused to take breath. 'You've struck a streak of bad luck. I don't suppose you'll give another winner for years, and I don't suppose I'll have another winning week for months.'

They stared at one another, two men weighted with the misery of the world.

'It'd be different if I was in funds,' said Evans. 'If I could afford to send out a classy circular to all clients, old an' new, I'd get 'em back. It's printing and advertising that does it, Mr. Bodd. My educated way of writing gets 'em eating out of my hand, to use a Shakespearean expression. I'm what you might term the Napoleon Bonaparte of Turf Advisers. It's brains that does it. I'm sort of second-sighted, always have been. I had to wear glasses for it when I was a boy.'

Mr. Bodd bit his lip thoughtfully. He was a businessman and a quick thinker.

'A few pounds one way or the other doesn't make any difference to me,' he said slowly. 'You've got to put it down before you pick it up. What about a share in my book, Evans?'

Educated Evans could scarcely believe his ears.

'Not a big share – say three shillings in the pound,' said Bodd, still speaking deliberately. 'Your luck's out, and you won't be giving winners for a long time – I've studied luck and I know. Most of your Somers Town mugs bet with me. That last big winner you sent out gave me a jolt. And it doesn't matter much whether you give winners or losers – you can't hurt yourself. A little punter is born every minute. *And* I'd put up the money for all the advertising.'

The sinister meaning of Mr. Issy Bodd was clear, and Educated Evans felt himself go pale.

'Get out a real classy circular,' Issy went on, 'with pictures. There's nothing like pictures to pull in the punter. Get a picture of a horse talking. It's an idea I had a long time ago. Have the words "Straight from the Horse's Mouth!" Silly? Don't you believe it! Half the people who back horses haven't seen one. Me and Harry Jolbing have got most of the street business in Camden Town and Harry's had a bad time too.'

'Do you mean that I'm to send out losers?' asked Evans in a hollow voice.

'One or two,' said the other calmly. 'Anyway, you'll send losers. It's worth money to you. If you do the thing well, and with your education you ought, we ought to get a big win.'

Evans shook his head.

'I tried to give losers to a fellow once,' he said, 'and they all won.'

'You couldn't give a winner if you tried,' said Mr. Bodd, decidedly. 'I know what luck is.'

That evening Educated Evans sat in his library, preparing the circular. He was the tenant of one room over a stables. When he slept, it was a bedroom; when he ate, it was a dining-room; but when he wrote, it was library and study.

And thus he wrote:

STRAIGHT FROM THE HORSE'S MOUTH
That sounds ridiculous to anybody who doesn't know
EDUCATED EVANS
(*The World's Premier Turf Prophet*)

But with Educated Evans that phrase has a meaning of
the highest importance and intelligence!
It means that he's got the goods!
It means that he's in touch with secret information!
It means that his touts and army of investigators have
unravelled a great Turf Mystery!

What a beauty!
What a beauty!
What a Beauty!

THE BIGGEST JOB OF THE YEAR!
Get back all your losses! Double your winnings!
Put down your maximum!

There was more in similar strain.

Mr. Issy Bodd helped. He got a friend of his to draw a horse's head. It was a noble head. The mouth of the fiery steed was opened and from its interior came the words:

'I shall win at 10 to 1!'

The misgivings of Educated Evans were allayed at the sight of this masterpiece.

To some two thousand five hundred people this circular was despatched. Most of the names were supplied by Messrs. Bodd and Jolbing, and the words 'Put down your maximum' were heavily underlined.

Despite the exceptionally low price at which the peerless information was offered, the response was not encouraging.

'It doesn't matter,' said Mr. Bodd. 'You can send them the horse whether they pay or not.'

The race chosen was the Stockwell Selling Plate at Sandown, and the selection of the horse occupied the greater part of the day before the race. A committee of three, consisting of Educated Evans, Mr. Bodd, and Jolbing, a prosperous young man who wore diamond rings everywhere except on his thumbs.

'Polecat?' suggested Evans. 'That horse couldn't win a race if all the others died.'

Mr. Bodd shook his head.

'He was a job at Pontefract last month,' he said. 'I wouldn't be surprised if he popped up. What about Coal Tar?'

'Not *him*!' said Mr. Jolbing firmly. 'He's just the kind of horse that might do it. He's being kept for something. What about Daffodil? He finished last at Windsor.'

Educated Evans dissented.

'He got left,' he said. 'Daffodil's in a clever stable, and Mahon rides, and they like winning at Sandown.'

'What about Harebell?' suggested Mr. Jolbing. 'She's never finished in the first three.'

'She's been leading Mopo in his work, and Mopo won at Newcastle,' said Mr. Bodd. 'That horse could win if they'd let her. No, I think the best one for you, Evans, is Grizzle. He's been coughing.'

Evans smiled cynically.

'The boy that does him told me that Grizzle is fit and fancied. In fact, Grizzle is the very horse I should have tipped for the race.'

The entry was not a large one, and there remained only five possibles, and two of those were certain to start first or second favourites.

'What about Beady Eye?' asked Mr. Bodd.

'It doesn't run,' said Evans, 'and there's no sense in sending a non-runner.'

'Gardener?' suggested Mr. Jolbing, laying a glittering finger on the entry. 'That's your horse, Evans.'

But both Educated Evans and Mr. Bodd protested simultaneously.

'Gardener belongs to Yardley and you know what he is,' said Evans reproachfully. 'I wouldn't be surprised to see Gardener win. The only horse that I can give is Henroost. He *couldn't* win!'

Here they were in complete agreement, and the committee broke up, leaving Evans to do the dirty.

That evening, with all the envelopes stamped and addressed and ready for despatch, Educated Evans strolled out for a little fresh air and exercise. At the corner of Bayham Street he met Mr. Hackett, the eminent greengrocer. Mr. Hackett was in wine, for it was early-closing day and he had spent the afternoon playing an unprofitable game of nap at his club.

'Oh! there you are, you perishing robber!' he sneered, planting himself in Evans' path. 'You ruiner of businesses! Educated! Why, you haven't got the education of a rabbit!'

Had his insults taken any other form, Educated Evans might have passed him by in contempt. But this slur upon his erudition roused all that was most violent in his usually amiable character.

'You're a nice one to talk about education!' he sneered in return. 'I could talk you blind on any subject – history, geography, or mathematical arithmetic!'

'A man who sells lies – ' began Mr. Hackett insolently.

'It's better than selling caterpillars disguised as cabbages and rotten apples,' said Evans heatedly. 'It's better than selling short-weight potatoes to the poor and suffering – '

And then, before he could realise what was happening, Mr. Hackett, all his professional sentiments outraged, hit him violently on the nose.

In three minutes the most interesting fight that had been seen in Camden Town for many years was in progress. And then a strong hand gripped Evans by the collar, and through his damaged optic he saw the silver buttons of London's constabulary.

The Miller was in the station when Evans and Mr. Hackett were charged with disorderly conduct, to which, in Mr. Hackett's case, was added the stigma of intoxication; and, in his friendly way, the detective went forth in search of bail. It was impossible, however, to discover the necessary guarantee for Evans' good behaviour. He could neither approach Jobling nor Bodd; and when The Miller returned with the information Evans was frantic.

'I've got some work to do tonight, Mr. Challoner,' he wailed. 'Three thousand tips to send out!'

The Miller hesitated. He was going off duty and he had a genuine affection for the little tipster.

'What are you sending out, Evans?'

'Henroost for that seller tomorrow. It ought to go before eleven o'clock,' moaned Evans. 'Couldn't you find anybody? Couldn't you stand bail for me, Mr. Challoner? I'd never let you down.'

The Miller shook his head.

'An official is not allowed to go bail,' he said. 'But I'll see what I can do for you, Evans. I suppose they've not taken the key of your expensive flat from you?'

'The key's under the mat, just outside the door,' said Evans, eagerly. 'Henroost – don't forget, Mr. Challoner. If you get somebody to do it for me, I'll never be grateful enough.'

At half-past eleven the following morning Educated Evans addressed a special plea from the dock with such good effect that the magistrate instantly discharged him. He did not see The Miller who was engaged in investigating a petty larceny; but, hurrying home, he was overjoyed to discover that the table, which he had left littered with envelopes, was now tidy.

He had spent a very restless night, for the occupant of the adjoining cell was an elderly Italian with a passion for opera, who had sung the score of *La Bohème* from opening chorus to finale throughout the night.

Educated Evans lay down on his bed and was asleep instantly. The sun was setting when he rose, and after a hasty toilet, realising his responsibility, he went out to discover the result of the great race.

A glance at the result column in the *News* filled him with satisfaction and pride, though he had at the back of his mind an uneasy feeling of disloyalty to his clientèle. The race had been won by Coal Tar, which had started at 10 to 1, and Henroost was unplaced. Thus fortified, he strolled forth to meet Mr. Bodd, and came upon him in Great College Street, and the face of Mr. Bodd was darkened with passion.

'You dirty little twister!' he hissed. 'Didn't you say you'd send out Henroost? You cheap little blighter! Didn't I put up the money for your something so-and-so circulars? Didn't I pay for the unprintable stamps that you put upon the unmentionable envelopes that I bought with my own money?'

'Here, what's the idea?' began Evans.

'What's the idea!' roared Mr. Bodd, growing purple in the face. 'You sent them out Coal Tar! It won at ten to one, and every one of your so-and-so clients had his so-and-so maximum – don't let Jolbing see you, he'll murder you!'

Dazed and confounded, Evans bent his steps to the police station and met The Miller as he descended the steps.

'Excuse me, Mr. Challoner,' he faltered. 'Didn't you send Henroost?'

The Miller shook his head.

'No, I sent Coal Tar. Just after I left the station I met one of our inspectors from Scotland Yard, who'd had the tip from the owner. Evans, your luck's turned!'

'As a tipster – yes,' said Evans, and weeks passed before The Miller quite understood what he meant.

THE GOODS

IT is an axiom that the best-laid plan of mice and men frequently falls to the earth with a dull, sickening thud. So far as man is concerned, the truism holds, though as to the disappointments and setbacks of mice we lack exact information.

Mr. Charles Wagon was not a great trainer in the sense that he filled the eye of the racing public. He was master of a small stable in Wiltshire, and had, as his principal patron, a Kentish Town publican – who was also a sinner.

He won few races, but when he did win, the horse was the goods. It had twenty-one pounds in hand and nitroglycerine in its stomach, for nitro is a great stimulant of sluggish racehorses, and under its influence a high-spirited thoroughbred does almost everything except explode.

Mr. Wagon came up to London to lunch with his principal patron, and they sat together in the gilded hall of an Oxford Street restaurant, and the patron, a gentleman who had not seen his feet for years, except in photographs, was inclined to be fulsome.

'I'll say this of you, Wagon, that you're a perfect wonder! Your stable costs me over two thousand pun' a year, but it's worth it. Now, what about this Little Buttercup?'

'He's as fit as hands can make him, and you can put your money down fearlessly,' said Mr. Wagon.

He was justified in his optimism. Little Buttercup had run six times and had never finished nearer than fourth, because Mr. Wagon was taking no risks. When a horse of his won, there were no 'ifs' or 'buts' about it. There was never an uneasy moment when it looked as though something was coming up on the inside to beat it. He preferred wet days or hot days, when a perspiring flank did not show or was excusable and, above all, he preferred a six-furlong seller.

'Nobody knows anything about it,' he said. 'My head lad's safe, and I've got such a fat-headed lot of boys that if they saw a winner they wouldn't know it.'

The patron fingered his empurpled cheek.

'The thing is,' he said, 'that this horse mustn't be amongst the arrivals or the probables. If my pals see that he's arrived they'll want to know all about it. If he's not in the list I can always say I didn't know it was running – see what I mean?'

Mr. Wagon nodded.

'I'll borrow a motor-box and send it over in the morning,' he said. 'Don't worry about that.'

'And there mustn't be a penny for him on the course,' said the publican – and sinner. 'I can get everything on, away. He'll win all right?'

Again Mr. Wagon nodded.

'Don't fret yourself about that,' he said. 'I'll give him a livener just before the race, and he'll dance home.'

'There's another thing,' said the publican – whose name was, most inappropriately, Holyman, 'keep them tipsters and touts off your ground. There's a fellow called Educated Evans round our way who's always nosing round for tips. It's people like that who ruin horse-racing. The Jockey Club ought to do something.'

'Trust me,' said Mr. Wagon.

In the next few days the training establishment which housed that equine giant, Little Buttercup, was the home of mystery. Little Buttercup was ridden by his trainer, and the horse was galloped at unlikely hours.

Mr. Holyman need not have feared Educated Evans. That worthy man was beyond asking for tips. His luck was out, and it was all the more annoying, even maddening, that passing the fish shop of Jiggs and Hackett, he had been moved to enter and to offer the sceptical Mr. Jiggs certain advice which had materialised. Evans had sent a loser to his dwindling list of clients, and by word of mouth had given a winner to a notorious twister – and this at a moment when he was reduced to choosing horses by the process of adding up all the car registration numbers he saw and selecting a horse that came to that particular number in the published list.

'Seven three four one,' muttered Evans, as a bus whizzed past. 'Seven and three's eleven, and four's fifteen, and one is sixteen. Sixteen is one and six, and one and six is seven.'

Then he would look down a handicap and choose the most likely seven.

He despised himself, but something had to be done. The fickle goddess of fortune must be lured into the right way. Men whose luck is dead out do things that they would not care to confess even to their intimates. Educated Evans spent whole days adding up the numbers of taxis and cars and buses, and on a certain morning was obsessed by the numeral 9.

Nine was the very last number he saw at night – the first that greeted his eyes when he came out to breakfast one sunny morning. Indeed, it was the 19th of May and Educated Evans, realising this remarkable coincidence, chose the ninth horse in the Braxted Selling Welter at Birmingham.

That morning Detective-Sergeant Challoner, C.I.D., strolled into Mr. Stubbins' coffee-shop off Ossulton Street, and a dozen people nodded politely as he sat down and ordered a cup of tea and a tea-cake.

'Good morning,' said The Miller genially to his *vis-à-vis*. 'Nice morning, Mr. Clew.'

'Very nice, Mr. Challoner,' said his *vis-à-vis*. 'It's a treat to be alive.'

'It is indeed,' agreed The Miller. 'I saw you last night in the High Street, didn't I?'

'Very likely,' said Mr. Clew, who was a large man in green-grocery. 'I usually go out with the missus for a breather.'

'Thought I saw Young Harry with you?' suggested the detective, as he sipped his tea. 'How's he getting on?'

'I haven't seen him for months,' replied Mr. Clew emphatically.

'Where's he living now?' asked The Miller in a careless, conversational tone.

Now everybody, or nearly everybody, in the shop knew that Young Harry was 'in trouble'. He had also been in the coffee-shop half an hour before the detective's arrival, but, yielding to the earnest advice of friends, had gone elsewhere.

'Don't know what he's doing now,' said Mr. Clew. 'Living in the south of London, I understand. He's got a job.'

'I want to get him another,' said The Miller truthfully, for Young Harry had broken and entered enclosed premises. To wit the garages of Grudger Bros., the eminent bakers, and had feloniously removed therefrom one hydraulic jack, one set of ring spanners, two sets of plugs, an inner tube, and a tin of petrol, the property of the aforesaid Grudger Bros. And he was wanted. And, what was more important, would be caught, for Young Harry was like hundreds of other Young Harrys, he 'hid' himself by going to stay with his brother-in-law whose address the police knew.

The little thief is the best friend of the police. He catches himself.

The Miller did not come to the coffee-shop for information. He came for Young Harry. He knew very well that every friend of Young Harry would be suffering from myopia and loss of memory, and that if Young Harry had stood before them that morning they would not have seen him, and if he had told them just where he would be at a certain time they would have forgotten the fact.

The Miller was sipping his second cup of tea when Educated Evans drifted in and on his sour face was a mask of gloom.

'Young Harry – no, Mr. Challoner, I haven't seen him in the last three years.'

Educated Evans had a few minutes before passed Young Harry at the corner of Stebbington Street.

He took the place vacated by Mr. Clew and ordered one hard-boiled egg and a cup of coffee.

'How's trade, Evans?' asked The Miller.

Educated Evans raised his eyes from the business of egg-chipping.

'It would be good if people acted honourable,' he said bitterly: 'but acting honourable is a lost art. When the celebrated owner of Franklin an' Vilna and other four-legged quadrupeds – which is a foreign expression meaning horse – dug up Come-and-Have-One, the highly renowned Egyptian, he was delving, so to speak, into the past, as it were, when sportsmen *was* sportsmen and acted honourable, paying the odds to ten shillings or a pound accordin' to the class of information.'

'I doubt if the tipsters flourished in the days of the Pharaohs,' said The Miller, biting off the end of a cigar.

'I bet they did,' said Evans, confidently. 'There's always been fellows that told what was going to happen. What about Moses?

Him that his mother found in the bulrushes and kidded it belonged to her aunt? What about Aaron, who went and predicted that his sons should cover Tattersall's like the grass on the field? What about – '.

'Who amongst your ragged-seated clientèle hasn't been acting honourably?' asked The Miller.

'Jiggs, the fishmonger, for one. I went specially in to see him yesterday, just as he was takin' the appendix out of a sturgeon, and I said: "Mr. Jiggs, you've got to have your maximum on Flying Sam," I said. "This horse has been tried to beat Harritown at ten pounds".'

'And did he stick his knife into you?' asked The Miller.

Evans shrugged his shoulders rapidly.

'Flying Sam won at "eights",' he said simply. 'Information *v.* Guesswork. Knowledge *v.* Picking 'em out with a pin. And what did I get for it? A cod's head – it cost me eightpence to disinfect my room afterwards. It shatters your confidence. And I've got a Fortune in my pocket! I've got a horse for a race tomorrow that can only lose if the race is abandoned. This horse is "The Goods". I've been waiting for him all the season. They tried him last Saturday after all the touts had gone home, and they brought Golden Myth from Newmarket, and tne horse *slammed* him. Won his trial with his head on his chest, pulling up.'

'Not Golden Myth,' murmured The Miller gently. 'He's at stud.'

'They brought him out of stud,' said Evans. 'It was either Golden Myth or some other horse. The boy that does him is the nephew of my landlord's cook, so I *ought* to know.'

'What is it?' asked The Miller, his curiosity fired.

'Little Buttercup,' said Evans in a confidential whisper 'The Goods! And don't forget I've got a mouth, Mr. Challoner.'

He strolled along towards Euston Road with The Miller, and it was at the juncture of that thoroughfare that the detective said:

'Evans, I'll introduce you to the king pippin of your illicit profession – Mr. Marky!'

The man he addressed was walking briskly toward King's Cross Station. He was a tall man, expensively attired, and at the mention of his name Evans gasped.

'Not *the* Marky, Mr. Challoner?' he said in an awestricken whisper, and found himself shaking hands like a man in a dream.

'Glad to meet you, Mr. Evans,' said the newcomer. 'In the same line of business as me, are you? Well, I hope you have better luck than I've had lately.'

In the presence of such majesty Evans was dumb. For Wally Marky was the greatest of all the sporting prophets. He was the man whose advertisements covered whole pages of the sporting Press – Wally Marky, The Seer of Sittingbourne – Wally Marky, England's Supreme Turf Adviser – Wally Marky, who never charged less than the odds to two pounds, though he didn't always get as much.

'Evans has a beauty today,' said The Miller. 'The Goods! Had it from the owner, didn't you, Evans?'

Evans nodded, and wished he was a million miles away. To deceive his clientèle was one thing; to ring a wrong 'un on the great Marky, with his thousands and tens of thousands of paying clients, was another. At the thought of the awful responsibility the tongue of Educated Evans clave to the roof of his mouth.

'What is it?' asked the interested Marky.

'Little Buttercup,' said Evans hollowly.

'Trained by Wagon, who dopes his horses. I've been on the look-out for that one. It hadn't arrived this morning. I wonder – '

Mr. Marky frowned.

'You've had it from a good source? I've a good mind to try my luck with it – excuse me.'

He turned away to the nearest telephone booth, and Evans began to breathe freely. In five minutes his shattered confidence had returned.

Educated Evans became more and more enamoured of the child of his fancy. Until that morning he had hardly known of the existence of Little Buttercup and had certainly never heard of Mr. Greenly, under which name the bashful publican raced. Even The Miller, who was not usually impressed, went away with a sense of opportunity.

It was the last despairing effort of Educated Evans. He hurried from shop to shop; he flitted through the Midlands Goods Yard until he was summarily ejected by a policeman; he called on every client, possible and impossible; and the burden of his tale was the passing swiftness and the inevitable victory of Little Buttercup. And, in course of time, he came to the Flamborough Head, that magnificent palace of glass and mirrors, whereof the reigning monarch was the apoplectic Mr. Holyman.

Mr. Holyman was in the bar, counting out little stacks of change for his barmaids to use; for he was one of those men who trusted neither his right hand nor his left.

'Good morning, Mr. Holyman.'

Mr. Holyman turned his bovine glance on Evans.

'Morning, Evans,' he said, almost cheerfully. 'I haven't seen you around here for a week. You'll have something with me?' he asked.

'You'll have something with me, Mr. Holyman,' said Evans, with quiet triumph. 'I've got a horse for you.'

Mr. Holyman shook his head.

'No, you haven't got any horses for me, Evans,' he said good-naturedly. 'Tips are out of my line, as you well know.'

'This isn't a tip,' said Evans, lowering his voice to an agitated quaver, 'this is a gift from heaven! It's a thing I've been waiting for all the year! This horse has been tried to give twenty-eight pounds to Town Guard, and the money's down.'

'What's the race?' asked Mr. Holyman, his interest mildly aroused.

'The Braxted Selling Plate, at Birmingham.' Evans looked up at the clock. 'You've got ten minutes to get on and share the good fortune that I've brought to the mansion and the hut, to the highest and the lowest.'

'I'll tell you something else, Mr. Holyman,' he said, 'it's never happened to me before. Who do you think I met this morning?' Here Evans was telling nothing but the truth. 'Marky!'

He stepped back to observe the effect of his words. The name of Marky is known throughout the sporting world.

'I met Marky – introduced to him,' said Evans, with the satisfaction that the average man might display were he relating a chance meeting with royalty. 'He shook hands with me, quite affable and gentlemanly. His luck's out, too. Us tipsters are having a bad time. So I gave him Little Buttercup – '

'What!'

Mr. Holyman's face turned a dark, rather vivid, shade of blue.

'You gave him what?' he howled.

'Little Buttercup. It's a pinch. The owner's a friend of mine – '

Mr. Holyman glared helplessly round, and the first thing he saw was a pewter pot. It missed the head of Educated Evans by inches.

There were only two runners for the Braxted Selling Plate. Mr. Wagon's jockey had weighed out before the appalling fact became known that Little Buttercup was Marky's Fear-Nothing Five-Pound Special. And Little Buttercup won by the length of a street. It took two mounted policemen and a stable lad to get him back to the paddock. The price was 8 to 1 on.

'What a beauty!' sneered The Miller when he met Evans the next morning, and Educated Evans shrugged his shoulders more rapidly than ever.

THE PERFECT LADY

'IF,' said Inspector Pine, emphasising his argument in the best platform manner by hammering his palm with his clenched fist, 'if horse-racing isn't – er – pernicious and brutalising, if it isn't low, Sergeant, how is it that it attracts the criminal and the law-breaker?'

It was a favourite argument of his – one which he had expounded on a dozen platforms.

'If racing isn't the sport of rascals' – his grey head wagged in an ecstasy of righteousness – 'why don't you see God-fearing men and women on the racecourse?'

Sergeant Challoner had heard all this before, but had not troubled to supply the obvious answer.

'The trouble with a good many people, sir, is that they think that if they don't like a thing, or if some form of amusement or recreation doesn't appeal to them, it must be bad. There are people I know who would shut up all the fried-fish shops because they don't like fried fish. I can give you a hundred names of God-fearing people who follow racing.'

He reeled off a dozen, and there were an illustrious few that even the inspector could not deny.

'It isn't because it's racing, it's because racing has many followers that the thieves follow it. If a million people follow the game, it's certain, by the laws of average, that a few thousand of them will be thieves – just as it is certain that sixteen thousand will have appendicitis and thirty-five thousand bronchitis. The few thousand look a lot because they're the only fellows you and I hear about.'

The inspector shook his head.

'I'm not convinced,' he said. 'Look at that rascal Educated Evans.'

'Evans is honest. He hasn't always been lucky, and he got two months for a larceny that he knew nothing about. I'm certain that if he could afford to pay for the proceedings he could get the conviction quashed.'

'I'm not convinced,' declared the inspector.

'Because you don't want to be,' said The Miller – but he said it to himself.

It was perfectly true that Evans knew thieves, and that association with lawless men was an everyday experience. He knew them because he lived poorly in a poor neighbourhood, and the majority of thieves are poor men. They do not thieve because they are poor – they are poor because they thieve.

Racing appealed to most of them because it held the illusion of easy money. Hundreds of dishonest women go to church for the same reason. A dismal face and a whining tongue produce clothes and blankets and small gifts of cash. If the annual conference of the Royal Society were the occasion of distributing largesse the hall would be thronged by cadgers displaying the same interest in Einstein's Theory of Relativity as old Mrs. Jones takes in the Lent services and the vicar's Sunday Afternoon Talks to Mothers.

Why, even at Rosie Ropes' wedding there were beaming ladies who had no interest whatever in matrimony, but had come because, at the cost of half an hour's sitting in an uncomfortable pew, they were assured of a good dinner and an afternoon's amusement, with wine and fruit thrown in.

It was not often that Educated Evans went to parties, for society and social functions of all kinds he did not hold with. But the marriage of Mr. Charles Ropes' daughter Rosie to young Arthur Walters was an event of such importance that he could not very well refuse the invitation, extended from both sides, to pop in for a glass of sherry wine and a bit of cake.

Not that Evans was a wine-bibber. He did not hold with such effeminate drinks, his favourite potion being a foaming beaker of bitter. The nuptials of the Ropes and Walters family were something more than an ordinary union. To Educated Evans it was the wedding of a Five-Pound Special to an Occasional Job Wire, for both parties represented consistent supporters of his.

The Ropes' house, where the do was to be, was in Bayham Street, Mr. Ropes being in the Government and entitled to wear brass buttons every day of the week; and the wedding breakfast – which to the mind of Evans was much like lunch – was as classy an affair as he had ever seen.

To Educated Evans fell the task of proposing the bride and bridegroom, which he did in sporting terms, as was appropriate to his renowned position.

'May they run neck-and-neck from the gate of youth and dead-heat on the post of felicity!'

Several other people proposed the bride and bridegroom, and most of them hoped that their troubles would be little ones.

After the bride and bridegroom had departed by car for Westcliffe-on-Sea, the harmony ran smoothly until, under the influence of port wine and an unaccustomed cigar, young Tom Ropes started snacking about education and horse-racing.

'It's my own fault,' said Educated Evans when he was relating the events to The Miller the following day. 'You can't touch pitch without being reviled, as Shakespeare says. It was the Flora Cabago that got into his head – boys ought to stick to Gold Flakes. If it hadn't been for her I'd have chastised him.'

'Her?' repeated the puzzled Miller. 'Which "her"?'

'Miss Mary Mawker,' said Educated Evans awkwardly. 'A friend of mine, and as nice a young woman as you've ever dropped your eyes on.'

'Pretty?' asked the interested Miller.

'As lovely as a picture,' said Evans, enthusiastically, 'and educated! We had a long talk about history and geography. What she don't know about foreign parts ain't worth knowing. She's got two lady friends, Miss Flora and Miss Fauna, that's been everywhere; she mentioned 'em all the time – '

'Flora and Fauna are terms meaning flowers and animals,' corrected The Miller gently.

'She's very fond of flowers,' said Evans, 'and she keeps rabbits, so practically it's the same thing. She's got the heart of a lion, and she's heard about me. The first thing she says to me was "Are you *the* Mr. Evans?" '

'And you admitted it?'

'There was nothing else to do,' said Evans modestly. 'She ups and ask me if I was the celebrated Turf Adviser that everybody was talking about – what could I do? Like the far-famed Sir What's-his-name Washington, when asked if he let the cakes burn, I couldn't tell a lie.'

'There must be times when even you get like that. I suggest that you were under the influence of drink.'

Educated Evans cast upon him the look of a wounded fawn.

'The wine was good – they got it from a grocer's in Hampstead Road that's selling off – but wine means nothing to me. I could drink a bucket without telling the story of my life. What wasn't wine was lemonade – which she drank, being a lady. And when young Tom started snacking and sneering she got up and said "If you lay a hand on my gentleman friend I'll push your face off." '

'She wasn't a titled lady by any chance?' asked the sardonic Miller. 'There's a touch of Mayfair about that observation. You'll miss not seeing her again.'

'I'm seeing her tonight,' said Educated Evans with a secret smile. 'We're going to the cinema together.'

'I hate you when you're coy,' said The Miller. 'Evans, this is going to interfere with business. I never knew that you were a lady's man, either.'

'I've had me lapses,' admitted Evans, and smiled reminiscently.

The Miller rubbed his chin thoughtfully, and his grave eyes surveyed the World's Premier Turf Prophet thoughtfully.

'I'm sorry I missed that wedding,' he said. 'Young Tom well dressed?'

'Like a gentleman,' said Evans reluctantly. 'I didn't know him – long-tailed coat, classy hat, patent-leather shoes, beautiful gold wa – '

He stopped suddenly.

'Yes,' suggested The Miller. 'Beautiful gold watch, you were going to say. Any rings?'

'I didn't notice,' said Evans hastily. 'Now I think of it, I don't think he had a watch on at all.'

Mr. Ropes, senior, was employed in a Government office. His son had also been in Government service – twice. The Miller had got him the job. Ropes, senior, was wont to confess that children are a trouble, and he had excellent reason, for young Tom was by nature and instinct a 'tealeaf', which, in the argot of his kind, meant that he got his living by finding things that had not been lost. His downfall was ascribed by his lenient parent to 'bad company'. In truth, there was no company that Tom did not make a little worse by his presence.

'Besides,' said Evans, 'Tom's going straight now – he's got a job.'

The Miller smiled.

'They always have jobs, Evans. But Miss Mary Mawker – where did she spring from? Is she a friend of the bride's or the bridegroom's or the best man's?'

'She's a friend of mine,' said Educated Evans stoutly. 'She may be acquainted with young Tom; I'm not saying that she isn't. But if she knew the kind of feller young Tom was she would, in a manner of speaking, recoil with horror!'

There was a very good reason why the straw-chewing Miller should be interested in the adornment of young Tom Ropes. There had been a burglary at Finsbury. A jeweller's shop had been entered and trinkets to the value of a few pounds had been abstracted. It was fairly well known that it was the work of a gang that young Tom ran with. The haul, however, had been disappointing, most of the jeweller's stock being in the safe.

The question of this simple burglary did not exercise the knowledgeable authorities so much as the information which had come to them that there had been a joining of forces between young Tom's crowd and Gaffer Smith's confederation. Gaffer was notoriously versatile, and there was nothing, from pitch and toss to manslaughter, outside the range of his operations.

Educated Evans met his Mary that afternoon in Regent's Park, a favourite rendezvous of his. For the occasion Educated Evans had dressed himself with unusual care, even going to the extent of paying three and sixpence that his scanty locks might be dressed to the greatest advantage.

Miss Mary Mawker was pretty in a bold way. She was a straight-backed, athletic girl, with a rosy face and a pair of hard blue eyes; and if her ankles were a little thicker than they should have been, and her hands slightly on the coarse side, she was to Evans' enraptured eye what Venus might have been with a little bit of luck.

She refused Evans' gallant offer to row her about the lake for an hour, and he was relieved.

'Never did like the water,' said Miss Mary Mawker. 'Every time I go to Paris I get seasick.'

'You're a bit of a traveller, Miss Mary,' said Evans respectfully.

'I must say I like travelling myself. I've often been to Brighton just for the day. Travelling broadens your mind,' he went on, 'it's education and enlightenment. Look at Christopher Columbus. Where would he have been if he hadn't travelled? And where would America have been? Even the Americans wouldn't have heard about America if it hadn't been for him.'

She nodded her head graciously.

'I suppose you're single, Mr. Evans?' she said, and Evans protested his bachelorhood with great heat.

'I only asked because so many fellows pretend they're single when they're not,' she said demurely, tracing figures on the gravel with the end of her umbrella. 'And when you find them out they say their wife's in a mental hospital, so they're as good as single. What a wonderful life you must live, Mr. Evans, going round to all these racecourses and seeing horse-races. It must be beautiful! And then, I suppose, the jockeys tell you what's going to win and you send it round to all your friends.'

Evans coughed.

'Not exactly. The jockeys very seldom know what's going to win,' he said. 'I used to rely on jockeys once, but after I'd been let down – never again! They mean well, mind you,' he said. One of them told me the other day – well, perhaps it's not gentlemanly to repeat his words. No, I never take any notice of jockeys. And as for trainers' – he shrugged his shoulders many times – 'you can't believe trainers. They're like the celebrated Ananias who turned round to have another look and was turned into a salt-cellar.'

'What a lot you know!' she sighed. 'Do you ever get excited when the horses are racing? I should simply be terribly excited.'

'Haven't you ever seen a race?' asked Educated Evans. 'Not,' he said disparagingly, 'that it's much to see. I simply don't take any notice of 'em. My man comes and tells me how much I've won or how much I've lost – a thousand one way or the other doesn't make any difference to me. When I'm going well,' he added, hastily. 'Of course, I'm not always going well.'

It occurred to him at that moment, that he might be conveying a wrong impression if he gave her to understand that he was exceedingly well off.

'I wonder you have time for racing at all, Mr. Evans,' she sighed. She had a habit of sighing. 'What with picking up the bits of

knowledge that you've got, and your education, and your clients'
– she was still tracing designs on the gravel. And then: 'I should so
like to see a real horse-race – though, of course, I shouldn't like to
go alone. I'd be so frightened. What I want to do is to go to a race
meeting with somebody who is experienced, somebody who knows
everything about it.'

Educated Evans realized she was referring to him.

'I should be glad to take you, Miss Mary,' he said eagerly. 'The
expense is, comparatively speaking, nothing at all. I don't suppose
you'd mind going in the Silver Ring?'

'What's that?' she asked in surprise. 'Is it a ring made of silver?'

Evans explained that the Silver Ring was the real aristocracy of
the Turf. In the Silver Ring men bet more fearlessly, and prices
were higher than in any other ring. Tattersalls, so far from being a
desirable place, was an enclosure in which the price-pincher flourished. She hesitated.

'I think I would rather go into Tattersalls, if that's the name,' she
said. 'But, of course, dear Mr. Evans, I wouldn't think of allowing
you to pay my expenses. I'm a very independent girl.'

Evans murmured his half-hearted protest.

'I am, indeed! And I heard Tom say he was going down to
Sandown on Eclipse Day. What is Eclipse Day?'

Evans explained again.

'Friend of yours, Miss Mary?'

'Who – Tom? Well, he's not exactly a friend, he's an acquaintance.
He's not the kind of man I would have any dealings or associations
with,' she said.

'That's exactly what I said to Mr. Challoner,' said Educated
Evans, triumphantly, and the smile faded from the girl's face.

'Mr. Challoner?' she said, a little sharply. 'Do you mean that
detective? Surely, you don't have anything to do with him? You're
the last person in the world I should think was a snout – nose, I
mean. Aren't I being unladylike?'

'In a way he's a friend of mine,' said Evans, a little taken aback.
'He has my selections so, in a manner of speaking, he's a client.'

Her face cleared.

'Oh, if that's all,' she said. 'I know these birds do bet on the sly,
and then they go round pinching the poor little street bookmakers,

don't they? I've read about that in the newspapers,' she added, quickly.

It was arranged before they parted that they should meet on the following Wednesday at Waterloo Station under the clock; and Evans, having despatched innumerable messages, both by hand and telegram, dealing with the outstanding possibilities of Glue Pot winning the mile seller, hurried forth to meet his lady.

The sight of her took his breath away. Never a more ladylike person had he seen in her simple blue suit and little white hat. Nothing flash, nothing ikey, just plain and ladylike. He was proud to be seen with her.

They travelled to Esher first class. For once in his life Educated Evans travelled on a first-class ticket. And all the way down he spoke on a subject agreeable to himself, namely – Educated Evans.

They were walking across the park when he broached the subject which was in his mind.

'If I was you, Miss Mary, I don't think I should have any truck with young Tom Ropes,' he said, but she raised her eyebrows.

'Why ever not?' she asked. 'Isn't that him in front?'

'Yes, with some of his leery pals,' said Educated Evans, 'so don't walk fast.'

'But why shouldn't I, Mr. Evans?' asked Mary. 'You're making me so terribly frightened. Isn't he honest?'

'He never robbed me of anything,' said Evans diplomatically.

'I should hate to think he wasn't honest,' said Mary Mawker, shaking her head. 'I can't abide people who aren't perfectly straight-forward, can you, Mr. Evans? What I mean to say is that if they're on the hook they're so unreliable. You never know where they are, do you? There's a friend of mine, she's got a fiancé, and she never knows his address. Sometimes he's at Wormwood Scrubs, some-times he's at Wandsworth – it's just wasting stamps to write to him.'

'Yes, yes,' said Evans, a little dazed.

He had no fault to find with her ladylike behaviour throughout the day. She stood on the top of the stone steps of the stand, and Evans went down to do her betting for her, and every time she won he brought the money back, and every time she lost she said:

'You must remind me to pay you that five shillings on our way home, Mr. Evans.'

The crowd was a tremendous one, as it always is on Eclipse Day, and just before the last race the sensible girl suggested that they should make a move to the station. When they reached the other side of the course, however, she changed her mind and insisted on seeing the last race. And then, and only then, did they make their way to the railway arch under which the passengers must pass en route to the station platform.

'Don't let's go any further. I saw some friends of mine,' she said. 'We'll wait here until they come.'

'You won't get a seat on the train,' he warned her.

'Oh, yes, I shall,' she said with a saucy toss of her head. 'You wait here beside me. Now don't you leave me, Mr. Evans.'

'Do you think I would?' breathed Educated Evans, tenderly, and he thrilled as she caught his hand and squeezed his little finger.

The stream of home-goers that crossed the park was now multiplied in size, and presently Evans saw young Tom Ropes, though apparently that youthful brigand did not see Evans, for he showed no sign of recognition.

The press was now tremendous. He and the girl had to flatten themselves against the wall and it was with difficulty that the crowd squeezed past. Every now and again someone would bump against Evans. Twice it was young Tom Ropes who also seemed to be waiting for a friend.

And then of a sudden there was a stir in the crowd. Somebody struck out, and Evans looked with open mouth at the strange spectacle of young Tom Ropes in the hands of The Miller. Where The Miller had come from, unless he had dropped through a crack in the arch, Evans could not guess.

In an instant the archway was alive with plain-clothes police.

'Let's get out of this,' said Miss Mawker hurriedly.

She had not taken two steps when somebody gripped her arm. Evans was on the point of asserting himself when, looking up, he recognised The Miller.

'Want you, Mary,' said The Miller pleasantly. 'We've got the rest of the gang, I think.'

'Look here, Mr. Challoner,' began Educated Evans, struggling to follow the sergeant and his captive.

In a quiet and secluded station on the other side of the line six bedraggled men were in the process of being ushered into a waiting police van when Evans, following The Miller and Miss Mary Mawker, came upon the scene.

'We've got the men but we haven't got the loot,' said an officer who was evidently in charge, and added, 'Hullo, Mary, had a good day?'

Mary made a reply which shocked Educated Evans beyond words.

'I suppose this somethinged "can" was snouting for you?' she said. 'Well, he's in it with the rest of us.'

'I know all about that,' said The Miller. 'Turn out your overcoat pockets, Evans!'

'Me?' said the horrified Evans.

'You,' said The Miller. 'I'll give you a clean bill because I know just how they brought you into it.'

In Evans' pockets were eight watches, seven notecases, five purses, two scarf-pins, and a lady's diamond brooch. Evans could only watch like a man in a dream as the property came to light.

'You were the carrier,' said The Miller on the way back to town. 'They always get a mug for that job. She planted you against the railway arch so that the gang should have someone to take the plunder as they found it. By the way, she's young Tom's sweetheart.'

'She ain't mine,' said Educated Evans, savagely. 'I'm done with wimmin!'

THE PROUD HORSE

EDUCATED Evans left the Italian Club, having lost £4 18s. at a game which was known locally as 'Prop and Cop'. He had propped so misguidedly and copped with such lack of brilliance, that the wonder was – as The Miller, to whom he confided his woes, told him – that he had any trousers left.

Yet Educated Evans was not an unhappy man; for that day had seen the success of his five-pound special. And on the previous Sunday 'Tattenham' had said nasty things about a trainer who was reputedly an enemy to all touts and tipsters, and had expressed his views on the same in the public Press.

Sergeant Challoner walked with Evans to the end of the mews wherein the educated man had his habitation. As they stood talking, the keen-eyed Miller saw a light shining at one of the windows above a stable.

'The Turners are up late,' he said.

'The kid's ill,' said Educated Evans shortly and, taking leave of the detective, he made his way rapidly along the uneven roadway. He did not go direct to his own room, but climbing the opposite stairs, came to a pause on a landing very similar to his own, and knocked at the door which led to the lighted room. He knocked gently, but the door was instantly opened by a haggard-looking woman.

'How is he?' asked Educated Evans quietly; and she made way for him to enter.

The room was a little better furnished than Evans' room, but it was less airy. On a stuffy bed lay a small boy, very wan and hollow-eyed. The perspiration glistened on his white forehead, but he grinned at the sight of Evans.

'Hullo, Mr. Evans!' he piped.

'Hullo, Ernie!' said Evans, sitting down on a chair by the side of the bed.

'Been to the races, Mr. Evans?'

'No, I can't say that I have,' admitted Evans.

'And I'll bet your horse didn't win,' said the child, speaking with difficulty, and fixing his solemn eyes on the bare-headed tipster.

'If you bet that you'd bet wrong, Ernie. It did win! I thought you was better or I'd have come home earlier.'

Ernie was an old pal of Educated Evans. They were in the habit of holding speech together across the intervening space which separated one balcony from the other. Mrs. Turner was a widow; her husband had been killed in an accident when working for the firm that owned the property where she lived. They had given her a small pension and, more important at that time, had given her the two rooms rent free for life.

The woman herself did not come into the purview of Educated Evans, for she was not interested in the thoroughbred racehorse, nor very greatly interested in Mr. Evans. But Ernie and he went walking together, surveying the spring glories of the park, and sailed boats on the lake.

He went to the door with the woman.

'What did the doctor say?' he asked in a low voice.

'He says he ought to go away into the country, and it's his only chance,' said the woman with a catch in her breath. 'He'll die if he stays here. The doctor's tried to get him into a convalescent home, but there's no vacancies; and I can't afford to keep him away for any time.'

'Mr. Evans!'

He turned to the bed.

The child had struggled up on to his elbow and was watching him with his odd, pitiful face.

'What about that prahd 'orse?'

'That what?' said Evans, puzzled.

'You told me you'd let me see a prahd 'orse.'

'Oh, a proud horse,' said Evans, correctly, and remembered his promise. 'What do you mean by a proud horse, Ernie?'

'You know, Mr. Evans – the 'orses that 'old their 'eads up in the air, they're so prahd. I'd like to see a prahd 'orse. I could sit all day and look at a prahd 'orse,' said the child, with a strange earnestness.

'Ain't there any proud horses round here?' asked Evans. 'What about Haggitt's?'

The child's pale lip lifted contemptuously.

"E isn't a prahd 'orse,' he said scornfully. 'Why, 'e 'olds his 'ead down like a cow. I'd like to see a prahd 'orse, Mr. Evans – them that champs their feet on the ground.'

Evans scratched his nose.

'Now you come to mention it, Ernie, I'll confess I haven't seen a proud horse for years. I think the motorcars must have knocked all the pride out of 'em.'

Evans crossed over to his room, feeling uneasy in his mind. Financially, things were not going too well with him, or he would have offered, without hesitation, to send the child away into the country. His was the kind of nature that goes out to children, and it hurt him even to think of that poor little chap in the stuffy bed in that hot and airless room. Once he got up in the night and looked out of the window. The light was still burning. When he did go to sleep it was to dream of proud horses, black as night with high, arched necks and frothing mouths and hoofs that pawed incessantly. And in his dream they were pulling a shabby little coach. And under the driving seat was a little white coffin.

He woke up sweating, pushed open the window. The dawn was in the sky and the air smelt sweet and good. The windows opposite were closed, hermetically sealed; the door was jammed tight and locked.

Evans turned on the light and sat down to study the day's programme published in the overnight paper, but he could not keep his mind on the possibilities of profit. Every entry was a proud horse with an arched neck that 'champed' the ground.

At the particular moment when the kindly heart of Educated Evans was lacerated by the thought of suffering childhood, a proud horse was being pulled up on the Wiltshire Downs. His name was Veriti. He had cost, as a yearling at the Doncaster sales, 13,500 guineas, and he was, so Mr. Yardley, the eminent trainer, told the owner in dispassionate tones, worth exactly 13,500 pennies.

'He looks good enough,' said Lord Teller, a shivering man who had been dragged out of bed to witness the wholly unsatisfactory trial in the cold hours of the morning.

'Unfortunately, my lord,' said Mr. Yardley politely, 'the London Cup is not a beauty show. If it was, I think Veriti would get very nearly first prize.'

Being the great Yardley he could talk to one of the newest of the peerage frankly and in plain words.

'He can do it if he would do it,' he said bitterly, watching the beautiful Veriti as he stepped daintily round and round the waiting circle; 'and it isn't lack of courage. It's just wilfulness – super-intelligence, perhaps.'

'What will you do?' said his lordship.

'I shall run him,' said Yardley. 'He'll start a hot favourite and when he finishes down the course knowledgable people will look at one another meaningly, and the *hoi polloi* will talk about another one of Yardley's mysteries, and yet another nail will be driven into my reputation.'

He walked over to the horse, smoothed its arched neck and patted it.

'You're a dirty dog, Jim,' he said. And his lordship learnt for the first time that the name under which a horse is registered is not the name by which it is known in a stable.

'You're a mouldy old thief! What's the matter with you?'

Veriti did not wink, but Yardley, who understood the very souls of horses, thought he saw a look of amusement in his eyes.

'You'll have one chance, my lad, and that's at Alexandra Park. A cart-horse can win at Alexandra Park. And if you don't behave yourself on Saturday, you'll go to the stud at nine guineas, and you know what that means!'

Veriti did not raise his eyebrows, but he raised his ears as though he understood. And really the question of his fee was less important to Veriti than his popularity. For the moment he was exceedingly unpopular, but that did not worry him.

Mr. Yardley was a painstaking and thorough trainer, and it was all to his advantage that veiled Press comments and innuendoes passed him by without making the slightest impression. He was that gentleman whose practice it was to run two horses in a race and win with the outsider. It was the popular idea that these results were cleverly planned. To such a suggestion Mr. Yardley merely offered a cryptic smile and the remark that horses were not machines.

He brought Veriti out two mornings after, and gave him a gallop with the two best horses in his stable. And he was not overwhelmingly surprised when Veriti won the gallop pulling up, because he was, as Mr. Lyndall would say, 'a horse of moods'.

'I suppose that means that you'll finish down that infernal course on Saturday,' mused Mr. Yardley, looking into Veriti's eyes – and it may have been a coincidence, but Veriti nodded.

Educated Evans had made up his mind to have a great day on the Saturday, for his punters were, in the main, people who speculated their maximum on that day. He had planned a grand circularizing of every name on his books with the winner of the London Cup. That he should have chosen Veriti is not remarkable, for Veriti had run second in the Chesterfield Plate at Goodwood. But somehow the zip had gone out of Evans' life that week. Morning and night, and sometimes in the middle of the day, he was to be found in the widow's room, sitting by the child, who seemed to fade before his very eyes.

Evans saw the doctor, a busy man with very little time to fuss.

'The child would be saved if you could get him away to the country and keep him there,' he said to Evans, when the educated man met him at the bottom of the stairs. 'I'm giving this advice, well knowing that this poor woman cannot afford to send the child away. I've done my utmost to find a free convalescent home for him, but I can't get him in anywhere.'

'What would it cost, doctor?'

'Five or six pounds a week,' said the doctor brusquely, and Evans' heart sank, for he was very near the end of his own resources, and his livelihood was a precarious one.

'Do you know what I think, Mr. Evans?' said the mother, coming outside the door on to the landing and talking in a hushed voice. 'I think that boy's life would be saved if he could see that kind of horse he's always talking about. It's funny how things run in your mind when you're ill. That's all Ernie wants.'

Evans went into the room. The child was lying with his wasted hands beneath his cheeks, his eyes fixed on vacancy.

'Hullo, Ernie, old boy!'

Evans patted his shoulder gently. The dark eyes turned up to meet the tipster's face.

'What about that prahd 'orse?' he said weakly.

'I'm going to see what I can do about it,' said Evans. 'I'll be bringing one down the mews, and then I'll carry you to the window, and you can see it for yourself. Mrs. Turner, don't you think you might have your windows open a bit?'

She was shocked at the suggestion.

'That's what the doctor's always saying,' she complained. 'That means that Ernie will lie in a draught and catch a cold.'

To Evans' discerning eye the boy was slowly sinking; and he spent the Friday afternoon, when he should have been attending to his business, in a vain search of the neighbourhood for any horse that bore the slightest resemblance to Ernie's description. Evans could not help thinking –

He had to go to Alexandra Park; there was nothing else to do. The child was getting on his mind; and everlastingly that thin, whining voice intoning, 'Want to see a prahd 'orse', rang in Evans' ears.

He himself saw one. In a half-hearted way he had sent Veriti to some fifty clients, and he saw Veriti finish a bad ninth.

And then a great idea was born in his mind, and he hurried out of the cheap ring along the road and into the paddock. That he got into the paddock at all without the necessary ticket was a tribute to his courage and resourcefulness.

He arrived as Veriti was being sheeted under the disapproving eye of the great Yardley; and surely Veriti was a picture of a horse. Unfortunately, they will not pay out on pictures, as Mr. Yardley had truly said.

'Excuse me, sir.'

Yardley turned and saw a face which for the moment eluded him.

'I know you. Who are you?' he asked, not being in the mood for polite conversation.

'You remember me, sir, I'm Educated Evans.'

For a moment Yardley glared, and then a twinkle came into his eyes.

'Oh, you are! I remember you, you rascal. What do you want? I've no tips for you and I'm broke.'

'I don't want any money, sir,' said Evans huskily, and oppressed by the fearful liberty he was taking. 'But is there any chance of this horse coming to Bayham Mews, sir?' he blurted.

'To where?' asked the startled Yardley.

'To Bayham Mews, sir – Camden Town.'

'There's a chance of him going into a cart, if that's what you mean. There's also a chance of him going into the cats'-meat shop,' said Yardley. 'What do you mean, my friend?'

Brokenly, incoherently, Educated Evans told his story, gulping out the plaint of little Ernie.

'A proud horse? What's a proud horse? Oh, I think I know what you mean,' said Yardley, slowly, and turned his eyes upon Veriti. 'He's proud enough, though God knows why,' he said, and chuckled in spite of himself. 'Yes, I think he'd fill the bill. But you really don't imagine I should send his lordship's horse to amuse a small slum child, do you?'

'No, sir,' said Evans miserably.

'Then you're a damned fool,' said Yardley. 'What's your address?'

Educated Evans, scarcely believing his ears, gave ample directions. At a quarter past six that evening, when he was sitting with Ernie, not daring to believe that the trainer would carry out his promise, there came a clatter of hoofs in the yard, and Evans dashed to the window.

Coming back without a word, he lifted the child in his arms and, in spite of Mrs. Turner's protests, carried him on to the landing. And there Ernie saw the proudest horse he had ever seen – a horse so proud that it refused to run with other horses, but invariably and sedately trailed in the rear.

'O-oh!' said Ernie, and his round eyes grew rounder.

Veriti never looked better. He had been stripped of his sheet, and his coat glistened in the afternoon sun.

'O-oh!' said Ernie. 'Ain't 'e prahd?'

And proud he was, with his head held high and his delicate feet picking a way across the cobbled stones.

For a moment the horse held the eye of Educated Evans; then, looking past him, he saw Yardley. The great trainer came slowly toward him and mounted the stairs.

'Is this the child?' he said.

'Yes, sir,' said Educated Evans.

'Looks as if a little fresh air would do him a world of good,' said Yardley. 'What do you think of my proud horse, laddie?'

'He *is* prahd!' said Ernie.

'I should say he was,' said the grim Yardley. 'Nothing infectious about this child, is there?'

'No, sir,' said the woman.

'I'll send my car for him first thing in the morning. The wife of my head lad will look after him, if he's well enough to travel.'

And so Ernie Turner went down into Wiltshire, and there was an amazing sequel. As though conscious of the compliment that had been paid to him, Veriti won the next time out, and won pulling up. He started at 100 to 7. The favourite, which finished down the course and started at 6 to 4, was also one of Yardley's. And in the paddock after the race, wherever men congregated, it was agreed unanimously that Yardley ought to be warned off.

A JUDGE OF RACING

THE honourable Mr. Justice Bellfont was a very human man with a wide knowledge of human affairs. If the name of Carslake had been mentioned in his court, he would not have said, 'Who is Brownie Carslake?' but would have told you the position Brownie occupied in last year's list of winning jockeys and his lowest riding weight. If he did not say this aloud, he would have exposed his knowledge *sotto voce*, for he had the habit of speaking his thoughts aloud.

On Saturday meetings you could see him at Kempton or Hurst, and he had even been known to journey north to witness the field of the Manchester Handicap emerge from the fog. He had a cousin who owned horses and a nephew who trained them. He was, in the sense of experience and knowledge, the widest judge that ever sent a lad for a stretch.

He loved horses; but even in the days when he was a prosperous junior, he never had more than a pound each way on Ormonde. And if there wasn't a horse in the field relatively as good as Ormonde, he did not bet at all.

He had a notoriously tender spot for the little thief, and a hard surface for the clever financiers who came at rare intervals before him, and his terse 'You will be sent to prison for seven years', had brought distress to many a family who were living in luxury on the money that papa had extracted from poor investors.

Therefore, it was, in a sense, an act of providence that Walter Holl came before him – for Walter, though a tea-leaf, was a good fellow and a well-meaning man.

In the clear grey of morning, before the shops are open and while milkmen are yet lying in their beds, Camden Town is a place of solemn splendour, and even her public houses have an especial dignity. Save for a belated cat or so making its weary way homewards after a night spent in reckless debauchery, nothing moved in High Street. The drone of a distant newspaper van chug-chugging to Euston, the twitter of the birds in Bayham Street and the distant hoot of a goods-engine at the Midland Goods Station, are the only sounds that break the sylvan stillness.

Detective-Sergeant Challoner – known as 'The Miller' because he chewed straws – had spent the night profitably in conducting a raid upon a snide factory just off Ossulton Street, and now, at peace with mankind, he stood surveying the desert of High Street.

A figure came shuffling round a corner, saw him instantly and faded out of sight.

The Miller did not move: seemingly he had not seen the wayfarer. Presently the furtive man peeped round the corner. He saw his enemy standing apparently oblivious of his presence, turned and walked back the way he had come, satisfied that justice was happily blind.

Mr. Walter Holl would have found it difficult to run, for he carried in his cloth bag a large quantity of lead piping and brass taps that he had acquired in the earlier hours of the morning from an untenanted house in Holloway Road.

He was half-way back to Great College Street when he heard the softest sound behind him, and turned to meet The Miller.

'Lord! Mr. Challoner, you give me a fright! Them rubber soles of yours ain't half quiet!'

'Been shopping?' asked The Miller pleasantly, his eyes upon the bulging bag.

'Them?' Mr. Holl asked innocently as he opened the bag and displayed his loot. 'They belong to a friend of mine, a plumber. He's goin' up to Scotland to do a job an' he asked me to bring the bag to the station for him – gave me five bob to do it. You see, Mr. Challoner, he got soused last night an' – '

'Come along and have a cup of coffee at the station,' said The Miller, 'and we'll talk over old times. How long ago is it since I took you for busting empty houses, Holl? Must be nearly three years.'

Mr. Holl fell in by his side, The Miller's hand affectionately gripping his arm.

'It's a cop,' said Walter, with the philosophy of his kind. 'I got these out of a house in the Holloway Road – number eight-nought-four, or maybe four-nought-eight. It's hard luck on me, because I was goin' to get a packet out of Telltale in the Victoria Cup. I've been workin' honest for two years, but what with this here unemployment an' Lloyd George bein' the Gover'ment, an honest man can't make a living.'

'Mr. Lloyd George has been out of office for many years,' said The Miller, and Walter sneered.

'This choppin' an' changin' of gover'ments is the ruin of the workin' classes,' he stated.

At the police station he was searched; before he was put into the cells he asked for a special favour.

'I'd be very much obliged, Mr. Challoner, if you'd ask Educated Evans to put a piece together for me, so as when I go a front of the old bubble an' squeak I've got, so to speak, a full answer.'

'Can't you afford a mouthpiece?' asked the sympathetic Miller, referring in this crude way to a gentleman learned in the law.

'Mouthpiece!' Walter was scornful. 'Why all these so-and-so lawyers 'ang together. Why, I see a picture the other day of two of 'em walkin' arm an' arm together – and they was on different sides in a murder! No so-and-so lawyers for me!'

'Moderate your language,' said The Miller. 'I'll tell Evans, though I don't know what he can do for you except to tip that you'll get time. In which case you'll probably get off.'

Educated Evans of Tapin House, Bayham Mews – he had a disconcerting habit of renaming his residence after big race-winners – was indeed a friend to the poor and afflicted, in addition to being the World's Greatest Turf Adviser.

And at that moment he was riding on the crest of a wave.

Camden Town, which had lost confidence in the man and the prophet, was slowly regaining its faith. For had he not given in rapid succession:

> Argo! What a beauty!
> Argo! What a beauty!
> Argo! What a beauty!

together with

> Mr. Clever!   What a beauty!
>
> Mr. Clever!   What a beauty!
>
> Mr. Clever!   What a beauty!

to quote his own admirable literature.

It was rumoured – mainly by Mr. Evans – that the West End bookmakers were panic-stricken. People had come to his flat and paid him real money to encourage him in his good work.

The Miller walked up the wooden stairs which led to Tapin House, and found one who described himself immodestly as The Wizard of Camden Town engaged in the study of the next day's programme. Evans received him gravely – as a man of property would receive a bailiff, or a successful author a reviewer; in other words, as somebody who was respected but did not count.

Briefly The Miller explained the reason for his visit. Evans shook his head.

'I've given up writin' out defences for common people,' he said. 'I'm too busy, as the well-known Sir Francis Drake said to the soldier when he was teachin' the young princes in the Tower to say their twice-times table. What with owners an' trainers an' what not writin' to ask me not to tip their horses; an' what with me correspondents at Lambourn, Newmarket an' Epsom sendin' me yards an' yards of winners, I've got no time to disgrace meself with Walter Holl. What's he done?'

The Miller told him, and Mr. Evans made an impatient sound.

'The man was certainly a client of mine in the past, but whether he acted honourable or not I can't tell till I've seen me books. I'll see what I can do.'

'What's going to win the Gatwick Handicap?' asked The Miller.

'Blue Nose,' said Evans indifferently. 'I'm not troublin' about that race – it's too easy. Give me somethin' hard, like the Victoria Cup.'

'Blue Nose?' queried The Miller.

Evans went to his bed, turned the pillow and produced a letter.

'Read that,' he commanded.

The Miller read.

Dear Sir,

    With reference to your enquiry, Blue Nose has done no work for six months and has a very bad leg.

Yours faithfully,

H. Haggit

'That Haggit,' said Evans profoundly, 'couldn't tell the truth to his doctor. What's more, he owes me one. So I wrote to him, knowin' that whatever he sent me would be a lie. Blue Nose is money for nothin'. Help yourself an' don't forget I've got to pay rates an' taxes.'

The Miller was impressed.

'And Telltale will win the Victoria Cup?' he hazarded.

Here The Miller voiced the opinion commonly held by all keen racing men. For Telltale had, so to speak, been flung into the handicap. He had been left – also, so to speak – ten minutes in the Newbury Cup and had been beaten by a short head by a great horse. Ardent sportsmen in Camden Town were going to Hurst Park in a fortnight's time to place their underwear at the disposal of the receptive bookmakers and, if truth be told, Mr. Walter Holl's divers larcenies and felonies had been performed or committed with the object of getting a little stock of money to invest in this gilt-edged security.

Educated Evans scratched his nose.

'He ought to win it,' he admitted. 'He ought to be able to fall down an' get up an' then win. But them bookmakers won't lay more than twoses an' more likely it'll be six ter four on the field an' twenty to one bar two. And that don't pay me an' my clients.'

He looked round cautiously, though there was no danger of being overheard.

'You're in the lore, Mr. Challoner; what about Dum Spyro? He's trained by Falston – he's the nephew of Lord What's-his-name, the highly celebrated judge.'

'You mean Mr. Justice Bellfont?' asked The Miller.

'That's him. Don't you ever get any tips at Scotlan' Yard? Don't judges put things in your way – they ought to. Where would they be without busies?'

The Miller chuckled.

'The judge doesn't give tips, you poor miserable man!'

Mr. Evans was deep in thought.

'If I thought Dum Spyro was on the job I'd take him to beat the fav'rite. But that Falston's so close that he's stuck together. He don't bet, but he wouldn't tell his own wife where he kept his shirts: he's that tight you couldn't open him with a pickaxe.'

The Miller went away and brooded on the immediate problem of Blue Nose. He was, in a way, slightly amused by the perverted reasoning of the World's Premier Turf Prophet. So was the station-sergeant and several form-studying constables. When Blue Nose won that afternoon by the length of a street they were slightly annoyed.

Mr. Evans spent the greater part of the evening composing an address which Walter could read from the dock. He had composed many such: generally speaking, they began in very much the same strain.

> May it please your Worship. It was said by the celebrated Shakespeare, 'The quantity of Mercy is not strange', therefore I ask your Worship, in the terrible position I find myself, an innocent man dragged ruthlessly to the bar of justice, to take a lenient view of a mere bagatelle committed under the influence of drink, that well-known curse.

The three hours spent in this labour were, however, so much wasted time, as he learned on attending the police court the next morning.

'Sorry, Evans,' said The Miller, 'but this will be an Old Bailey case. We found a lot of stolen property in his house, and he is certain to be fullied.* He tells me he did a bit of work for you in the past two years?'

This was true. Mr. Holl had earned many an odd shilling. He had run a few errands, scrubbed the educated man's floor, and once had distempered the walls of his bed-sitting-working-room.

'If you go up before the judge and say a few words for him, you might save him a lagging,' suggested The Miller – a scheme which at first filled the World's Champion with quaking fear, but which afterwards had certain attractions.

Educated Evans had participated in many police court proceedings, but he had never yet attained to the distinction of making an official appearance at the Old Bailey.

By great good fortune, Mr. Holl was fullied in time to catch the

* *Fully committed for trial.*

next week's sitting of the Central Criminal Court. Kind friends, one and all, whipped round to supply the funds necessary to secure the services of that eminent barrister-at-law, Mr. Chubble-Chine, a very young man who knew just as much of the world as can be viewed from the court of Caius College, Cambridge, and Pump Court, E.C.4. Educated Evans, wearing his check trousers and nearly gold horseshoe tiepin, his almost white bowler hat on the side of his head, strolled into the hall of the Old Bailey, the observed of all observers.

'It's curious, Mr. Miller,' he said modestly, 'how a feller gets known. All them people know me . . . I'm so to speak, the sinicure of all eyes.'

'They think you're Woddle, the forger, surrendering to his bail,' said The Miller coldly, 'and listen, Evans: when you get up in front of the judge, don't talk too much – it's Bellfont.'

Figuratively speaking, the ears of Educated Evans pricked.

'The highly famous Lord Bellfont – him whose nephew trains Dum Spyro?' he asked, and The Miller nodded.

'That's a bit of luck,' said Evans thoughtfully. 'When he sees the kind of man he's got to deal with, I bet he'll ask me into his private room an' have a talk – '

The Miller's eye was cold.

'The only private room you'll ever be asked into,' he said, 'is one of twenty in the basement, which has a lock on it and a peep-hole where the warder can see that you're not committing suicide.'

Nevertheless, Mr. Evans was not depressed.

It was two o'clock that afternoon when Mr. Holl stepped brightly up from the bowels of the earth into the dock. He pleaded 'Not guilty' in a chirpy voice.

At a quarter to three, Educated Evans walked into the witness-box and, having solemnly sworn to tell the truth, leant negligently on the ledge of the box.

'You are,' said the youthful counsel, 'a very well-known sporting journalist?'

Evans was momentarily staggered at this description.

'In a sense and in a way I am.'

The saturnine figure on the bench glared at him.

'Are you or aren't you?' he rasped.

'I am, my dear Lord,' said Evans, and went on to answer questions

which were intended to prove, beyond any question of doubt, that
Walter Holl was between whiles a hard-working man, a good father
and a kind and loyal friend. Counsel for the prosecution did not
even trouble to cross-examine him.

Not so Mr. Justice Bellfont.

'When you say you are a sporting journalist, what do you mean?'
he demanded.

'The fact is, my dear Lord – ' began Evans.

'There is no need for you to be affectionate,' said his Lordship.

'The fact is,' said Evans, a little wildly, 'I'm what you might term
the World's Champion Turf Adviser and Prognosticator. I'm the
gentleman that gave Braxted at 20 to 1 – what a beauty, dear lord!
Also Tarpin – '

'Oh – a tipster!'

It is impossible to convey all the scorn, derision, contempt and
condemnation in his Lordship's tone.

'Yes, my dear sir – my dear Lord, I mean – I'm a prophet. As
the well-known and highly respected John Bunions, the celebrated
composer of Robinson Crusoe and his man Friday, said – '

'A tipster!'

His lordship's lips curled.

'A prophet an' Turf adviser, dear my lord,' murmured Evans.
'The same address for twenty-five years; not one of them "gone
today and come tomorrow" people. As the far-famed Lord Winston
Churchill said, "Jer swee – I'm here!" '

The judge leant back in his padded chair; the cold malignity in
his eyes made Mr. Evans shudder.

'You infernal rascal!' he muttered. When he was annoyed, he
invariably spoke his thoughts aloud. 'You robber; you ought to be
in the dock!'

And then:

'You have the audacity to come here to certify a man's character!'

'Yes, my dear Lord,' said Evans faintly.

'You send out your inf – your prophecies as to what horse will
win?'

'Yes, dear – my Lord.' Evans in his terror was swaying in the
box.

'And you have the – really – I am amazed at your audacity! Do
you profess to be able to predict horses that will win races?'

Evans nodded – he hoped respectfully.

'I believe you are a swindler!' said the judge firmly. 'I believe that you are obtaining money by false pretences.'

The educated man saw the prison gates yawning wide to receive him. Cold perspiration trickled down his nose. The hands that gripped the ledge were clammy – the court spun round him.

But the unconquerable spirit which is latent in every prophet sustained him, in a last desperate effort to justify himself:

'The fact is, dear Lord – dear mister . . . my Lord,' he stammered, 'it's easy. Now take Telltale – he can't help winnin' the Victoria Cup . . .'

'Not a ghost of a chance,' muttered his Lordship. 'Not with Dum Spyro in the field . . .'

So low he spoke that only Evans heard him. Then, aloud, and with a stern look in his eye:

'Stand down, sir!' he said. 'The fact that the unfortunate prisoner has nothing better in the shape of witnesses than a wretched swindling tipster, is proof of his friendlessness.'

He let Walter off with a three months' sentence.

Evans staggered out of court like a man in a dream. The Miller spoke to him, but he did not hear. In Newgate Street he found a taxi and drove back to Bayham Mews.

That evening, Detective-Sergeant Challoner made one of his frequent calls at the Hall of the Prophet and found Evans in his shirtsleeves struggling with a duplicator which even a child could work. Round and round the little cylinder was turning, and with every revolution there appeared a quarto sheet, wet with violet ink. In silence The Miller picked up a sheet and read:

EDUCATED EVANS

The World's Champion Turf Profit and Racing Adviser Owner of the following high-class performers under both Rules:

RAW MEAT   TOMMY HAKE   SHIN SORE
EYEBALLS   WIGGLE WAG   JERUSALEM MOKE

Educated Evans, commonly called 'The Whizard of Camden Town' (same address for 30 years) has given some of the biggest selections the world has ever known.

BRAXTED 20/1! What a beauty!
BRAXTED 20/1! What a beauty!

TARPIN 11/1! What a beauty!
TARPIN 11/1! What a beauty!
Educated Evans begs to announce that one
of the
BEST JUDGES OF RACING
BEST JUDGES OF RACING
BEST JUDGES OF RACING
has kindly given him the winner of
THE VICTORIA CUP
This horse has 21lb. in hand of TELLTALE:
This horse is trained by
A RELATION
of the best Judge of Racing and
IS TRYING.
Send P.O. for 5/- to Educated Evans, Tapin Lodge, Bayham Mews.

'What is the horse?' asked The Miller.
'Dum Spyro,' said Evans rapidly. 'I had it from Lord Bellfont himself – didn't you see him give me the wink?'

THROUGH THE CARD

'I've often wondered,' said The Miller reflectively, 'why a man of your education and ability doesn't find another way of earning a living, Evans. I admit that it's better than thieving, and more desirable than a good many other methods of earning a livelihood that are followed by mutual friends. But it's a little precarious, isn't it, or do you make so much money that you expect to retire?'

Educated Evans scratched his chin and looked up at his visitor who was a frequent caller at the little room over the stable which was Evans' dwelling-place, and he had come that morning at a very unpropitious and depressive moment, for Evans had sent out twelve consecutive losers, and it almost seemed as if he would never touch a winner again.

So depressed was he, that he was engaged in his favourite course of study, which was the sixth volume of Chambers' *Encyclopaedia* which began at the Humber and finished at Malta.

On these and on all matters in between, except perhaps such subjects as the habits of the Lecythidaceae, which was a little above him, he was an authority. He knew all about Robert Lee and Pope John, Japan, and Iron, and International Law, and Ink and Indiarubber, and Incantations, and Lick Observatory and the Liturgy, because these were dealt with in the volume. And he had no other volumes.

He was half-way through a learned article on 'The Use of Lights in Public Worship' when The Miller's big frame loomed up in the doorway.

'I owe three weeks' rent,' said Educated Evans despondently. 'The woman who washes me shirts won't let me have 'em back until I pay her up all the back. I owe twenty-three and twopence for gas, and I've got four and sixpence that I borrowed from Li Jacobs. That's the money I've saved!'

'What do you do with all your money?' asked The Miller in quiet wonder. 'You must make a lot sometimes, Evans.'

'Some people,' said Educated Evans, 'like the celebrated Henry the Eighth who married twenty-five wives, do in their stuff on horses and women. You have to be a king to do it in that way. I've done all mine in on horses without the assistance of any young lady.'

He got up and went to the mantelpiece and filled a pipe, and the fact that he was reserving the end of a cigar that lay by its side was sufficient evidence that his position was a parlous one.

'I've done with horses from now onwards,' said Educated Evans. 'It's phantom gold,' he said recklessly. 'Find me a job; I'll take it.'

'Higgs wants a man,' suggested The Miller.

'Higgs!' said the scornful Evans. 'Do you think I'd work for a man like that? He's a twister. A ten-pun' note wouldn't pay what that man owes me for information supplied at great cost – you've no idea of my expenses what with travellin', giving money to stable boys and head lads – '

'You're amongst friends,' said The Miller soothingly. 'Don't let's tell the tale. What about Mr. Walters? He'd give you a job.'

Evans shrugged his shoulders.

'Am I the kind of man who'd work for a fellow like Walters?' he asked, haughtily. 'A man, so to speak, who makes a mock of education? No, Mr. Challoner, I'll see what Saturday brings in. And if Roving Betty doesn't win the Duke of York Stakes, then I'll have to look around. I'm not grousing' – he was very serious now – 'but somehow I've never been able to touch big money, Mr. Challoner. Facts been against me.'

'You mean Fate,' said The Miller.

'I'm talking about bookmakers more particularly,' said Educated Evans. 'I've never been able to bring off a coup. Not a real coup. Of course, I've bragged a lot in printin' – I wish I had the money that I've spent with Dickens the printer – but between friends, if I may presume, I've never touched the money that I've always dreamt about. I'm a bit of a dreamer, Mr. Challoner.'

'So I've noticed,' said the other, not unkindly.

'I can sit here,' said Evans, tapping the book in front of him, 'and dream as only educated people can dream, I've ridden Derby winners, I've owned the biggest sprinter of the age, I've taken a hundred thousand pounds a day out of the ring – in my dreams. And, mind you, I wouldn't be without 'em for anything. Of course, I never shall take a hundred thousand out of the ring, and I'll never get that cottage and field.'

The interested Miller sat down.

'Let's hear about your cottage and field, Evans. That's a new one on me.'

'I've got an idea of a beautiful little cottage in the country. I saw one advertised for sale the other day on the back page of *The Times*. Five thousand pounds! Me doing the kitchen gardening and making a bit by selling flowers and teas for cyclists – if they drank beer they'd fall off – and a horse in the field. Get an old selling plater and breed from her. That's my idea of happiness.'

The Miller puffed slowly at his long cigar.

'And it's not a bad idea either,' he said. 'But if you had the money you'd do it in, Evans.'

'Not me!' said Evans decisively. 'If I ever touch for a bit – and God knows I never shall – I'd give up buying *The Sportsman* and take in *The Christian Herald* – and it's more exciting anyway. I took a bus down to Kent the other day for a bit of fresh air, and it's a nice ride. There's a place with about two acres – a little cottage, an old well, just like in the pictures. Why, I'd be a king there!'

'What would it cost?'

'Two thousand pounds. I saw the owner. Kidded him I might be buying it one of these days,' said Evans dismally. 'Me buy a house! Why, I couldn't buy a rabbit-hutch!'

Friday afternoon saw Evans, with his dwindling stock of envelopes, folding what he knew was his last appeal to an incredulous public. Most of the circulars were delivered locally. Saturday brought him a solitary five-shilling postal order. Evans went without breakfast that morning and carried his overcoat to a repository near at hand and received in exchange ten shillings and a ticket.

He stood on the kerb, his hands in his pockets, the picture of dejection, staring blankly at the White Hart, the landlord of which had once welcomed him as a friend, and the shadow of ruin was upon him.

Evans was not a great drinker. His magnificence in his cups had led to so many awkward and embarrassing moments that he had abandoned the practice with no great regret, for drinking to Evans was one of the most expensive forms of recreation.

In his pocket he had 30s. and if he carried out the mad idea which possessed him that morning and went to Kempton Park he might starve on the morrow.

So brooding, The Miller passed him on his motorcycle and, seeing the melancholy figure, stopped his machine and got off.

'How did they come in, Evans?'

'They came in one by one,' said Evans bitterly. 'The first one has arrived; the second may come at any time between now and Christmas. I've got a dollar, and it cost me more than that for envelopes.'

'Can I lend you a fiver?' asked The Miller, but Evans shook his head.

'You'll never get it back,' he said miserably.

'Take it,' said The Miller and, thrusting the note into his hands, moved off.

'Don't forget Bactive Lad,' Evans called after him, the ruling passion strong even in death.

He stood with the note in his hand, and then a sudden resolve came to him, and he crossed the road and walked into the saloon bar. The proprietor was not visible, but the head barman eyed him suspiciously. It seemed that the news of Evans' poverty had spread throughout the land.

'A double Scotch and soda,' said Evans firmly.

He had never drunk whisky before in the morning, but he felt that he must do something or die of sheer inanition. He threw the five-pound note on the counter and tossed down the drink at a gulp.

'I'll have another,' he said, and when he had had the other and had leant against the bar, frowning thoughtfully for fully five minutes without saying a word, he came to a sudden decision.

'Going to Kempton, Evans?' asked the barman.

Educated Evans turned his stony eyes on his interrogator.

' "Mister Evans", if you don't mind,' he said haughtily. ' "The Honourable Mr. Evans", my good feller.'

'I'm sorry,' said the barman, aghast.

'You took a liberty,' said Evans, 'that no common man should take with an educated gentleman.'

He brushed some invisible dust from his sleeve, and with a shrug of his shoulders walked out.

Providentially a taxi was passing and Evans hailed it.

'Waterloo, my man,' he said. 'Get there in ten minutes and I'll give you a fiver.'

Happily the driver recognised him.

'What's the hurry, Evans? There are plenty of trains.'

'I have a special train,' said Evans, gravely, and fell into the taxi. He intended to step in, but he fell in, for his foot slipped.

Mr. Evans alighted at Waterloo with greater *éclat*. He stepped out of his cab on to the foot of Henry B. Norman, an American million-aire and an excellent sportsman.

'Say, haven't you any feet of your own to walk on?' said the plutocrat.

'Pardon,' said Evans in stateliest manner, and threw five shillings at the taxi-driver. 'As a gentleman I apologise. As a gentleman you accept. God bless you!' And he seized the hand of the astonished millionaire and wrung it. 'Come and have a drink,' said Evans.

Mr. Norman's eyes narrowed.

'I guess you've had almost as much as you can take, my friend,' he said. 'You're all lit up like the Hotel Doodah!'

'Come and have a drink,' insisted Evans, closing his eyes. He always closed his eyes in these circumstances; it lent him a certain dignity which was impressive.

Now Mr. Norman was waiting for a friend who had not turned up. He was going to Kempton Park because, as the owner of an American stud, he was keenly interested in English racing. But that morning, when he had left his valet's hands, he had not the slightest idea that at eleven-thirty he would be standing in the public bar drinking whisky with a disreputable gentleman who hinted mysteri-ously at his noble birth.

'It's not generally known,' said Evans, leaning affectionately on the counter, 'that my father was the fourteenth Earl of Pogmore. I'm not sure if it's Pogmore or Frogmore, but what does it matter?'

'Precisely.'

'You're an American. I knew in ten minutes,' said Educated

Evans, nodding his head wisely. 'That's wunner things I learnt at Eton.'

'At Eton?' repeated the staggered American.

'I was brought up at Eton and Harrow,' said Evans, 'but it's not generally known.'

'Who the dickens are you, then?' asked the American, thinking that he had by chance happened upon a member of the shabby nobility.

'Lord Evans, of Bayham House – of Bayham Castle, I mean,' said Evans.

'Going to Kempton?'

'I'll go through the card. There isn't a horse running today, my dear American fellow, that I don't know everything about. Owners, trainers, jockeys – ' he waggled his hand expressively '– I get everything!'

It was at that moment that the millionaire's friend found him.

'Goodbye, Mr. Evans, or Lord Evans, as the case may be,' said Norman, good-humouredly.

He shook hands with his host, and was half-way to the door when he stopped.

'I'll give this poor soak the surprise of his life,' he said, and taking out five clean, crisp notes from his pocket-book, 'A present from the United States,' he said, and slipped them into Evans' hand.

Things were going remarkably well with Evans.

He arrived at Kempton by a very ordinary train. The Miller, who had ridden down on his motorbike, watched him open-mouthed as he strolled into Tattersall's, slamming down a ten-pound note.

'Here, what's wrong with you, Evans?' The Miller tackled him as he entered Tattersall's ring.

'Ha, Miller, I owe you a fiver, I think? Take it, my good fellow.'

He waved the note in the air, and The Miller, anxious to avoid a scene, took it.

'Miller, old boy' – he gripped the detective's arm – 'I've got summun to tell you. I'm not what you think I am, dear old boy.' He forced back the tears that had come into his eyes with an effort, blew his nose, and repeated: 'I am not what you think I am.'

'You're soused,' said The Miller reproachfully.

'No, no, old boy, I'm not soused. I'm an unfortunate man, dear Miller.'

His attentions were becoming more than embarrassing, he had his arm affectionately round The Miller's shoulder – as far as it would reach.

'Dear old boy, I'm the nat'ral son of the Earl of Evans! Now you know!'

He stepped back dramatically, and came into collision with a bookmaker who was taking a light lunch.

'I'm not that either,' said Evans, in reply to the bookmaker's observation. 'I'm – '

He looked round for The Miller, but the latter had seized the opportunity and vanished.

The horses were at the post when Evans, sitting on the steps of the stand, his head between his hands, suddenly woke with a start. Fumbling with his card, and walking to the nearest bookmaker, he demanded so loudly that it could be heard almost all over the ring:

'What price Midget's Pride?'

'Eight to one to you,' said the bookmaker.

Evans dropped a roll of money in his hand and with some difficulty the bookmaker counted it.

'Twenty-three pounds seventeen and sixpence. Do you want it to this?' he asked incredulously.

'To that,' said the grave Evans.

'Take back the silver. I'm not betting that way.' He thrust the coins into Evans hand. 'A hundred and ninety-four to twenty-three Midget's Pride. You needn't take a ticket. I'll know that dial anywhere.'

Midget's Pride won cleverly. Evans was unaware of the fact until the bookmaker hailed him.

'Hi, you! Come and get this money you've robbed me of!'

Evans thrust the notes into his pocket and went into the bar. When he emerged he was another man. His eyes were bright, his head was high. He had lost his hat.

The second race was a two-year-old seller. A horse started a hot favourite at 13 to 8. Evans took 6 to 4 to all the money he could find in his pocket.

Just before the last race The Miller was standing by the rails discussing with a brother professional the appearance of several well-known faces in the ring when he saw Educated Evans strutting along the alley-way that led from the paddock.

'Good morning, Miller. Good morning, my man,' he said, with a lordly wave of his hand.

'Been through the card?'

'Right through the card. Look at this.' He put both hands in his pockets and drew forth notes in such profusion that dozens fell to the ground. 'Let 'em be,' said Evans loftily. 'Leave 'em there for the common people. I've just seen the Stewards about the dead-heat in the last race. Disgustin'!'

'There wasn't a dead-heat in the last race, you damned fool!' growled The Miller. 'The winner was a clear length in front of everything else.'

'It looked like a dead-heat to me,' said Evans. 'I distinctly saw two horses.'

As the field was going to the post Evans staggered to the leading bookmaker of Tattersall's.

'Good morning, Mr. Slumber,' he said. – In other times and circumstances he would have trembled to approach the great man. – 'What price Standoff?'

The great Harry Slumber surveyed his customer with a calm and critical eye.

'Seven to one.'

'Lay me forty-nine thousand to seven thousand and the money is yours,' said Evans gravely.

It was then that The Miller thought he ought to interfere.

Evans woke the next morning with a feeling that by some tragic accident his head had been caught between steam rollers and slightly flattened. When his hand went up, however, he found no difference in the shape. He was aching in every limb and, staring round, he found he was in a room of familiar appearance.

There was a steel door and a grating, a bell-push, a hard, leather-covered pillow and a blanket. The bed itself was a wooden bench. A large jug of water slaked his burning thirst and then, just as he was going to ring the bell and ask for information, a lock snapped and the door of the cell opened. The Miller looked at him and shook his head.

'What a nice man you are, Evans!' he said bitterly. 'After I'd taken the trouble to bring you home and put you to bed!'

'What did I do?' asked Evans.

'What did you do?' said The Miller. 'You came and kissed Inspector Pine, that's what you did! I thought he'd have killed you.'

Evans groaned.

'I've had such a wonderful dream. I dreamt I'd been to Kempton and won thousands.'

'Three thousand two hundred pounds,' said The Miller calmly, 'and you're a lucky man to have it.'

Evans jumped up as if he had been shot.

'Did I go through the card?' he asked hollowly.

'You went through the card, and the boys would have gone through you if I hadn't been there,' said The Miller. 'Evans, you're a disgusting fellow. And here comes Inspector Pine,' he said, 'to ask if your intentions were serious.'

SPORTINGALITIES

A SELECTION of the thumbnail sketches of racing personalities which Wallace contributed to John Bull in the Twenties is included here to show how he could catch a character in a few paragraphs. They demonstrate too, how he was not afraid to say what he thought of the faults and more unpopular sides of those whom he depicted. He did not hesitate, for instance, despite his whole-hearted admiration for him, to mention Lord Derby's habit of saying just what he thought which led him at times into indiscretion, and to describe Lord Lonsdale's ferocity towards those appearing before him on enquiries. In fact it was those qualities in these two great characters which brought them into conflict later on.

Lord Lonsdale's behaviour in the Stewards' room was a by-word amongst owners, trainers and jockeys, especially the latter. Joe Childs, the royal jockey, has related how on one occasion he stood up to him so successfully that his fellow Steward, Lord Durham, remarked, 'Perhaps it would be best if I took the chair', and Tommy Weston, Lord Derby's jockey, was said to have done much the same with the result that Lord Derby believed that Lonsdale (for whom he never had a high regard, saying after one enquiry that he had been treated by him, 'like a criminal' and he would certainly have endorsed another grandee's verdict on his fellow peer, 'almost an emperor and not quite a gentleman') had it in for him and his horses. After the Weston episode he wrote to his trainer, the Honourable George Lambton, in his usual trenchant style: 'I am therefore thinking of writing to Topham saying that I wish my name taken off the list of Stewards as I cannot serve with Lord Lonsdale, and for the future, if he is to be a Steward, I shall decline to enter horses. There is no doubt he is half-witted, but it is no reason because he is half-witted he should have this down upon our stable.'

Nor, in writing about Lord Astor, was Wallace afraid to put in pithy *comment upon his father's unpopularity. Waldorf Astor, unlike his son, was not a well-loved man. He had a mania for privacy and expended his great wealth on ensuring it, bringing down condign penalties on those he fancied had invaded it. To such lengths did he carry this that when he purchased the Cliveden estate from the Grosvenor family on hearing that its river banks held attractions for boating parties on the Thames, he spent thousands building a high wall around the entire estate, thereby earning for himself the sobriquet, 'Walled-off' Astor.*

Lord Carnarvon was, of course, to gain far greater fame off the racecourse as the discoverer of King Tutankhamun's tomb, which took place only some six weeks after Wallace's sketch of him appeared, and a few months later he was dead, giving rise to the widely circulated story of 'the curse of King Tut'. Nevertheless he was a not inconsiderable personage on the Turf. Always eccentrically dressed, 'Wearing', his son says, 'a unique sort of low-crowned felt hat of a shape never seen on any head but his own, and a frayed bow tie, shod, whatever the smartness of the occasion, with brown shoes — "that fellow's, damn brown shoes" as a great personage once observed — he could count on a special welcome.' He had had considerable success with horses bred by himself, numbering amongst many others victories in the Ascot Stakes, the Stewards' Cup, the Doncaster Cup and the City and Suburban, but it was, as Wallace points out, his quiet determination to carry on 'through fair weather and foul' which made his sudden death a sad loss to the Turf. Herbert Jones, the jockey whom Wallace included in his gallery, was a great raconteur and he may or may not have been the originator of one of the best of the stories of Wallace's occasional eccentricities on the Turf which, again, may or may not be apochryphal. One of Wallace's endearing foibles, which cost him a lot of money, was that he always believed the best of his horses however useless they were, and jockeys who returned to criticize them were frequently discarded without warning, never to ride for him again. As he was both well-liked and generous this was a fate to be avoided and many were the stories hatched up by riders to cover their mount's shortcomings and excuse their failures. On this occasion the jockey returned to Wallace with what he thought was a tale to tell which would protect him from Wallace's wrath and resentment. 'He's green and very backward,' he said on dismounting 'What he needs is a bit more time.' 'But,' was Wallace's sad reply. 'He's nine years old already!'

LORD DERBY

I DON'T know how many years ago it was when Lord Stanley (as he was then) stood up in the House of Commons and hinted darkly at the fate which would be mine if it were proved that the stories I was writing about the Boers' treatment of our wounded should prove to be false.

Nothing did happen to me, for my stories were accurate, and I lived to understand the young under-secretary, and, understanding him, to admire him more than I have ever admired any man that occupied a Ministry of the Crown.

Here is an Englishman who might stand as a sealed pattern of and for all Englishmen. His honesty is stupendous, his habit of truth an outrage of all the canons of political practice. There never was a straighter, cleaner and (in his younger days) more impetuous, and because of these very qualities more indiscreet, man.

But the habit of saying what he thought was his greatest asset, annoying as it was to those who writhed under the acid of his honesty.

No one man in England did more individually to win the war than he. He raised whole divisions in his recruiting campaign, and served us in France at a very critical period of the war.

What he did for us and the world when, as Ambassador to France, he moved (waded would be a better word) through the pestiferous atmosphere of political intrigue, we shall never know. We shall, I feel sure, live to see a Derby Administration, for at this moment he is the strongest man in the Conservative Party.

Apart from the King, Lord Derby is the dominant figure in the sport of horse-racing. He has been a loyal and consistent supporter of the Turf, and I hope and believe that his reward is coming.

Pharos, in my judgment, is the best two-year-old we have seen this year. If he has a better, or if Pharos stays. . . May we all be at Epsom next year to cheer him when he leads in the Derby winner.

SOLOMON B. JOEL

THE first time I met Solomon Joel was in Johannesburg. I
think it was Carl Hanau who introduced us. In those days
he was as often called 'Jolly Soul' as 'Solly Joel', and he has
still a very keen sense of humour. Which is remarkable, for the
accumulation of great wealth is very destructive to a sense of fun.
And he has not been without his private worries. Nevertheless, I
don't think he looks very much older than when I glimpsed him
some twenty years ago.

It is queer, remembering his enormous wealth, that one hears so
little to his discredit. I cannot think of another millionaire about
whom some dark and sinister stories do not circulate. Either they
are mad or mean; have strange and horrid amusements, or are
secretly suffering from some incurable malady.

'X.? Oh yes, poor X. isn't to be envied. He is worth three
millions, but they say he has to be fed with a spoon.'

Or else there are tales of this kind:

'It's sad about Z. – worth three millions and hasn't been sober
for years. He has a bottle of whisky for breakfast, and never goes
to sleep before he has drunk a magnum of Bollinger.'

But nobody ever hints that Solomon Joel drinks or has mysterious
tastes. In spite of his millions he is the most normal man I have ever
met. I have never had business transactions with him; but I am told
that there are many people who have had who wish he *would* drink!
Undoubtedly he is a pillar of the Turf. His horses are run out, and
he spends liberally to keep his stable at the top. The fiasco of
Pondoland's Derby was probably the greatest surprise he has had in
his racing career, for those who should have known better advised
him that, despite Pondoland having been stopped in his work, he

could 'fall down and get up and then win!'. Pondoland did not fall down, and he did not get up, and he did not win. Some day, however, Pommern's success will be repeated – and on Epsom Downs.

ALEC TAYLOR

MR. ALEC TAYLOR is really a gentleman-farmer. He has a stable of horses, but you always feel that the stable of horses is a side-line, and the really important business of life with Mr. Taylor has something to do with mangel-wurzels. I might remark in passing that farming is one of the mysteries I have never solved, and that I have only the vaguest idea as to whether farmers grow wheat or tulips.

But I know he is a farmer because when I was at Manton last year, a local authority spoke to me for an hour about Mr. Taylor's crops, and never once mentioned his stayers.

Such men as he are the high priests of Turfdom. You can no more imagine the English Turf without a Taylor than you can imagine Lord Lonsdale without a cigar. He is one of the non-betting trainers and there is a story that he once had a stone certainty at Newmarket, and was urged by one of the stable connections to support his horse.

'What price is it?' he asked cautiously, and was told that it was 7 to 4.

'Then put me a fiver each way,' were his instructions. It will be admitted that a man who backs his 7 to 4 horse for a place cannot be put into the category of dashing betters.

It is customary to refer to the Taylors as 'wizards', and the title of 'Wizard of Manton' is almost an hereditary one; but the wizardry of Mr. Alec Taylor is reducible to hard work, sound judgement and, as I have said, a patience that is hardly human. The present holder of the title, like his father, is a specialist in long-distance races and with uncanny precision he can 'place' his charges to win.

There is no stable which holds fewer mysteries than Manton –

very rarely indeed is a ready-made winner sprung upon the market – except in the case of two-year-old horses, the merits of which are necessarily dark. Manton is too big for trickiness.

A delightful simple, charming man, without an atom of snide and with a great fund of human kindness, he is nevertheless something of an autocrat. Owners who want to race their horses off their legs, and who wish their animals to run at this, that and the other meeting, do not patronise the Manton stable. He is a trainer of infinite patience and wisdom, and granted that he has excellent material to work upon, he is in some measure responsible for its excellence.

BERT JONES

S OME day, all that Ibanez did for the bull-fighter in *Blood and Sand* – the book, not the play – somebody will do for the jockey. We shall have a real and understanding picture of his early struggles, the brutalising effects of voluntary starvation; we shall learn of the human parasites who prey on him and receive perhaps a convincing picture of his inner life when success has come and mysterious thousands appear on the right side of his passbook.

If ever I wrote such a book and I should be compelled to take a type for a hero, I should certainly choose Bert Jones to fill that role.

He stands, not only for the romance, but for the humanity of jockeyship. Herbert Jones has ridden for two kings and has won three Derbies. He has been attached to one stable for thirty years and has been riding in public for more than twenty. And he is still riding winners. There is no 'safer' jockey in the saddle for the betting owner – as a rider of 'difficult' horses he has no peer.

But I like Bert best for his unfailing humour. He is a man who is absolutely unspoilt by the success that has come his way. It takes a great deal to amuse a writer of humorous stories, but I have laughed until I was helpless at the stories of his army experience. He was one of the Zepp fighters, and the tale of Bert's introduction to the anti-aircraft gun can only be told by himself in his own inimitable language.

There is no more generous soul than his, and his views of race-riding are worth hearing. Danny Maher is the greatest rider he has ever known – of Danny he speaks with genuine affection.

It is difficult to realise that Bert was riding winners before Tod Sloan began his meteoric career on the English Turf; that he saw the coming and the going of the Reiffs, and had two Derbies to his

credit before a diminutive Master Frank Wootton came in knicker-
bockers and Eton collar to ride his father's horses.

At the age of forty-one he is still a master horseman and can hold
his own with the youngest and the strongest. A good fellow and a
lovable fellow, may he carry the royal livery for many years – there
is no cleaner, straighter man riding today, and no man more worthy
to ride the horses of the First Sportsman of the Land.

LORD LONSDALE

IF LORD LONSDALE had not been born the heir to an earldom, or if that interesting event had occurred four hundred years ago, we can imagine him commanding a privateer and harassing the galleons of the Spanish Main. Heaven gave him the soul of an adventurer, and Fate ordained that he should live respectably and wear top hats and, on occasions, white trousers, and invariably a large and fragrant cigar.

He is one who has roughed it in many countries of the world. An intensely masculine man, he was once described by an American reporter as 'the rough-neck peer', and for a very excellent reason, for he has no place in the boudoir. One could not picture him playing croquet on the lawn and I should imagine that he has never written poetry in his life. He is a man who has done a great deal for British boxing and not a little for the Turf. As a Steward he is rather terrifying, and there are many jockeys riding today who would sooner stroke the neck of a full-sized and vociferous dragon than rub him the wrong way.

I sometimes think that in his passion for clean riding he is not always quite fair to the jockey who is hauled into the objection room, but the jockeys manage to survive his ferocity and probably a little loud-pedal music is good for their souls. He is noisy in the best sense of the word, a rider to hounds and a most excellent 'master'. It is a legend that he cannot pass coverts without causing considerable heart trouble amidst the 'varmint'. To the adventurous the adventurous go. I remember that it was in Lord Lonsdale's handsome dining-room that the Legion of Frontiersmen were launched on a career which has been made glorious by their deeds in East Africa. He was the foster father of the movement. He is immensely English both in his tastes, his blunt honesty, and his love of the good games that are characteristic of the nation. The coster loves him and to the coster's wife he is the ideal of an English gentleman. I don't know what his age is and I will not even look up my *Who's Who* to discover. He is a lad and will always be a lad to the end of his days. May they be many.

LORD ASTOR

Lord Astor's lamented father was, I suppose, one of the most unpopular Americans that ever settled in this country. He brought from the land of equality and freedom the methods and the manners of the Grand Seigneur. He had a ruthless way with anybody who trespassed on his property; he hated publicity; he most intensely disliked the Press; and apparently he disliked as intensely Americans. I am not quarrelling with him for his aloofness, and the fact that he made no effort to gain popularity in the land of his adoption must stand to his credit. He certainly gave us in his son, the present holder of the title, an excellent sportsman, a patriotic minor statesman, and a very charming personality, which even the advent of his wife into the world of politics has not obscured. A man who races on a grand scale, he has contributed to Turf history in no small degree. Although he has not yet won a Derby or a St. Leger, he had, in Craig an Eran, a horse which in my judgement was infinitely superior to the defunct Humorist – whose death no lover of the English thoroughbred can honestly regret. It is true to say that it was not Humorist, but Donoghue, who won the Derby of 1921; and had the jockeys been reversed there is no doubt whatever that Craig an Eran would have, as they say, 'trotted it'. Astor has multifarious interests. He is a newspaper proprietor, with a reputation for generosity. He is a great landowner, and he is a man destined for Cabinet rank. I am told that he will win the Derby of 1923, but this I will never believe. It is extremely improbable that a man can have, for three years in succession, horses that are of Derby class. None the less, we shall wait with confidence to see his pretty colours carried first past the post in the great Epsom classic. On the Turf it is impossible to buy success at the first time of asking, but it is a fact that given lavish outlay and patience, the classic winner must sooner or later come to the plucky owner who refuses to accept every adverse buffet of fate as final.

Lord Astor will win as Lord Derby will win the race on which he has set his heart. Maybe they will run a dead-heat!

LORD CARNARVON

F I went to any race meeting and failed to meet Lord Carnarvon, I should feel that there was something radically wrong somewhere. Lord Carnarvon is in a class by himself as an owner. He is what I would term a handicap man, and few of his horses have had pretensions to classic achievement.

Whether this prominence in handicaps is part of a considered policy I do not know. If it be, then it is a sane policy and is accompanied by fewer disappointments than go with the classic hope. It is certainly a policy which yields more profitable results. Maybe in Lord Carnarvon's case it is not a settled policy at all, but sheerly accidental.

That he is a 'good owner' from the trainer's point of view is evidenced by the length of time his horses have been trained by Mr. Dawson. Looking round the big personalities of the Turf, I can find only half-a-dozen other men who have stuck to one trainer through thick and thin. I have not before me a list showing Lord Carnarvon's winnings for the past decade, but I have the impression that they have fluctuated less than those of his rivals. When I talk of classic aspirations I had forgotten for the moment the bad luck which robbed him of last year's St. Leger. Undoubtedly Franklin would have won that race nine times out of ten.

Lord Carnarvon is something of a philosopher, being endowed with the ideal temperament for ownership. I do not remember having seen him greatly elated, or deeply depressed, by success or failure. Nor do I remember any of his fancies starting at very long prices. A horse of his that has a chance is fairly widely advertised; there is little mystery about any animal that carries the scarlet and blue. I regard him as a type of owner that the Turf cannot spare.

Some men come with a flourish of trumpets and a mile-long string of thoroughbreds, head the list of winning owners for a season or two, and then, when the luck turns, grow sulky and gradually vanish from the Turf.

Men like Lord Carnarvon go on year after year maintaining a reasonable stable and sticking at the game through fair weather and foul. They are the stabilisers of the Turf, the exact and steady quantities that are so necessary to the sport. We owe much to Lord Carnarvon for the consistency of his support.

GOLDEN RULES OF RACING

CATCH YOUR
JOCKEY!

IT doesn't seem half a dozen years ago that whenever pressmen met and the jockeys came up for discussion the air grew blue with violent condemnation. We passed through a period when the jockey vintage was about the worst the world has ever known.

Every owner who needed sure guidance for his thoroughbred went abroad, either to America, or to France, to find a rider. Americans flowed into England: Danny Maher, Skeets Martin, the Reiffs; from Australia, Brownie Carslake, Frank Bullock, and one or two others I would rather not mention; and it looked as though the Jockey Championship had gone with all the others.

Today we have one of the finest bunches of jockeys ever collected together in any country. I mention Brownie first, because Brownie Carslake is a particular friend of mine. He is a well-read man, and charming companion. His cynical wit has kept me amused for hours. As a jockey he is super-excellent.

I hate to have backed a horse and to find Brownie lying within a length of it at the distance, because his finishing power is extraordinary, and time and time again I have seen him snatch a race from the fire, as it were, and in one furious drive land his mount a short-head winner.

People may imagine that being a personal friend of a jockey has a great advantage, in that one receives extraordinary lucrative tips. But the truth is that Brownie has only given me one tip in his life! That was about my own horse!

He is very much an owners' jockey. He is reticent to his nearest friends, and it is very rarely indeed that Brownie's mounts start favourite.

He says that the best jockey he has seen is Donoghue. He has never wavered from that opinion, and I think that he is justified.

Steve, in addition to riding at a weight which is beyond the dreams of men of his age, has all the riding qualities of a great jockey. No man can handle a horse as he does, get more out of it at the finish, or deal more effectively with problems of pace. It doesn't matter what is the length of the race, or the course, Steve is a master at all distances and over all tracks.

I would not say that he was the best distance race-rider – that distinction, I think, must go to Joe Childs, the King's jockey. Joe has an uncanny knowledge of pace; knows just where to make his effort, just how to nurse his mount for the final effort.

Gordon Richards' secret is his balance; and Brownie Carslake, who has a good word to say of every jockey, is never tired of pointing out to the uninitiated the characteristics of this wonderful little rider.

Richards is a young man whom success has not spoiled. He is still the same modest little fellow that he was when he was riding as an apprentice to his master. His loyalty to his first stable is a legend to the Turf. There isn't a straighter jockey licensed.

If you ask Richards what is going to win a race in which he is riding, he will probably reply: 'I am.' He has got faith in his mount, he tries from start to finish, and he is never done trying till the post is past. I saw last year at Hurst Park a race in which it seemed almost inevitable that he could not finish in the first three. His horse was beaten at the distance, yet Richards did not cease to persevere and snatched a head victory on the post.

Gordon Richards is nothing like what a jockey ought to be. Physically, he is all wrong. His body is too long, his legs are too short, and he must take nearly a No. 7 in hats! On a horse he is inelegant and his riding appearance is not improved by his use of a long rein.

But everything else is right. Gordon has the maximum of vigour and driving force, wonderful balance, a great sense of distance and, usually, the knowledge of what most of the horses in a race have done besides the performances of his own mount. He is always thinking about his job, and when beaten wonders what he has done wrong.

His social aspirations are nil. He is probably the only fashionable jockey who doesn't know a night club. His chief hobby is reading boys' magazines and even if he does drive a large car he does not fraternise outside his own class. His greatest friend is his fellow jockey, Sirett.

He has spent most of the winter turning down retaining fees, for he remains loyal to the men who made him – Martin Hartigan and Captain Hogg. But he will also be seen wearing the Union Jack colours of Lord Glanely this season [1928]. So his already large bank balance is going to be enormously increased. He says one of the worst horses he has ever ridden is the Lincolnshire entry, Chichester Cross, and in this race rides Jugo.

So far he has not been anywhere near winning the Derby, but hopes to do so this year for Lord Dewar. If he does this he will probably imitate another jockey of recent years and celebrate it by taking his sweetheart to the pictures. If he ever adopts a family motto it will be 'Cool Head Wins!'

Charlie Smirke is another dashing rider. If his style is not so pretty, he gives a push and an urge to his mount that is equalled only by Carslake.

Yet another jockey I should consider amongst the first three or four would be Michael Beary. Michael is an artist in the saddle; he rides at a light weight, and he has very strong finishing powers – as I know to my cost, for when he defeated Warrior's Star, at Brighton, last year he robbed me of the greater part of a thousand pounds. Michael is a most cheery companion, a real good fellow, and, like most Irishmen, a born raconteur. His story of how a spirit came to his private room in the Rutland Arms at Newmarket, and lifted the table three or four inches from the floor, is one which is well worth repeating, if it were possible to tell the tale in his own inimitable style.

Which of these jockeys would one choose for one's own horse or for the horse on which one had made a heavy bet? Probably, if the weight were very light indeed, one would take that veteran, Kenneth Robertson, who is a better jockey now than ever he has been in his life.

The jockey is a very vital factor in racing. I would be content with any of those I have named, would even go farther afield and take boys like James and Taylor and be sure that my horse would be well ridden. I should not be surprised to find whatever horse Beary rides finishing in the first three at Lincoln.

FIND A TRAINER

IT is easy to find a trainer for your horse. There are thousands of them – licensed and unlicensed. Give 'em the horse and they'll get the licence!

There isn't a stable boy who does not think that he is as good, or nearly as good, as the guv'nor; and, generally speaking, the average jockey regards himself as a trainer, not so much in the making as already made.

It is perfectly true that there are quite a number of jockeys who can be, and are, of the greatest assistance to the owner and the trainer, and can offer them information from the knowledge they acquire during 'riding work', but these are exceptions.

Carslake, for example, is not only a trainer, but has held a trainer's licence, and has a large number of winners to his credit on the Continent. Donoghue, who has never held a trainer's licence, is also an expert.

The difference between a perfectly trained horse and an imperfectly trained horse is about two seconds in five furlongs. If you count two you will realize perhaps better just what the art of training means.

For two seconds represents ten lengths, and many a good horse has failed to win, not only an important handicap, but a classic, because he hadn't just that little bit of polish which only years of experience of training and observation could have given him.

I will name no names, but I once saw a horse that should have won both the Derby and the Two Thousand Guineas fail in these races because his trainer, although a knowledgeable man, lacked just that little bit of experience.

Who are the great trainers? Alec Taylor has retired and left his stable to a very capable man. Many of the old warriors of other days have passed out of the game, but some brilliant men still remain.

My mind naturally goes to John Watson, who trains for the Rothschilds, because I know him, and have known him for years as a master of his art. Unfortunately, he has had very poor horses to deal with in the past few years. The cleverest trainer cannot make bad horses into good horses, but John Watson is one of the best men at the game.

It would be invidious to place, or attempt to place, trainers in their order of merit. There are so many who are surpassingly good. Jack Jarvis, for example, Frank Butters, Captain Gooch, Charlie Peck, Stanley Wootton, Felix Leach, Atty Persse, and the Leaders, to name only a few.

If one were to be asked who is the best trainer in England today (and at the very writing of the words I find I have omitted Fred Darling, a top-notcher, from my list), one would be faced with a task of considerable difficulty. I should put on the top line, Charlie Peck. Here is a man of extraordinary patience and knowledge. He trains, as you know, for Jack Joel, who told me the other night that he had a very good lot of horses in his stable this year.

He has Philammon and Priory Park in the Lincolnshire Handicap, and there can be no question at all that Philammon is the better at the weights. The only doubt is whether a light-weight jockey (Burns) can get the best out of this animal. If he can, then Peck may very well have the winner in his stable.

Atty Persse is a brilliant trainer but, alas! has not the cattle he once had. Apelle is in his stable, and this brilliant performer may add to his laurels at Ascot this year. He is nothing like as good as he was before he ran the Grand Prix, but that he is a first-class performer no one will question.

Dick Dawson has yet to train a Derby winner for H. H. the Aga Khan. He has charge of Buland, who was a big, unfurnished two-year-old, and who won like a real good one at Kempton last back-end.

I suggest that Buland, Fairway, and Sunny Trace will be the best of the three-year-olds this year. I have omitted Hermit II, who did not strike me as being a stayer, but here I may be mistaken. No notice need be taken of his failure at Newmarket in his last race – he was far from being well.

Fred Darling, a famous trainer of Derby winners, as his father was before him, has Lord Dewar's good colt, Sunny Trace. This is one distinctly to keep in mind – it is not unlikely that he will figure prominently in all the classics.

Harking back to Dick Dawson, I see there is a suggestion that Ranjit Singh, another of the Aga Khan's horses, which won at Doncaster over a mile, has been talked up as a classic possible. At the moment I am not absolutely sure in which of the classics he is engaged, but I do know that he is or was, at least 10lb. behind Buland.

Earl is another capable trainer. He was not in the first flight of jockeys, though he was always a capable horseman. As a trainer of horses he has been extraordinarily successful.

Stanley Wootton is not only a trainer of horses, but one of the best 'masters' of jockeys. His stable produces more capable apprentices than any other. Stanley does not get the top-notch performers; he is more of a handicap specialist.

He has in his stable a horse that may create a surprise in the Lincolnshire Handicap – Orbita. Sir Alfred Butt's good-looking sprinter can obviously stay, for only last Saturday he ran a good second in a hurdle race at Kempton, which means that he is at least fit and well. A great point in so early a race as the Lincoln. Stanley is the most brilliant of our young men, who wins an incredible number of races and is, perhaps, one of the best judges of plating form in the country.

FIND A BOOKIE

THERE are bookmakers and bookmakers. There are those who advertise and those who tout and those to whom business comes because of their reputation for straight dealing and solidity.

There is the charming gentleman on the rails who will lay you the odds to a thousand; there is the little battler on Epsom hill whose stock in trade is a few shillings, an unbounded faith in providence, and the ability to run faster than his pursuers.

Of the 15,000 licensed bookmakers in England you can count the crooks on the average string of beads. As a class, bookmakers are more honest than any other I know.

There are bad bookmakers, just as there are naughty clergymen and reprehensible doctors, but when you are dealing with the average commission agent you know that you are dealing with a man whose word is his bond, and who will pay you to the last farthing what he owes you.

When you consider how business is done in Tattersall's ring you realise just what is the standard of the bookmaker's morality. Hundreds of thousands of pounds change hands in the course of a week, and there is no written obligation on either side to pay, no formal acknowledgment, nothing but the spoken word and a line scribbled in a book. Disputes as to bets are very rare.

The bookmaker's bad debts are enormous, for there is, alas! an enormous proportion of dishonest punters.

Last year a well known firm of agents were introduced to a young man apparently in a good position. He betted with the firm for a week and won £1,200. The next week he lost £2,500. When asked to pay he very coolly informed the bookmaker that he had no intention of paying.

Not only did they lose the £1,200 he had won on the first week, but they had to pay the betting tax on the sum he had swindled. They had no redress. If he were sued, he could plead the Gaming Act and go scot free.

That is not an isolated case. I have known case after case similar to this. The starting-price man is similarly defenceless.

There is a class of man who lives on swindling bookmakers. He opens accounts in various names and proceeds to back half a dozen horses in a race – backing a different horse with each bookmaker. In the course of a week it is pretty certain that he will have a winning balance with one of the agents – the rest he ignores.

One of the most remarkable cases I have met was that of a man of good education who served a term of imprisonment for forgery.

A friend of his boyhood, desiring to help him, told him that he could stay at his flat – an expensive place in Park Lane – for a month after his release, the owner being abroad at the time.

On the day X. was released from prison and installed in his handsome lodging he wrote to fifty bookmakers saying that he was a visitor from Canada and had been recommended by Lord —— (his absent host) to open an account.

In every case a credit was granted. In the course of the week the ex-convict, who had no intention but to victimise the bookmakers, had won over £12,000!

He had the intelligence and the decency to stop betting after that. The bookmaker is there to be shot at.

The punter, when he is choosing a bookmaker – I am referring to the honest punter – has a wide choice. He is perfectly safe in betting with the firm which advertises regularly in the sporting Press. And for this reason; newspapers which accept bookmakers' notices exercise the most scrupulous care before they admit an announcement to their columns.

I would always advise the punter, big or little, to open a credit account – though I advise this with certain reservations. What I could not advise is the practice of sending money to Scotland, unless you are very sure of the firm with which you are dealing.

The law of the land is peculiar in relation to betting. If I were a bookmaker and you sent me a bet and accompanied that bet with the amount of the stake, I should be liable to severe penalties.

If I had an office in Scotland and you sent me the same bet and the same money, I should still be liable if I opened the envelope and extracted the money and bet in Scotland; but, for some extraordinary reason, I am not liable if I send the envelope back unopened to my office in London and extract the money there!

Scores of tricks are employed to rob bookmakers, and in consequence more disputes arise over ready-money betting than any other kind. The Scottish bookmaker has to exercise an eternal vigilance, and it occasionally happens that quite honest people are very much inconvenienced.

The trouble about opening a credit account is that a backer, especially a reckless backer, loses all sense of money value. It is quite a different matter scribbling '£5 to win' on a telegraph form, and producing from one's pocket a crisp £5 note which looks and feels like money; and with the credit better there is that fatal Friday when, having had a bad week, he makes a determined effort to 'get out', usually with disastrous results to himself.

Credit betting too often leads to a man losing much more than he can afford; but for the intelligent punter, who can exercise a little self-control, it is the safest method.

Among the greatest of the bookmakers there are those who do not advertise. Others, equally great, secure their clients by a system of touting. I know one firm that has an agent in every big London club, who is all the time finding mugs – this particular firm does not want any other kind of backer.

The modest punter finds what he hopes will be his victim in the advertising columns of reputable newspapers, and my experience has been that he has no cause to regret such a method of choice.

RACING-STABLE SECRETS

THERE is a quiet paddock at Newmarket, miles from the race-course, and so far away from the hustle and roar of the ring that you forget racing has any existence. Round three sides of a square runs a neat array of horse-boxes.

But what there is of immediate interest for me is the paddock, where a mare is cropping the grass and a long-legged filly foal is throwing up her legs in sheer joy of life.

I saw her a few hours after she was born. She stood with her legs wide apart, staring at me with big, dark eyes.

Some day she will be a 5 to 4 proposition, and Poland Street will be blowing money to the course for her, and I shall be making to everybody the old conventional statement that 'She's pretty useful, but I'm not quite sure whether the going isn't a little too hard.'

The dam is a gallant winner, the sire is a great swell of a horse who won important races at Ascot and Newmarket.

He has had fifty children, none of whom he has seen – which, if I may be permitted the cynicism, is, if not an ideal, at least a comfortable, condition of fatherhood.

The great drama of racing starts in this paddock. The wise stud-groom, who is called up at all hours of the night to usher little 6 to 4 chances into the world, is he who rings up the curtain.

He has got his troubles and his anxieties before the foal is born; he will have more for a few days after its birth.

Some of them come into the world in very sorry shape, with bad legs, bad joints, seemingly useless for racing, though they have a trick of growing into shape.

The first year of a foal's life is fairly uneventful. After Christmas he becomes a yearling, and for the greater part of the year has a perfectly delightful time. By then he has grown into something that looks like a racehorse.

There was one great owner who invariably picked out his Derby entries from a field of yearling colts, and chose them by the speed they showed in galloping from one side of the paddock to the other.

But your expert judges by shape and conformation, gives mental points to shoulders, legs and quarters, heart room, neck and head.

To the average man and woman who are not acquainted with horses, one looks very much like another. Your racing expert, seeing three horses at exercise on Newmarket Heath, will tell you their names, because one is entirely different from the other.

Throughout this country and in Ireland there are many huge stud-farms, some of which are devoted entirely to the production of horses which will race in the owner's name.

There are others, like Sledmere, where horses are bred for sale. In all of them the mating of stallion with mare is almost an exact science.

Occasionally – and this is generally in the little stud-farm – a horse will be bred experimentally. By no method of reckoning can the breeder tell whether the result of his experiment will be good or bad.

The late Mr. Croker bred on these lines, and produced animals that were freakishly good. Horses like Prospector were experimentally bred, and I think that is true also of Irish Elegance.

In the case of such studs as those controlled by Lord Derby, horses are bred for 'home use'. They go automatically into his training establishment at Newmarket, and in course of time make their appearance on a racecourse.

For the selling breeders there are some wonderful markets, the greatest of which are the Doncaster Sales. To Doncaster, on the four days of the meeting, go the cream of the studs, and here the high-water mark of values is reached.

The biggest gamble in racing is not on the racehorse, but in the sale ring. The prizes are few, the disappointments are many. I am always amused when the great breeders demand State subsidy.

When you remember that some studs sell hundreds of thousands of pounds' worth of stock which does not produce a penny for the unfortunate purchasers, you realise that it is the owners rather than the breeders who require subsidy.

Sir Victor Sassoon paid 12,000 guineas for Fete. He may have won a race for him, but I can't remember it, and it certainly wasn't an important one.

Gay Baby was sold to the Aga Khan for 10,500 guineas; she may make a good brood mare, but she certainly had no other value.

Mr. Morriss, who bought Manna, also bought Sample at 9,200 guineas. Sample has done nothing, nor did Shiraz, for which Sir Charles Hyde paid 8,200 guineas.

Looking down the long list of horses that fetched over 2,000 guineas, it is very rarely that one's eyes rest upon a winner, even of a small race.

Last year Quarrat-al-Ain was purchased for 12,500 guineas. She is outstanding, because she, at any rate, has won two good races; but Farman Farma, also bought by H. H. the Aga Khan, for 9,100 guineas, has done nothing. Possibly his best purchase was Blenheim, for which he paid 4,100 guineas.

Yet year after year the great owners assemble at Doncaster, and the competition is keener than ever. There are also sales at Newmarket throughout the year, and probably at these some of the best bargains have been secured.

Michael Beary bought two horses, one for 300 guineas and one for 70 guineas, that have won races, and one of these, Queen's Orb, may in the long run prove to be as good as, if not better than, the 12,500 purchase Quarrat-al-Ain.

Between the Doncaster Sales and the Goodwood Cup what an immense period of trouble time!

Some of the colts who come up to the sales are already entered in races. They were entered before they were born in the Produce Stakes, where not the offspring, but the sire or dam is nominated.

There is a delusion that a Derby horse is entered at birth. He is not in fact entered till he is within a few months of being a two-year-old.

If you are a student of the *Racing Calendar*, you will find races closing which are not run until 1931, and in some cases 1932, but these events are antiquated affairs which have little or no value so far as racing is concerned.

The young horse's trouble begins in September or October, when he is broken. At the end of a long leading rein, he is subjected to the indignity of a dummy saddle.

He had already been introduced to a bit, and becomes gradually accustomed to the strange thing that is strapped to his back.

I have known the training start much earlier, and I have seen the dam of a sturdy foal trying to push the dummy from her progeny's back.

Some horses take to the new and terrifying experiences very quickly; others fret; others go wild; but in the end the perseverence of the trainer quietens them, and they carry the saddle, and, before the cold days have come, they will carry a boy on their backs.

There is no life harder than a trainer's. He is up at cock-crow, and, if he is conscientious, he supervises the feeding of every horse in the stable. There are some training establishments where there are fifty or sixty horses.

I confess I have an intense admiration for the little heroes who attend to those wild animals. I am filled with awe when I watch these diminutive lads go into the box and treat a big, upstanding horse as though he were a rabbit. Horses have no intelligence whatever, but they have excellent memories, and the majority become attached to one of these mites. There are a few, however, who will become attached to nobody. They are savages from their birth.

Every horse has an individual character. I know one that would never sleep in the dark, and had to have a light in his box at night. I know of scores who can only be pacified by the presence of a goat in their box.

If the horse is a friend of man, the goat is certainly a friend of the racehorse, and I have never been into a single training establishment that did not possess a goat in their box.

It is difficult to understand what sedative qualities a goat possesses, but at least three of my wife's horses require the constant companionship of a billy.

Early in the morning the horses are taken out. The 'first lot' – that is to say, the horses required for races that are near at hand – do their bout of cantering, and then the 'spares' go out.

To the trainer every horse is a separate object of consideration. He watches their development, he knows just when the cantering should develop into half-speed gallops; he can tell, without any other evidence than his eyes, when a horse is ripe for racing.

It is a great mistake to believe, as some people do, that all horses in a training establishment are tried before they race.

Some trainers never send their horses the full distance over which they must race. I have seen a horse second in the Ascot Stakes, which is two miles, that was never galloped more than nine furlongs.

The trainer knows that one of the easiest things to do is to 'leave a race on the training-ground' – that is to say, take so much out of a horse in a trial that he cannot do his best in the race.

Races are not won on the trial ground; they are won in the stable.

No house mistress watches her boarders as shrewdly and as carefully as a trainer watches his horses.

There are a hundred-and-one diseases which can attack them, and they all seem to be more or less infectious.

Heelbug will devastate a stable; strangles, coughing, and certain mysterious diseases which can only be diagnosed by a veterinary surgeon – and not always accurately diagnosed at that – attack the stable from week to week.

Some horses have nerve storms at the sight of a racecourse; others are so delicately constituted that the appearance of a jockey in colours is quite sufficient to throw them into a bath of perspiration.

A very large proportion of these highly-strung racehorses have private habits, some stupid and some vicious, which are hard to eradicate, and which are dangerous because a horse is a very imitative beast, and one bad horse in a stable will often corrupt the rest.

A trainer has been interesting himself about the horse's future long before it seemed that he had any.

He has made entries for races months, and sometimes years, ahead, and there comes a time when, as a two-year-old, the youngster has 'shown him something for it', and he is sent off to have his first experience of the real game.

He may travel by train under the care of a lad, or, more likely in these days, he will travel in a luxuriously appointed motor horsebox, which will take him to the racecourse stable, where he usually arrives overnight.

The next morning is a fairly anxious time for the trainer. The first symptom of nervousness or physical ill-being is the inability of a horse to eat his breakfast. Well for the trainer if he may boast to his owner that the colt 'did not leave an oat'.

He may have been roughly tried and represent a good thing to bet on. But the trainer will necessarily warn his owner that the youngster is new to the game and may run green – in other words, though he has the ability to win, he may not have the technique.

He is probably unused to being handled by a strange jockey; the unaccustomed sights of the racecourse may interest him too much, and his mind may be on the novelty of his surroundings rather than upon the business of racing – for a horse has to be taught to race.

How many people depend for their living upon that slim thoroughbred that comes flying up the straight?

There are scores of professional backers, there are hundreds of bookmakers, there are the tic-tac men, who signal every variation of price.

Far away, almost out of sight, a man is watching Tattersall's through a telescope; nearby is a telephone fixed to a telegraph-post.

And at the end of that wire is a humming office, into which money or its equivalent is pouring, and which must be transmitted or 'blown' to the course; money that has come from all over the country from starting-price bookmakers who are anxious not to be caught by this new youngster who is reported hot.

Another wire goes into the office of a news agency, where a man sits at an instrument like a piano and will tap out the result of a race, to be reproduced on thousands of tapes.

Whether he wins or loses, the colt does put money into circulation. He is circulating money all the time.

His board fee is £5 a week, every entry absorbs from £2 to £25, the jockey who rides him receives three guineas if he loses and a nominal five guineas if he wins, plus the present which every owner makes.

There are jockeys who can earn, and have earned, from £20,000 to £25,000 a year. There are men who are riding today with the greatest success who have found it difficult to live upon their income.

Some spectacular win on their part has changed the whole of their career, and from being neglected they become the jockeys most in demand.

Money will circulate in the rings, although such big owners as the Aga Khan, Lord Derby and Lord Glanely do not bet.

How do they make racing pay?

At first sight Lord Derby makes it pay very well, when he stands at the head of winning owners, as he did last year, with £63,919 to his credit.

In four years Lord Derby has won £160,000 in stakes alone. But has he made it pay? The answer to that would be in all probability – barely.

But he makes it pay in another way, as so many other owners do. All the time he is building up the reputation of sires.

There are horses at stud that earn from £16,000 to £20,000 a year for their owners, and that is where the real profit from racing comes.

A two-year-old goes through his career, and alarums and excursions accompany his progress. Then comes Derby Day and the supreme test.

By great good luck he is a winner and a potential money-earner for the stud.

He is kept jealously for the important engagements, and ends his career probably as a four-year-old by winning first the Gold Cup at Ascot, and the Goodwood and Doncaster Cups, and he, too, goes to stud.

And to him comes a matron with an Oaks record behind her, and so racing ends where it began – with the mare in the paddock and a new aspirant for classic honours nuzzling at her side.

LORD DERBY'S
RACING MEMORIES

*I*t is a measure of Wallace's versatility and of his ability to mix with all men on the Turf from the highest to the lowest that, just after a year had elapsed from his writing the memories of 'Ringer' Barrie, he was entrusted with recording the racing life and recollections of Lord Derby, then probably the leading pillar of the Turf and the most influential of all the ruling few of the day. The compilation of these memoirs entailed a succession of interviews with the subject and a friendship was then formed which remained a lasting one and which, as mentioned in the Introduction, conferred benefit to racing in general far wider than the personal trust and affection engendered between two uniquely talented men from backgrounds which could scarcely have been more different. These memoirs were written in 1924 and, apart from their intrinsic interest and historical value, they shed a light on the characters of both men – Lord Derby's open-mindedness in talking freely to his interviewer and Wallace's hard work and meticulous research on a subject which had caught and captivated him.

Although much has indeed changed in the intervening years, the common-sense of Lord Derby's reflections on ownership and breeding and the qualities necessary to attain success – not excluding luck – have not. These and the skill with which Wallace elicited and put down his subject's thoughts and opinions ensure that the matter has not dated except, perhaps, as regards the value of money when one reads that Lord Derby headed the breeders' list in 1923 with a sum of £39,275!

A ROMANCE OF THIRTY YEARS' RACING

ABOUT the name of Lord Derby is the golden haze of romance. A great statesman, an instinctive soldier, and a world-famous diplomat, he represents success won by such sheer personality and genius as would have brought him to the front even if he had not been born with all the advantages of a great name and great traditions.

To millions of people who have no very great interest in high politics, the name of Lord Derby is associated with the sport of kings. The Derbys have for hundreds of years been illustrious figures on the Turf.

'It was the practice of my ancestors,' Lord Derby told me, 'to plant at Knowsley a grove of trees to celebrate the outstanding victory of a horse, and these groves are known by the horses' names. Some of the avenues bear names which cannot be traced in any works of reference – horses that have passed beyond human remembrance!'

The association of the Earls of Derby with racing is almost lost in the mists of history. To describe Lord Derby were a thankless task, for he is familiar to almost every man, woman, and child in these islands. Tall, broad-shouldered, a clear-eyed, smiling man, with an unwrinkled face, he is 'of no age'. President Wilson once said to me: 'Derby is the most English Englishman in England.' And that is a fair description.

He is a man without illusions, impatient of the chicanery which is associated with politics, blunt sometimes to the point of offensiveness, invariably truthful, transparently honest; he maintained the respect of the French in the darkest hour of their suspicions, and the confidence of his own people even at a moment when public idols were tumbling.

I should imagine that he had made many enemies but kept none. You cannot continuously resent sincerity even when, from your point of view, it is misapplied or wrong-headed. Honesty has the virtue of justifying its offences.

As I have said, the house of Stanley has raced throughout the ages, but never on the extensive and successful scale which has marked the regime of the present holder of the title. The name of Derby was imperishably attached to this great sport when the twelfth earl instituted first a race for three-year-old fillies, which he named after his Woodmansterne residence, The Oaks, following this institution with another race for colts, which thereafter bore his title.

'It is difficult to know what was the genesis of the Derby Stakes,' said Lord Derby. 'Our ancestors were less businesslike but perhaps a little more sporting than we, and if they arranged races without keeping a record of their transactions it is pretty certain that the race or matches were run to the letter of agreements entered into on the spur of the moment.

'After dinner, when the bottle passed and men were inclined to extol the virtues of their horses, matches were booked and conditions laid down which sometimes persisted through the years, as in the case of the Oaks and the Derby. I have no doubt that at these convivial meetings great races were arranged which did not survive their first celebration.

'At any rate, the idea of the Derby Stakes for colts was something of an inspiration, something, too, which must have taken the fancy of the gentlemen who owned stables of horses, with the result that the Derby Stakes is now the greatest of racing institutions, and has its replicas in every part of the world.

'There are Derbys in America, in Africa, even in Germany, I believe; whilst in Rumania one fortunate gentleman has won the Derby twenty-three years in succession! I am very happy to have won it once!'

Racing, of course, has always been popular in England. There are records of races held in the twelfth century at Smoothfield – that is, Smithfield – these meetings combining the purpose of horse-fairs and race meetings; and in Stowe's translation he tells how 'the jockeys are boys expert in the management of horses, which they regulate by means of curbs and bridles, sometimes by threes and sometimes by twos, as the match is made, and prepare themselves for the contest. Their chief aim is to prevent a competitor from getting before them.' An excellent and admirable ambition!

Even in the reign of Richard I, knights rode at Whitsuntide over the three-mile course for 'forty pounds of ready gold'; and it will be news to many that King John, of Runnymede fame, kept a stable of horses. There was racing on the Roodee at Chester in 1500; whilst the passion of the merry monarch for Newmarket is well known.

'Racing had been the subject of legislation, and in 1739 an Act was passed to prevent racing by weak horses, and which also prohibited prizes of less value than £50.'

Few people, I imagine, realise that racing prizes are governed by the law of England!

The Oaks was instituted in May 1779 and was won the first year by his lordship's own filly, Bridget, which he himself bred from Herod out of Jemima. His lordship was not so successful in the Derby: it was a few years later that a horse of his won those historic stakes. With one exception, as far as I can recall, the Earls of Derby have played a prominent part in racing ever since.

The late earl was a great lover of the thoroughbred, and I think Lord Derby will agree that his father did a great deal towards making possible his own extraordinary successes; though it would also be fair to Lord Derby and to his trainer, the Hon. George Lambton, to state that it is due to the new blood introduced by Lord Derby, who is a keen student of breeding, that his triumphs have been accomplished.

'I have in George Lambton – and I say this with all respect to other gentlemen engaged in training – the greatest trainer in England,' said Lord Derby emphatically. 'Not only great in judgement, but great in his generosity. I shall never forget his act of unselfishness which probably won me the St. Leger of 1923. He had Tranquil under his care, but was not satisfied with the progress the filly was making. A lesser man would have worked away to have got her as fit as he possibly could, with the knowledge that she was not quite good enough.

'Mr. Lambton thought the matter over and decided that what

Tranquil wanted was another training ground. She had grown tired of galloping at Newmarket. He sent the horse to another trainer – Charles Morton, of Wantage – handing over, as he knew, the kudos which would be his if the horse won. But that, of course, didn't worry him; his object was to win the race for me and how Tranquil justified the move is history.'

That the Hon. George Lambton is a wonderful judge of the thoroughbred was proved by the purchases he made at the Doncaster sales on behalf of his Highness the Aga Khan. Amongst those purchases were both Diophon and Mumtaz Mahal, the latter of whom won £14,000 in stakes, the former taking, amongst other rich prizes, the 10,300 sovs. which goes to the winner of the Two Thousand Guineas, Diophon winning £18,445 in all. The horses purchased by George Lambton were Mumtaz Mahal for 9,100 gns., Hajibibi for 4,000 gns., Diophon for 4,000 gns., Salmon Trout for 3,000 gns., Charley's Mount for 2,600 gns.

'Yes, it is true that I began racing in my father's lifetime,' said Lord Derby, 'running horses under my own name and in my own colours; and though, of course, I had nothing like the success which afterwards came to me, I won my share of races.'

He was twenty-eight when he registered his colours – black, white belt and cap; this was in the year 1893, and between 1893 and 1904 he had won 83 races of a value of £31,351, his best years being 1896, when he won £6,933, and 1897, when he won fifteen races of a smaller value.

Lord Derby has had a great deal of luck with his purchases, the dam of Sansovino being a case in point; and the first winner saddled by Mr. Lambton was a horse which had been running unsuccessfully in Count Kinsky's colours. This was Greywell, an aged grey horse by Marden out of Seakale. These were the days when men like Colonel North were carrying all before them, and I suppose there are many today who will remember the nitrate king's colours, pale-blue and primrose stars, which were so popular with the little betting folk throughout the country.

Greywell certainly did not look a very good purchase to the uninitiated, and there were some who regretted that the young hope of the House of Stanley had not made a better start in his racing career. Nevertheless, Greywell, under Mr. Lambton's care, improved to a remarkable extent, and at the Liverpool July Meeting

– Liverpool is Lord Derby's pet meeting – he won the Liverpool Plate, a mile handicap, Fred Finlay being the successful jockey.

Greywell was the only representative of Stanley House to run at that meeting, at which Colonel North won five races. 'I think Greywell won again,' Lord Derby told me, 'a welter handicap for qualified riders, at Leicester. Rickaby rode him with 5lb. extra and won.'

That same year Lord Derby secured a chestnut filly, Hettie Sorrel, by Peter out of Venus' Looking Glass. She was two years old at the time, and had already won three races for Mr. R. B. Brett.

This game filly, thoroughly exposed as to her form, was entered in Lord Derby's name for the Kempton Park Nursery Handicap, and, carrying 7st. 7 lb., which included a penalty, she gave the late Tommy Loates a winning ride. That she could not only sprint but stay was proved when she won the Ditch Mile Nursery, at Newmarket, carrying 8st. Though Hettie Sorrel did not win as a three-year-old, she proved a very excellent dam, and gave Lord Derby a useful progeny to win races in the black and white.

A third purchase of this year was Sprightly, a bay gelding by Galliard out of Sad. Lord Stanley saw him ridden by Lord Molyneux at the meeting where Greywell won at Liverpool and, pleased with his appearance, negotiated his purchase. The gelding was a little bit better than a plater, and he justified the young owner's judgement by winning a selling plate, being bought in for 480 gns. He won again at the Derby November Meeting, beating four others in the Quorndon Plate, and the year after was sold to Lord William Beresford. Sprightly was by no means an extinct force, for he was exported to India and won Lord William the Viceroy's Cup.

At the Second October Meeting held that year (1893), a mile selling plate was won by Haymaker, carrying Lord Dunraven's colours, and at the subsequent auction, Haymaker, a four-year-old bay colt by Springyfield out of Lady Binks, was purchased by Mr. Lambton and won at the Autumn Liverpool Meeting, the Wavertree Welter Handicap. Haymaker did not win a race the following year, though he ran ten times.

In fact, the year 1894 was a fairly thin one, only two races, of a total value of £335, being credited to the white belt, one of these being won by Sprightly before he was acquired by Lord William Beresford. The other race was the Sefton Park Plate at the Liverpool

Spring Meeting, which was won by Golden Blaze, a filly by
Hampton out of Meteora, which did not catch the judge's eye again
that year.

'No,' said Lord Derby, 'that did not represent the ebb of my
racing fortunes. In 1904 I won one race of a hundred sovereigns!'

There is no royal road to success on the Turf. The wealth of the
Indies cannot acquire a Derby winner, and success can only come,
as it comes in other walks of life, as a reward of patience, persever-
ance, and judgement. The owner who succeeds is he who does not
expect miracles to happen, and for a Derby winner to fall into his
lap, but rather gives his time to a study of the all-important question
of breeding, learns to analyse the qualities which constitute the
racehorse and forever strives to produce the ideal blend of blood.

'Those who believe that lavish expenditure on bloodstock automatically ensures success in the sport of racing are foredoomed to
disappointment,' said Lord Derby. 'The price of success, like the
price of liberty, is eternal vigilance. The racehorse is a peculiarly
complex product. Certain lines of stock are forever deteriorating,
other lines are improving. Sometimes, for no apparent reason, there
flashes up an amazing burst of quality. A horse, queerly or
unfashionably bred, develops into the champion of his age and then
fails to transmit any of his qualities to his stock!'

One has seen this occur in human beings, Shakespeare, born of
commonplace parents, is an illuminating genius, an isolated speck
of dazzling light that burns up like a new star and dies, leaving no
trace. The sire every owner seeks is he of steady quality. The
inexplicable genius is mistrusted, and rightly. The freakish horse
that can cover five furlongs in extraordinary time is less popular
than the steady plodder that can win a race over a distance in average
time, and can always pull out at the end just that little bit of 'ego'
that enables him to assert his superiority. And it has been this sturdy,
placid fellow, this good-hearted, game mare, without any electric
achievements to its credit, that has been the core of Lord Derby's
racing fortunes.

In the course of this little history great horses make their unobtrus-
ive appearance, unheralded by ecstatic paragrapher or by the profound warnings of those writers who specialise on the breeding side
of racing. Nobody watches them canter down to the post; few

notice them come back: and yet these horses were destined to make history on the Turf.

'It goes without saying that it was always my ambition to break the traditional bad luck which has attended our colours and win the Derby. That, of course, is every racing man's desire, as his Majesty the King very truly said in his telegram to the Press Club on the occasion of the Derby luncheon. Sansovino's victory was a very happy day for me, and all the happier because there was no fluke in it, and because I anticipated, so far as one dare anticipate such things, his winning.'

We who were the witnesses of that event will not readily forget the scene on that grey day, when the skies were streaming and the ground a quagmire. Every quality of heart and muscle were required to negotiate that terrible hill and to battle against the atmospheric conditions.

It was not too much to say that the eyes of the world were looking for the white cap and the black jacket, and when it was seen moving forward as the field swept down towards Tattenham Corner, how many thousands asked themselves the question: 'Is it really and truly possible for an Earl of Derby to win the Derby?' And when that game horse shot out of the ruck, and, coming on ahead, galloping like a lion, flew down the straight lengths ahead of his nearest pursuer, what a cheer went up from the rain-soaked crowd! The shout that greeted Lord Derby as he came out of the unsaddling enclosure was the most amazing roar of delight I have ever heard on Epsom Downs. In that fierce yell of exultation was expressed the Englishman's love for a good sportsman and a good horse. I cannot help feeling that the gallant Sansovino took second place, even in that minute of his supreme triumph.

Patience and courage are the two qualities essential to ownership. The man who starts racing, even though he has unlimited capital at his command (which Lord Stanley had not, for the income of the eldest son of the House of Stanley was not an extravagant one), must be prepared for disappointment. Classic winners may be picked up for a song – Spearmint and Comrade are two cases in point – but, as I have said before, the man who sits down and waits for miracles is going to end up his racing career with a sore heart and a depleted pocket.

The year 1895 was a good one, the best Lord Stanley had had.

He won ten races of the value of £2,784. It started unpretentiously
with a win at the Liverpool meeting by a very humble selling plater,
Bellincione, and the quality of this animal may be judged by the
fact that it was sold at the subsequent auction for 150 guineas, and
did not, so far as I can see, run again.

A more important win was that by Melange, a brown colt by
Melanion out of Amalgam, which won the Middlesex T.Y.O. Plate
at the Hurst Park Whitsuntide fixture, Rickaby riding.

He was now getting together some very excellent two-year-olds,
and at the July Meeting at Liverpool he exploited Birch-rod, which
won in a canter, and there being only two runners, odds of 9 to 1
were demanded. The filly was well-named, being by Hazlehatch
out of Fright. She ran subsequently unplaced in nursery handicaps
at Kempton and Newmarket, and at the Autumn Meeting at Liverpool was fourth to Arctic, Imposition, and Lord Derby's Canterbury
Pilgrim.

It was, I believe, the first notable instance of rivalry between
father and son. Canterbury Pilgrim was later to make history at the
stud, and there is no doubt that this particular field, in which Birch-
rod was placed fourth, was a very smart one, for when the filly was
pulled out again on the Friday she was made favourite for the
Downe Nursery Stakes and won by six lengths from sixteen others.

Lord Derby is not a betting man, and this explains why, when
Birch-rod was seen at Derby a week later in the Friary Nursery,
she was allowed to start at 100 to 8. Although she carried a 10lb.
penalty, she won this race fairly easily.

Another good winner was Red Wing II, a three-year-old bay filly
by Carlton out of Red Spider. She won the Londesborough Handicap of a mile at York in August, the September Stakes at Sandown
Park, and the Newmarket Oaks at the Second October Meeting,
her three races contributing more than £1,000 to Lord Stanley's
modest total.

Golden Blaze, after disappointing a dozen times, won a mile
handicap at Newmarket, and though she won fairly easily, her many
failures took something out of the stake-book.

'When an owner's winnings are totalled at the end of the year,
no deduction is made for the very considerable amount of money
lost in forfeits and failures. A horse may cost his owner £200 or

£300 and actually show a loss on the year, even though he wins, if the stake he secures is a small one.'

That is a fact which the public overlooks. It costs £50 to run a horse in the Derby, £100 to run him in the Two Thousand Guineas, and considerably more to run him in races like the Eclipse Stakes. There may be a debit of £500 or £600 against his name in the book before he picks up a £300 race. His winnings, however, are put to the general total; and at the end of the year, when envious people read that Mr. So-and-So has won £10,000 in stakes, the unfortunate 'winner' may be drawing a cheque to cover the difference between his 'winnings' and the cost of keeping, training, and entering his horses.

The following year, Lord Stanley's winnings bounded upwards. In that year he won twelve races, of a value just short of £7,000. To this Birch-rod contributed pretty considerably; she started off by winning a Mile Plate in the Leicester Meeting, and later placed to Lord Stanley's credit the Champion Breeders' Biennial Foal Stakes of a mile, worth £945; she followed this up by winning the Norfolk and Suffolk Handicap at Yarmouth.

Birch-rod's victory at that venue will long be remembered. Something like a cloudburst occurred over the famous Norfolk seaport. It had been raining all the morning, but just before the start of the race it came down with a vengeance! One could scarcely see the horses until they were right on the post, and some idea of the quantity of rain that fell in the few minutes that it took for the horses to get to the post and return may be gathered from the fact that not only the rider of Birch-rod, but the other riders, when they went to the scale, were found to be carrying 2lb. overweight! The stewards were at once notified, and there was a consultation; other riders were weighed, and it was found that all carried more or less the same quantity of moisture, and the weights were passed.

Chiselhampton and Curable were two three-year-olds who added to the growing tale of winners. Curable was a chestnut colt by Friar's Balsam out of Engadine, who, starting favourite, won the Chaddesden Stakes of six furlongs at the Derby November Meeting, Otto Madden being the successful jockey. Chiselhampton won the Sandown Foal Stakes over the Eclipse course, of £1,724, by far the biggest stake that had come Lord Stanley's way. It was a very hard race, Rickaby only just winning by a head from F. Martin on

Gulistan, with Morny Cannon a short head behind on the Duke of Westminster's Conroy.

Chiselhampton was a very game son of Hampton, and in spite of the hard race won again the following year.

But by far the most consistent performer of the year was that excellent horse Melange, who won four races in succession, of a value of £2,000. Tommy Loates beat the stable jockey, Rickaby, at Brighton; Rickaby was riding Chasseur, which had, only a week or so before, won the Stewards' Cup. Chasseur was regarded as something to bet on, but Lord Stanley's game horse had no difficulty in beating him. He followed this up by winning at the Doncaster Leger meeting, the race being the Cleveland Handicap of a mile.

The versatility of Melange is emphasised by the fact that he easily smashed a big field for the Great Eastern Railway Handicap at the Newmarket First October Meeting; whilst he went on to win the Liverpool St. Leger over a course of 1¼ miles.

The year 1896 was a triumph for the Stanley colours, for Lord Derby won the Oaks with Canterbury Pilgrim, a filly that had been purchased by Lord Stanley on behalf of his father at the sale of the Duchess of Montrose's stud. How little did he guess that he was buying the grandam of his first Derby winner! We may trace a very large proportion of the success which has attended Stanley House to the acquisition of this great mare.

This period of Lord Stanley's racing career is in many ways most fascinating. For the purchase of Canterbury Pilgrim, no less than the acquisition of such an excellent performer as Melange, was bringing him into a class of ownership which every lover of the thoroughbred desires to reach. Melange was a money-spinner, the type of horse that could always be relied upon to do his best, and it is to this honest type of thoroughbred that England owes its pre-eminence in the breeding world.

In the following year Melange won the Molyneux Plate at Liverpool, was second to Bewitchment for the Great Eastern Handicap at the First October Newmarket meeting, and won the Third Welter Handicap at the Houghton Meeting, following this up by winning the Warbreck Plate at Liverpool.

The House of Stanley has had an affinity for the Liverpool Cup, and Lord Stanley began his list of remarkable successes in 1897 with his good horse Chiselhampton, Sam Loates riding. Again he won by a head, as he had done at Sandown, this being his third success of the year, for he had won the Middlethorpe Stakes at York and the Northampton Handicap of one and a half miles.

It has never been part of the Stanley House policy to run two-year-olds 'off their feet'. Their engagements are few, and they are given plenty of time to develop before they are asked any serious question. A three-year-old colt by Surefoot-Queen Bee – The Guide, won three races this year [1924] in Lord Stanley's colours and helped to bring his total up to fifteen races won, three in excess of the previous year, though they were in point of value some £2,600 less than 1896.

The year 1898, which saw the outbreak of the Boer War, and incidentally sent Lord Derby to South Africa, brought another Liverpool Cup to his buffet. This was won by Golden Rule, a chestnut horse by Royal Hampton out of Meteora. It was Golden Rule's only victory of the season, and he subsequently ran ten times without success. Finally he was sold out of a selling race only to win races for his new owner.

It is a tradition that owners at Ascot do not object, except in very flagrant cases of misconduct or fraud; an unwritten law which has been broken of recent years. And although it cannot be said that there was any objection to The Reeve (a three-year-old son of Goldfinch), who won a Biennial, the *Racing Calendar* of that period notes that:

'The owner of The Convict (Mr. C. D. Rose, the banker, who afterwards gave a £1,000 stakes for stayers to contest at Newmarket), though he made no objection to the winner, complained to the Stewards of the manner in which Rickaby rode in this race, and they called Rickaby before them and cautioned him.'

The Reeve only won a head from The Convict, which was favourite, but he subsequently won a race at Newcastle, and at Thirsk, in Lord Farquhar's name, won the Newby Plate. He followed this up in the autumn with a victory in the Great Lancashire Handicap, this time running in Lord Stanley's colours.

I should imagine that the most important race of the year for Lord Stanley was the Southport Two-year-old Stakes at the Liverpool Summer Meeting, for here he won his first race as a breeder, the horse being Lisbeth, who was out of his mare, Hettie Sorrel.

'There is no sensation quite like seeing a horse of your own breeding win,' said Lord Derby. 'That to me is more than half the joy of racing. One may buy a good winner and get a lot of satisfaction out of the victory; but to see one of your own babies win – the little thing that you have seen as a long-legged foal, and whose dam has raced in your colours – that, I think, is the greatest pleasure of all.'

There is no finer illustration of the reward of patience than the case of Loreto, a chestnut colt by Bona Vista out of Lottie, who won the Liverpool Plate for Lord Stanley in the spring of the following year. Loreto had run four times as a two-year-old without winning, and fourteen times as a three-year-old with as little success.

The impatient owner who wishes to get rid of any horse that doesn't win after three attempts would have long since disposed of the colt, but Mr. George Lambton is a man blessed with vision, and though Loreto would have worn out the patience of most men, he kept the horse in training, and not only had the satisfaction of winning at Liverpool by ten lengths, but he also took the Warwick Welter Handicap, carrying 12st. 3lb.

After running a dead heat with False Step for the Visitors' Handicap at the Newmarket First Spring, he was beaten by a neck by Innocence for the Prince of Wales's Plate at the Epsom Spring Meeting, and finished up the year by winning the Berwick Welter Handicap at Brighton, and walking over for a race at York.

As a rule Stanley House makes no mistakes when it lets any of its horses go, but in the case of Golden Rule, which had won the Liverpool Cup of 1898, there was perhaps an error of judgement; for after being sold out of a selling plate for 400 guineas, he won races for his new owner at Epsom, Newmarket, Doncaster and Manchester.

The Boer War took Lord Stanley from racing to the sterner contests which were being fought out on the veldt. In 1900 Mr. Lambton sent out a good winner in Pellisson, a half-brother to Red Wing II. Pellisson won three races out of eight, starting off with the inevitable victory at Liverpool and ending with the almost as inevitable victory in the Liverpool St. Leger in the autumn. Between these he sandwiched the Great Tom Plate at Lincoln.

Pellisson and Loreto (who won the Babraham Plate at Newmarket and the Visitors' Handicap at Ascot) were the only two winners that Stanley House sent out, but these contributed between them £2,450.

Pellisson continued his victorious career the following spring, taking the Liverpool Spring Cup in a canter, and winning the Rothschild Welter plate on Easter Monday. He wound up the season by winning the Grosvenor Cup, also at Liverpool.

In the autumn of that year, the war being over, Lord Stanley was one of the acting Stewards at Liverpool: an appointment which he celebrated by winning the Duchy Plate with St. Levan.

By this time the Stanley stud – I use this term to differentiate between the greater stud controlled by Lord Derby – was settling down into a very live proposition. Melange had passed into his new sphere of activity, and in 1903 one of the first of his get, a colt out of Kilmorna, started the season by winning a match, and followed this up the next day by winning, appropriately enough, the Stanley Stakes from Lord Dunraven's Livia.

In this year Pellisson, carrying 8st. 8lb., and ridden by Danny Maher, won the Great Cheshire Handicap from Lord Dunraven's Morganatic.

Maher, at the height of his fame, was now riding regularly for Stanley House. He won at Windsor on Mixed Powder, and on the same horse at the Liverpool Autumn. He also rode Flamma when it won the 56th Triennial Produce Stakes the first time out.

From 1904 to 1907 Lord Stanley won nothing of note, and practically ran no horses. In the following year the death of his lamented father produced a change in his affairs which was to have a very considerable effect upon his racing fortunes. As Lord Stanley he had won 82 races valued £31,251. As Lord Derby he was to win more than that amount in one season.

LORD DERBY AND HIS BEST HORSES

The Story of Swynford and His Triumph

THE late Lord Derby had played an important part in the shaping of history, and his death removed a great figure and a fine gentleman.

'His earliest recollection of racing,' Lord Derby once told me, 'was being taken by his father to see Iris win the Oaks.'

That was in 1851, and Iris ran in the colours of the then Lord Stanley. The Earls of Derby, by the way, have won the Oaks on four separate occasions: in 1779, with Bridget, from a field of twelve runners – this was in the year of the Oaks' foundation; in 1794, with Hermoine, one of the famous Arnulls riding – eight runners; with Canterbury Pilgrim (F. Rickaby) in 1896; and with Keystone II, in 1906.

The late Lord Derby, although a keen racing man, was so completely occupied with his ministerial and his diplomatic duties that he might not have taken up racing again with the same zest when he returned from Canada a man of fifty-four, but for the knowledge that his son was an enthusiast. It was the queerest coincidence that Lord Stanley, as he was then, received Greywell (his first winner) as a present from his father, so the present Lord Stanley won his first race with Young Pegasus, who was presented to him by Lord Derby.

The record of the passing of the old earl finds a place in the *Racing Calendar*.

'A meeting of the Club [Jockey] was held at Ascot on Wednesday. Lord Durham, as Senior Steward in the place of Lord Stanley, who was absent, explained to the members present that, owing to the death of Lord Derby, which had occurred suddenly on the eve of the London Meeting, it had been found impossible for that Meeting to take place as arranged, and he asked the members to accept the suspension for this year of Rule 9, which fixed a meeting to take place in London in June, and agree to postpone any business which should have taken place at that Meeting to the Meeting in Newmarket in the first July week.'

Lord Durham then read a letter which he had received from the Senior Steward (Lord Stanley) notifying his resignation owing to the death of Lord Derby. His lordship said that, much as they regretted it, they would have no option but to accept the resignation, but in replying to Lord Stanley's letter, he felt sure that it would be the wish of everyone present that he should express their regret at the step which Lord Stanley had found it necessary to take, and to thank him for his valuable services as Steward.

Lord Durham also said that he was convinced the members would wish him to take the earliest opportunity of recording their deep sorrow at the death of Lord Derby. His Majesty the King (Edward VII) desired him to expressly associate his name with that of the Club in deploring the loss of his old and valued friend.

Mr. Brassey was appointed to take Lord Stanley's place, and for the next year the colours of the Derbys were absent from the Turf.

In 1909, however, Lord Derby was appointed Steward of the Club to take the place of Sir Daniel Cooper, who had died.

A few of his horses ran, either in Mr. George Lambton's or in Lord Durham's colours, but their successes were unimportant.

Lord Derby, in the days of his father's lifetime, had well and truly laid the foundation of his great stud when he had purchased Canterbury Pilgrim. Curiously enough, what was thought to be the important purchase at that sale was Roquebrune, which Lord Derby made strenuous efforts to buy. But Sir James Miller would not be denied, and Roquebrune went for 4,100 sovs., which in those days was considered a ridiculously high price. It was then that Lord Derby purchased Canterbury Pilgrim for £1,800. She was the dam of Chaucer and Swynford, which was the best horse Lord Derby has ever owned.

To the present head of the House of Stanley must be credited the buying of Gondolette, the dam of Sansovino, and Anchora, which belonged to the late George Edwardes, and bred Lord Derby nothing but winners, including Scapa Flow, the dam of Pharos.

To Mr. Alston, the manager of the stud, a very great deal is due. I think Lord Derby will agree that his wisdom, patience, and discretion are responsible for a large measure of the triumph which has attended his colours.

Lord Derby began racing again in 1909, and his colours were carried on Cocksure II in the Queen's Prize on the Easter Monday of that year. He started favourite at 6 to 4, with Danny Maher in the saddle, but ran up against a good stayer, if a somewhat erratic performer, in Wuffy, being beaten three lengths, with Santo Strato, Mr. Leopold de Rothschild's useful horse, behind.

Though he had not then been re-elected a Steward of the Jockey Club, Lord Derby was one of the acting Stewards at the Kempton meeting. The black and white was to be seen prominently placed in the course of the year.

He was third to White Eagle and Dean Swift in the City and Suburban with Lafayette, but he had no winner either there or at the Newmarket First Spring Meeting. Lafayette's third to these two excellent horses in the City was something of an achievement, though this indeed was not his best performance, for White Eagle was better than the average handicapper, while Dean Swift's liking for the Epsom gradient is a matter of Turf history.

Lafayette was by Begonia out of Iroquois, he was bred in France, and the fact that he subsequently beat Woolwinder by a head (in the March Stakes of 1¼ miles, Newmarket) demonstrated the excellence of the field, for Woolwinder should have won the Derby two years before.

He went on to win at Kempton at the Jubilee Meeting; whilst at the Second Newmarket Spring, Marchetta, a chestnut filly by Marco out of Hettie Sorrel, a prolific dam of winners, won the Breeders' Stakes on the Rous Course, 'any price' being offered against Lord Derby's filly.

I think it was in this race that a bookmaker offered a hundred pounds to a cigar against Marchetta, an offer that was taken by a man who thought so little of Marchetta's chance that he paid over his cigar before the race was won!

Marchetta was ridden by F. Rickaby jun., the jockey who met a gallant death in the War whilst controlling a tank in action. Although she subsequently ran several times during the year, Marchetta did not win again as a two-year-old.

Naturally he did not have a runner in the Derby, because, by the terms of the race, the death of the nominator voids an entry, and all the late Lord Derby's horses which had been put into the race were automatically withdrawn.

Lord Derby had run no horses at the Liverpool Spring Meeting, but Liverpool Summer saw the winning debut of a very first-class performer in Brig of Ayr, an Ayrshire filly out of Santa Brigida. J. H. Martin was the jockey, and she beat Counterpoise by a neck. She had had four unsuccessful outings previous to this, and ran twice unplaced subsequently.

Another Bridge – Bridge of Earn, a three-year-old – was second at this meeting to Faithful Don, but on the third day of the meeting the traditional Derby luck was revived when Well Done won the Sefton Plate at 5 to 1.

He was an Irish-bred four-year-old colt by Ballyalbany out of Well Chartered, and his history was a curious one.

He had been brought over from Ireland by Mr. Sargent to win the Horton Selling Plate at the Epsom Summer Meeting, and gambled on. He was ridden by the late J. Thompson, starting at 5 to 2 in a field of twenty. The good thing materialised, for he won by three lengths, and at the subsequent auction Lord Derby gave 650 gns. for him, a fairly high price in those days, and won five races that year, besides the Sefton Plate.

He won the Rangemore Plate at Derby in September, the Croxteth Plate at the Liverpool Autumn Meeting, starting at 100 to 8, the Chatsworth Plate carrying 9 st., (including 10 lb. extra) at the Derby November Meeting, and the Emscote Welter Handicap carrying 9 st. 9 lb. at Warwick, beating big fields every time.

I have always regarded the instance of Well Done as a classic proof of the value of running horses out. In spite of his victories, this honest animal generally started at an equitable price (on one occasion at 100 to 8), and though he went on from win to win, the natural suspicion of the punter, used to horses being 'readied', made it possible for those who systematically followed the fortunes of Stanley House to get a good price to their money.

Bridge of Earn, defeated at Liverpool, was pulled out to win a gentlemen riders' race at Brighton, whilst at the Warwick Autumn

Meeting, in addition to Well Done's victory, Lord Derby's Queen's Journal, a three-year-old by Florizel II, out of Glasalt, won the Warwick Handicap from Lady de Bathe's Black Sea and nine others, and subsequently won the Buckingham Plate at Windsor.

The death of his father had, as I say, made void many classic engagements for the excellent stock which was sheltered in his stable, and it was necessary that they should run in handicaps, and this is one of the reasons why horses like Queen's Journal and Bridge of Earn were to be found in all sorts of odd little engagements.

Bridge of Earn did not win again that year, the nearest to victory being a third to Santeve and Symon's Pride for the Liverpool Autumn Cup; but Lafayette won the Duchy Plate at Liverpool on the day that Well Done was successful.

It was in this year that Lord Derby brought out a two-year-old for the only race (the Exeter Stakes) he ran at that age. This was the mighty Swynford, who was unplaced in this one outing.

The year 1920 was one of important events for Lord Derby's stable. It began modestly enough with the victory of Glacier in an Apprentice Handicap at the Newmarket First Spring Meeting, and was continued over the old St. Leger course at the Doncaster Spring Meeting, when Glacis won the Chesterfield Plate, a handicap for which there were thirteen runners, and though it carried the welter weight of 9st. 11lb., it started at 11 to 2, and in a close finish won by a neck.

The more important victories of the year began at Ascot, when he won the Ascot Derby Stakes with Decision, by Count Schomberg out of Be Sure. Frank Wootton rode and beat Admiral Hawke, Major Eustace Loder's disappointing animal, which started favourite.

In the Hardwicke Stakes, Swynford made his winning debut. The race for some reason was regarded as almost a certainty for the American Whisk Broom, who was, I believe, the property of Harry Payne Whitney, whilst a good second favourite was Marajax, running in the name of Mr. H. Lytham, this being the racing name of the present Sir Edward Hulton. Marajax was ridden by Stanley Wootton, who is now a famous trainer, but was easily beaten by the horse that was destined to win Lord Derby's first St. Leger.

With the Ascot Derby and the Hardwicke Stakes to his credit, his lordship might be said to have had a very good Ascot.

At the Newmarket First July Meeting, Marchetta, who had scored such a sensational success as a two-year-old, was brought out in a field of twenty-five for the Soham Plate, and won this carrying 6 st. 10lb. and starting at 10 to 1.

This was one of the red-letter days in the annals of Stanley House, for the next race was won by Lord Derby's Premier, a Persimmon colt. This was the Duke of Cambridge Handicap, and Frank Wootton rode. The last race of the day also went to the black and white, Wootton again being the jockey, and Decision the horse.

From now on the record of his racing is a chronicle of equine champions, each supreme in his own sphere, and each to prove, not only his excellence on the Turf, but at stud. A son of Chaucer, Oliver Goldsmith, came out at the Lingfield Summer Meeting, and won the Great Foal Plate.

Winners were now coming in rapid succession. The Newmarket Second July Meeting saw Meadow Chat win the Khedive Plate, and on the Thursday, Queen's Journal came out and beat Joyful, Eaton Lad, and ten others for the Summer Handicap, starting at 9 to 1. Carrying 14lb. extra, Queen's Journal continued his winning career by taking the Goodwood Plate from the favourite, Declare, and Mr. W. Hall Walker's Royal Realm. There were eleven runners, and Declare was a good favourite.

But the real field day (if that term can be misapplied to cover more days than one) was at Liverpool that year. Lord Derby started off by winning the T.Y.O. Selling Plate with Glucose filly on the Wednesday, the Cup Course Selling Handicap with Corrie Glass on the Thursday, and on the Friday he took three races in succession: the Jolliffe T.Y.O. Plate was won by Oliver Goldsmith (Frank Wootton): the Sefton Plate by Marchetta (F. Rickaby, jun.); and the Liverpool Cup by Swynford, who started favourite in a field of twelve at 11 to 4, and had behind him such horses as Dean Swift and Succour.

Those who watched the race saw in Swynford the potential winner of a St. Leger, though there were some who scouted the idea of Swynford beating the Derby winner, Lemberg, who had covered the course in what was, until then, record time: 2 mins. 35 secs., a time which was not beaten at Epsom until Spion Kop's Derby.

'Swynford is the best horse I have ever ridden,' Frank Wootton told me at Doncaster, when I reminded him of his win, and time has proved that, if he is not the most brilliant horse that has ever been foaled, he is certainly the stoutest.

It was not from Lemberg that the danger came. The despised outsider, Bronzio, which had won at a sensational figure at Newbury, came at the last moment to challenge the great Swynford, and in a desperate finish, where Wootton showed all his brilliant artistry, Swynford won by a head, with Lemberg beaten off a length and a half.

Time has proved beyond any dispute that the best horse won.

In the three years 1921–22–23 alone, his stock won races valued at £87,673!

LORD DERBY AND HIS BEST HORSES

The Sterling Performances of Stedfast

LORD DERBY's interest in racing has ever been personal. There are owners that have no especial call to the Turf, but who have maintained expensive stables either because it has been a family tradition to do so, or that there is behind the race-track the solid business inducement of the stud and the enormous returns which are sometimes available from this source long after a horse or filly's racing career is finished.

To Lord Derby his horses are a very personal matter. He is no stoic who can watch his colours flash past the post ahead of the field without displaying the least sign of emotion. The horse for the moment is part of himself; his colours are the guerdon of the House of Stanley, and I have seen his hand tremble at the sight of the black and white in the fore of a field of horses.

There is a business side to his racing – but he never bets, and the fact that a fluent victory may increase the value of the horse as a stallion, or put a higher price on the produce if it be a mare, has no bearing whatever upon his feelings in these thrilling moments.

I have never met an owner less influenced by the pounds, shillings, and pence of racing than he. If his horses have chances in near-at-hand races, he proclaims the fact. And yet, for all his frankness, he is loath to induce others to bet.

'I am really afraid to tell them how well I have tried Sansovino,' he told me at the annual Derby lunch at the Press Club, 'for fear I make them back it and it loses.'

To such a man the improvement in his racing fortunes meant

something more than a totalling up of stakes won. There was the imponderable quality of pride in his horses' achievements – something which is not expressible in terms of gold and silver cups, and in periodical cheques from Messrs. Weatherby. His position as a pillar of the Turf is, of course, independent of his place as a winning owner.

If he never had a horse in training he would have been a vital factor in the sport. Both as Steward and Senior Steward he was a man of extraordinary ability, jealous of the honour of the sport.

To go back to the St. Leger of 1910, there was a disposition in certain quarters to discount Swynford's narrow win, and it was pointed out that Bronzino, Mr. James de Rothschild's horse, which had run him to a head, could not be described as anything within the first class. This hasty criticism was discounted almost immediately, for on the Friday following Wednesday's St. Leger, Bronzino came out and beat Bachelor's Double and Royal Realm for the Doncaster Cup. Royal Realm on his day was a very useful horse indeed, and Bachelor's Double has transmitted his fine qualities to scores of good class racehorses.

Another good winner this year was Hair Trigger II, a bay filly by Fowling Piece out of Altcar, who, after running three times without winning, won in succession the Astley Stakes at the Liverpool Summer Meeting, the Breeders' Foal Plate at Kempton in September, and the Boscawen Post Stakes at Newmarket, a total of £2,111. Frank Wootton (who, by an odd coincidence, I can see at this moment, his flat being opposite to mine!) was the jockey on each occasion.

Petschau was another two-year-old winner for Lord Derby. This filly was royally bred, being by Persimmon, King Edward's Derby winner, out of Loch Doon, who, if I remember rightly, was also in the royal stable. Petschau won the Hythe Maiden Plate at Folkestone, and followed this up by a victory at the Newmarket First October Meeting.

There were, undoubtedly, some fine two-year-olds at Stanley House this year, and the most promising was a Chaucer colt out of Be Sure, who, with a little luck, might have credited the stable with its first Derby winner. This was Stedfast, who made a promising beginning by running third to Lowlander and Sallie of Navarre at the First October Meeting. He followed this up by a victory in the

Prendergast Stakes, beating Wrinkler a neck, with Harry Payne Whitney's Dame d'Or colt third. He was the outsider of the three, and he won fairly comfortably, in spite of the narrowness of the margin.

George Lambton never hurries his two-year-olds, and the fact that Stedfast was not exploited until late in the autumn was typical of the stable policy. Stedfast carried 9st. 10lb. when he won the Hook Plate at Sandown from eight others, and, despite his weight and the opposition, odds of 3 to 1 were betted on him, and he wound up his first season by winning the Witherslack Plate at Liverpool, Danny Maher being in the saddle and the odds being a little more prohibitive, for the layers demanded 5 to 1.

Another royally bred one was Marie Legraye, a brown filly by Diamond Jubilee/White Lilac, who scored her one success at the Houghton Meeting.

The ruthless policy of weeding out horses that were not quite first-class has always been pursued by the Stanley House master. In this way Lord Derby got rid of horses which subsequently won for other owners, but I cannot trace that he ever disposed of a good one, or one that made any mark at the stud.

A bay filly by Chaucer out of Ejector was sold out of a selling plate to Lord St. Davids for 500 guineas, and though I have seen some of her stock running, she has never cut a great figure at the stud.

Swynford finished up that year with £10,694 to his credit, a highly respectable sum; and although, in the following season, he was beaten by Lemberg in the Coronation Cup at Epsom, he won the Hardwicke Stakes at Ascot, and the Princess of Wales' Stakes at Newmarket at the First July Meeting (from Lemberg) and beat the same horse in a canter in the Eclipse Stakes, winning in all, as a four-year-old, £15,813.

Although this does not compare very favourably with the enormous totals made by triple-crown winners, remembering the kind of races in which he ran, and the bold policy pursued by his trainer, and that these included only one of the classics, Swynford's performance is an outstanding one, and his total remarkable for many reasons.

In the Eclipse Stakes 11 to 10 was laid on Swynford, and 9 to 4 against Lemberg (who had dead-heated with Neil Gow in the previous year).

Harking back to the horses that have been sold out of the stable and have won for other owners, I might take the case of Well Done. This horse was sold out of the stable and was bought by Mr. Charles Hibbert, the Midland bookmaker, and although he failed to win in 1910, he won several races for him in 1911 and was subsequently sold at auction to Lord Cadogan, who won a selling race at Doncaster with him, buying him in for 700 guineas, and in the following spring won the Battyany Plate at Lincoln, Well Done starting at 100 to 8.

'Some people use selling plates as a medium for gambling,' Lord Derby once told me, 'but when I put a horse in a selling plate it is for the obvious reason: I want to get him out of my stable.'

The year 1911, or, as most people remember it, 'Sunstar's year', opened in ominous fashion from the point of view of Stedfast's Derby prospects. He was very much fancied by the general public; and though he failed in the Union Jack Stakes at Liverpool, being beaten by Seaforth and Athelstan (the latter being a horse which he had well trounced the year before), he was expected to make amends in the Two-Thousand Guineas. It was here, however, that Sunstar gave some hint of his merit, and Stedfast could get no nearer than second. I doubt very much whether the racing public expected him even to reach this position, for he started at 100 to 9, Sunstar being second favourite at 5 to 1.

The hope of Newmarket that year was Pietri, Mr. Leopold de Rothschild's horse, who was beaten out of a place.

When Sunstar and Stedfast met at Epsom, the positions were confirmed. They met in the Derby, a race which will be remembered for many years, not only because of the extraordinary performance which Sunstar put up, but because the race was a signal for the bursting of one of the worst thunderstorms that England has known: a storm in which some of the people on the Downs were killed by lightning.

The luck was against Lord Derby, for Stedfast made a very bad beginning and was coming with a wet sail at the finish and would, with any kind of fortune, have given Lord Derby his first triumph in the Epsom classic. Sunstar won on three legs, for he was a lame horse, and, if I remember rightly, did not run again.

This was Stedfast's last defeat as a three-year-old, and it is a curious fact that, although he won eight races subsequently, in none of these did he start at odds against. He won the Prince of Wales' Stakes at Ascot, with 5 to 1 betted on him, and was pulled out again to win the St. James' Palace Stakes, when the bookmakers demanded 5 to 4. He ran away with the Atlantic Stakes at Liverpool, at 6 to 1 on, and his 'race' for the Sussex Stakes was a match, and here 25 to 1 was asked. The Great Yorkshire Stakes at York fell to him at 7 to 1 on, and he walked over for the Doncaster Stakes, whilst in the Jockey Club Stakes he beat Lemberg, Swynford's old opponent, who was asked to give him two stone. In this latter race Lord Derby also ran Hair Trigger II, who finished third.

Stedfast's last race of the year was in the Kingsclere Stakes at Newbury, where he beat Prince Palatine and one of the Duke of Portland's horses, odds of 6 to 5 being laid on him.

As a three-year-old he brought stakes to Stanley House valued at £15,719, of which £7,481 was the stake money of the Jockey Club Stakes. Though defeated in the Derby, it was expected that the black and white would figure very prominently in the Oaks, and Hair Trigger II had certainly good credentials, though she could do no better than finish third to the dark Cherimoya, which, if I remember rightly, was trained by Charlie Marsh and was making her first appearance on a racecourse.

She was subsequently third in the Coronation Stakes at Ascot, and won a small race at Lewes. She was not the luckiest of fillies, or she should have won at least two races in which she was second, but she subsequently won the Nassau Stakes at Goodwood, the Lennox Plate at Hurst Park in August, the Park Hill Stakes at Doncaster, the Great Foal Stakes at the First October Meeting at Newmarket, and the Newmarket Oaks.

It was another good Ascot for Lord Derby's colours. He ran eight horses and won four races, with Stedfast, King William (who had been a better favourite than Stedfast in the Derby), Hair Trigger II and Swynford. His Ascot winnings totalled £7,712.

In scanning a year's record of a winning stable one is apt to forget that, sandwiched between the victories recorded in the stakes book, are quite a number of failures. We pass over the defeats of Glacis, Persephone, Corncob, Decision, Bridge of Allan, and concentrate our minds on the successes of Swynford, Stedfast, and Hair Trigger II.

'If I had to say what is the chief qualification for ownership,' said Lord Derby, 'I should put "patience" first, as you have done. The owner who loses his head, who finds all sorts of obscure reasons for his horses' failures, who considers a change of trainer every time he gets some unexpected setback, should not own racehorses. A large slice of philosophy should be part of the moral equipment of all men who register their colours. Without this, ownership is a fretful, unhappy business.'

Whatever King William might have been on the home gallops, he was obviously an inferior horse to Stedfast on a course. This was proved time and time again, notably in the St. Leger, when he could get no nearer than third to Prince Palatine, who had been beaten, at a few pounds' difference in weight, by Stedfast at Newbury. King William was nine lengths behind the St. Leger winner.

He had some compensation for this defeat when Decision won the Alexandra Handicap at Doncaster. Decision was a half-brother to Stedfast.

Another winner for Stanley House this year, after several failures, was Persephone, a Persimmon filly out of Princess Melton, who won the Coventry Plate at Warwick and the Ormonde Stakes at Newbury, though she started without a quotation in the market.

Usually, Lord Derby's colours are not seen out at Lincoln at the beginning of flat-racing, for they are generally in reserve for the Liverpool Spring meeting, which immediately follows. But his first winner of 1912 was The Bann. He was backed down to 5 to 4, in spite of the huge dimensions of the field, and he duly won.

The Bann subsequently won a race at Warwick and one at Pontefract, but subsequently ran badly.

In this year Lord Derby won the Manchester Cup with Donnithorne, a brown colt by Chaucer–Hettie Sorrel, beating the ill-fated Bronzino, with Mushroom third. I don't think Donnithorne ever won again. He was a three-year-old and carried the featherweight of 6st. 4lb.

Stedfast came out to walk over for the Rothschild Plate at Manchester, and went on to win the Coronation Cup at Epsom, subsequently taking the Royal Stakes at Newbury, the Hardwicke Stakes at Ascot, and was beaten a short head in the Eclipse Stakes by Prince Palatine, both horses carrying the steadier of 10st. On this occasion Danny Maher rode Stedfast, and in my judgement rode a very good race to get as close; for subsequently, in the Jockey Club Stakes, Prince Palatine gave Stedfast 13lb. and beat him by half a length.

In his second season Stedfast won over £10,000, for he added to his other trophies the Champion Stakes at Newmarket and the Atlantic Stakes, whilst his second in the Jockey Club Stakes was worth £1,700 to his owner.

'Stedfast was a good horse, though it would be absurd to say that he was anything like as good as Swynford, who was the best horse I ever owned. It is too early yet to place Sansovino accurately. There is no doubt that he is an amazingly good horse.'

LORD DERBY'S
UNLUCKY RACE

THE breeding of horses so that the best qualities of a long line of successful racehorses shall be so blended and amalgamated that only that which is fine and courageous and good-tempered shall be transmitted, is a delicate and baffling business. Every year we learn something new about that mysterious thing, heredity. All manner of people have contributed to our knowledge.

There was once an Austrian abbot who was regarded as being a little mad because he spent so much of his time grafting sweet peas and examining the result of his labours. Mendel, in his abbey garden, did something for English racing. He taught us the principle of dominant strains, and incidentally brought us to an understanding of Nature's amazing tendency to reproduce only the best kind.

It would be a mistake to look upon Lord Derby's 'luck' as though it were the result of haphazard choice and happy-go-lucky breeding. The basis of luck at racing is good, solid judgement. You could no more pick out your sires and dams with a pin than you could pick winners by that simple method. Pharos was not lucky to win at Kempton nor at Newmarket recently. You can trace his easy victory to the judgement which Lord Derby showed in buying his grand-dam, Anchora, from the late George Edwardes' stud, the care and discretion shown in the mating of Phalaris and Scapa Flow; to days and nights of study and thought on the part of those responsible for the management of the stud; and last, but not least, to the quiet patience of his trainer, George Lambton, who in spite of all disappointments, persevered with the horse that should have won the Derby of 1923 in a canter.

The year 1912 saw the introduction to racing of Light Brigade, a brown colt by Picton out of Bridge of Sighs. With this useful colt Lord Derby won the Highclere Nursery, valued £827, beating that very useful horse, Sleipner, and nineteen others. Robbins was the jockey, and the horse started at 100 to 8 against. In the Free Handicap at Newmarket, Light Brigade ran second to Mr. Jack Joel's Jest; but at the Liverpool Autumn Meeting, won the Liverpool Nursery, starting a hot favourite, with Frank Wootton in the saddle.

There are thoughtless people who sometimes ask why it is that Lord Derby's horses win so frequently at Liverpool. I say 'thoughtless' in the sense that they infer that these horses are 'kept' for these meetings in the North. There never were horses that are run straighter than those that carry the black and white; and the very simple explanation is that Liverpool is Lord Derby's home meeting, that he likes to see his horses win at Aintree, and that in many cases their preparation is timed for those meetings.

They may go for races before or after, as they do, and win them, and even then carry their penalties successfully at Liverpool. But if it is a fact that Lord Derby would rather see his horses win at his home meeting than at any other, it is equally a fact that his object in racing is to establish the excellence of his sires-to-be, and he would certainly not jeopardise their reputation by missing an important engagement, whether it was for Liverpool or elsewhere.

If you examine the records of the Derby family, you will find that they have won on almost every course in England. Whether they have won at Worcester, I do not know, but if not, then this is one of the few meetings where the black and white of the Stanleys has not been to the fore.

Another useful winner of 1912 was The Tylt, a bay filly by Spearmint out of Altcar, who won several races that year as a three-year-old, including the Stayers' Handicap at Gatwick, ridden by one of Mr. Lambton's apprentices, the Liverpool St. Leger, and His Majesty's Plate, at Doncaster. The Tylt was a natural stayer and a game one.

The year before the War, 1913, as most racegoers will remember, Easter fell very early, and the Kempton Park and Leicester fixtures preceded Lincoln and Liverpool. It was not until the latter meeting that Lord Derby's colours were carried successfully.

Light Brigade was one of the money-spinners of the year, and his performances were unequalled by any of the Stanley House horses, for Light Brigade, after taking the Knowsley Plate, at Liverpool, won ten races in succession. He took the Column Produce Stakes at the Newmarket Craven Meeting; the Hurst Park Yearling Plate, run on Whit Monday; the Midland Breeders' Foal Plate at Birmingham; the 60th Triennial at Ascot; the Northern Derby at Newcastle; the Great National Breeders' Produce Stakes at Redcar; the Durham County Produce Plate at Stockton; the Duke of York Stakes at York; the Great Yorkshire Stakes at York; and the Riverdale Three-year-old Plate at Windsor. A clear proof of Lord Derby's indifference to where his horses won, so long as they enhanced their reputation, for, of the ten races won by Light Brigade, nine were won on different courses!

With 8st. 12lb., a fairly heavy weight for a three-year-old, he was made third favourite for the Duke of York Stakes, but finished unplaced, the race being won by another three-year-old, which, with 8st. 6lb., carried Danny Maher to victory. This was Florist. Light Brigade did not succeed in getting into the first three. He was next beaten a neck by Mr. J. B. Joel's Blue Stone, giving that useful performer 9lb., for the Select Stakes at Newmarket. In this race, Cigar started favourite and finished third.

The Cambridgeshire has never been a lucky race for Mr. Lambton, for both Diadem and, later, Phalaris, were beaten on this trying nine furlongs. Light Brigade was equally unfortunate: carrying 8st. 5lb. he was unplaced to Cantilever, the leniency of whose handicapping was emphasised by the fact that although he carried 7st. 12lb., this included a 10lb. penalty for winning the Jockey Club Stakes. When they had met at Stockton in the Durham County Produce Plate, Light Brigade had given 9lb. to Cantilever and had beaten him two lengths, so that the reversal of form was rather remarkable.

Light Brigade in his ten races won stakes of £7,726.

Stedfast, as a five-year-old, was beaten for the Burwell Plate at Newmarket in the spring by Tracery and Jackdaw, starting favourite; but he won the Chippenham Plate at the First Summer Meeting, after having been beaten a length and a half by Prince Palatine for the Gold Cup at Ascot. This was the race which saw an extraordinary incident. As the field was turning into the straight, a lunatic dodged under the rails, brandishing a revolver, and brought down

Tracery, Whalley being seriously hurt. This incident must have affected every jockey and horse in the race; for, although there is no doubt that Prince Palatine was a pretty useful performer on his day, there is less doubt that he was nothing like the animal his enthusiastic admirers claimed him to be.

Stedfast won the Limekiln Stakes and The Cup at Newmarket, beating Lord Cadogan's Marco Fraser, ridden by Maher, starting at the unremunerative odds of 33 to 1 on.

The Tylt, now a four-year-old, won the Northumberland Plate with 7st. 13lb., the price being 9 to 1 against.

This year saw the debut of Young Pegasus, who, although it came from Lambton's stable, subsequently ran in the colours of Lord Stanley, Lord Derby's son, being a gift horse. Young Pegasus, who was by Chaucer out of Princess Melton, did not run as a two-year-old, but as a three-year-old won the Sandringham Foal Stakes at Sandown, the St. James' Stakes at Kempton Park, and the White Rose Stakes at York in August. His performances stamped him as a useful animal, and he brought £3,643 in stakes to Stanley House.

This was a year of good two-year-olds. Stornoway, Sir Edward Hulton's good colt, being one. A brown filly by Desmond, out of Veneration II, Glorvina, was considerably fancied to beat Stornoway in the Gimcrack Stakes, but was unplaced. Glorvina, however, won the Mersey Stakes at Liverpool in July, and the Maiden Plate at Kempton Park, whilst Willaura, a chestnut horse by William the Third out of Brilliantine, won the Lewes Handicap, the Round Course Welter Handicap, at Kempton Park, and the Castle Handicap, at Windsor, ridden by F. Rickaby.

Stanley House also sent out a beautifully bred two-year-old in Dan Russel, a colt by Chaucer out of Hettie Sorrel, who won three races out of five – the Convivial Produce Stakes, at York, the West of Scotland Foal Stakes, at Ayr, and the 66th Triennial Stakes, at Newmarket.

The only other winner that year that I can trace was Spean Bridge, who won three little races. Spean Bridge was by Spearmint out of Santa Brigida, and was a three-year-old.

LORD DERBY'S TRAGIC LOSS

THE year 1914 was not a particularly notable year for Lord Derby's colours, though there is no doubt that, given the opportunity, the three horses who credited the stable with something over £6,000 in stakes might have made Turf history.

Dan Russel won the Chester Vase, ridden by F. Bullock, the Home-bred Three-year-old Cup at Gatwick, ridden by F. Rickaby, who afterwards found a hero's death in the War, and the Knowsley Dinner Stakes at Liverpool Summer Meeting.

Young Pegasus won the Hylton Handicap at the Liverpool Spring Meeting, carrying 7st. 13lb., and starting at the surprising price of 100 to 8. Later he won the Croxteth Plate at Liverpool, a good sprint, whilst Light Brigade won the Bridgeman Stakes at Liverpool, the March Stakes at Newmarket, and the Atlantic Stakes, being ridden in each case by Rickaby.

The War placed the great owners of racehorses in a peculiar position. There has ever been a noisy section of the public who are inimical to racing, and who found in the War an opportunity, as they thought, for killing this sport – and, incidentally, this very important British industry. Their cry was a plausible one. They said in effect: 'Whilst our soldiers are fighting and dying on the fields of France and Belgium it is disgraceful that horse-racing should continue as though there were no war.'

To them horse-racing was merely an amusement for the rich, the idle, and the worthless. The same argument was used against the theatres, and it seemed at one time as though the efforts of these fanatics would succeed. But happily there were intelligent men in the Cabinet, who realised that racing not only supported thousands of workers, but that the export of bloodstock from this country was a most important trade.

Lord Derby, who was to become an assistant to Mr. Lloyd George at the War Office, was one of the people who did not lose his head. The case for racing was fought out with not a little bitterness, and eventually it was agreed that a restricted programme should be followed, and that there should be racing, at any rate, at Newmarket, the headquarters of the Turf, provided that no special trains should be run, and that racing people should go by road. And this at a time when the petrol supply was causing the authorities the gravest anxiety!

Lord Derby immediately plunged into the business of winning the War. He was the most wholehearted supporter the Government had. He was certainly the greatest recruiting agent that England has ever known. I would not like to say at this moment how many divisions he raised by his personal efforts. There is only one word that can describe his labours for the country, and that word is 'magnificent'. A great-hearted, impetuous man, his fiery eloquence brought tens of thousands of men to the flag; his honesty, the cleanness of his life, his very faults, helped to inspire confidence, and Lancashire responded to a man.

It was not till 1915 that the restricted programme was fully applied. At the Liverpool Spring Meeting Mr. George Lambton sent out Marchetta filly (by Radium) to win the Sefton Park Plate, the Ormonde Stakes, at Chester, and, later in the year, the First October Nursery. George Lambton, who had been one of the greatest of our amateur riders, a fearless man to hounds, and a member of a fine fighting family, must have chafed to see the younger men going out to war. But he had been for many years a cripple; his back had been in plaster as the result of a fall, and life had been something of an agony. In the circumstances, and remembering his zest for a fight, it was the cruellest of bad luck that his health did not permit his joining up. He stayed behind to carry on, whilst Lord Derby, leaving his horses to look after themselves, so to speak, plunged into war work with characteristic whole-heartedness.

Young Pegasus was a winner at Newmarket in the spring, taking the Peel Handicap, and, carrying Lord Stanley's colours, won the Cambridgeshire Hunt Plate at the Second Extra Meeting, in July, this being the substitute for the Royal Hunt Cup, the Ascot meeting, of course, being abandoned.

Lord Derby found time, however, to organise a New Derby Stakes, the race being over a mile and a half, for 100 sovs. each, with 1,000 sovs. added, this sum having been given by Lord Derby, so that it may be said that, even as his ancestor instituted the Derby in the eighteenth century, so did Lord Derby institute the New Derby Stakes during the War. It will be remembered that the race was won by Mr. Sol Joel's Pommern.

The two-year-olds which won this year were Canyon, a bay filly by Chaucer-Glassalt, and a brown colt by Polymelus out of Bromus. The latter was afterwards named Phalaris, and was destined to be the sire of Pharos, and incidentally, of Phalaros, both of whom won at Kempton Park recently.

Canyon won the Maiden Plate, the Bedford Two-year-old Plate, and the Bretby Post Sweepstakes at Newmarket, whilst Phalaris won the Stud Produce Stakes, and the Redmere Nursery Plate, in September. He started favourite at 9 to 4, and won easily from nineteen others, carrying 9st.

Joyous Gard, a three-year-old, by Spearmint, won the Teversham Three-year-old Plate, whilst Dame Prudent – who, by the way, has a very useful staying two-year-old running at the present moment, won the Kirtlin Plate. It is unnecessary to say that all these races were run at Newmarket.

Canyon was an extraordinarily good filly, and although she was difficult to train, George Lambton managed to deliver her at the post in the following year to win the One Thousand Guineas.

We have now come to an era in which names familiar to the racing public appear with considerable frequency. The Stanley House stud was established, and had passed from the region of hope and diffident optimism to accomplishment.

'I was, of course, so absorbed in the great problems of the War,' said Lord Derby, 'that all other interests were subsidiary. Yet it would be absurd to suggest that I gave no thought at all to the progress of my young horses.'

But for some outside interest no man of his dynamic qualities could have sustained the terrible strain which every member of the Government was called upon to endure. Mr. Bonar Law and Mr. Lloyd George had their golf, Mr. Asquith his books. His horses must have been a veritable godsend to a man of Lord Derby's temperament, though he took very little part in the great game, and left everything to his brilliant trainer.

In France, where the Government recognised the necessity for keeping the minds of the people freshened by sport, racing went on, even when air raids were of almost daily occurrence. The French recognised the necessity for keeping bloodstock up to the highest notch.

A reference to the stud reminds me of the tragedy which overcame Swynford. It is best told in Mr. Lambton's own words.

'I was training him for the Jockey Club Stakes, and one September morning, two days before the race, we were out on the July course. Curiously enough, that very morning, when riding out to exercise, Frank Wootton had said to me: "Nobody knows how good this horse is now. I don't think there is anything he couldn't do, from five furlongs to five miles." Half an hour afterwards he smashed his fetlock joint to atoms in a steady half-speed gallop.

'I shall never forget that morning. There were only two horses in the gallop, and they had to pass a haystack which hid them from view for a moment or two. I watched them go behind it, and then only one horse came on. I galloped straight down and found Swynford standing on three legs. It was an hour and a half before we could get Mr. Livock, the veterinary surgeon, and an ambulance, and then it was nearly an hour before we could get the horse into it.

'The task of getting such a great big horse out of it on three legs seemed impossible. It was a wonderful piece of work on the part of Mr. Livock to accomplish it. Personally, I never spent a worse day in my life.'

Fortunately for bloodstock, Swynford was a wonderful patient, and though it seemed impossible that this miracle could be accomplished, he was saved for the stud.

From his breeding it was expected that Phalaris would train into a stayer. His sire was Polymelus, a horse that has got Derby winners. But Phalaris was not to fulfil hopes in this direction. It was very doubtful whether he could stay a yard over seven furlongs in a truly run race, though he has certainly transmitted some of his father's staying power to the stock which he subsequently sired.

Phalaris started the 1916 season by winning the Beaufort Stakes at the Second July Meeting at Newmarket. This was run over six furlongs, and he was a fairly comfortable winner. He took the St. George's Handicap, value £877, at Windsor the same month, ridden by J. H. Martin, starting at 7 to 1, and winning by six lengths from Argos and Torloisk. At the Second October Meeting he won the Royal Stakes across the flat, one and a quarter miles, at Newmarket. But though this journey is a trying one, it has very often proved something of an illusion. Horses have won across the flat who are essentially sprinters, in the sense that six furlongs is their best distance. A case in point was Top Gallant, who won the Newmarket Stakes in record time, yet cannot get a mile in a true run race.

LORD DERBY'S
HOME-BRED WINNERS

C ONTINUING with Lord Derby's 1916 record, we now come to a beautifully bred filly in Nun's Veiling, by Roquelaure out of Canterbury Pilgrim, who won two out of her eight races this year. She was then a two-year-old, and great hopes were entertained that her progeny would reproduce some of the brilliant qualities of her parents. I believe she has foaled one or two winners, but I cannot remember any of great account.

Tortona won three out of seven races, including the Bishopsgarth Three-year-old Handicap, at Stockton, the Kedington Handicap, at Newmarket, where she gave 12lb. and a beating to that well-known performer King Sol, who was then, I believe, owned by Mrs. George Lambton. King Sol was a three-year-old at the time, and carried 6st. 13lb.

Tortona also won an Apprentice Race at Newmarket. This year saw the winning debut of Scapa Flow, who was, as is known, a three-year-old by Chaucer out of Anchora, the dam of Pharos. She won the Bramber Plate at Brighton in October, the Stockton Autumn Handicap, and the Scarborough Stakes at Newmarket. When Lord Derby brought Anchora from George Edwards' stud, he undoubtedly secured a bargain.

It is curious how some names remain in the memory, and others fade out so that, although they have classic form to their credit, it is with the greatest difficulty that one can 'place them'.

Although only a few years have passed since Ferry achieved her victory, how many of us recall the fact that she won the One Thousand Guineas for Lord Derby? Ferry was by Swynford out of

Gondolette, and was therefore own sister to Sansovino, and I believe that it was the encouragement received by this victory that induced Lord Derby to mate Swynford again with Gondolette, with the happy result that Sansovino lived to carry the Stanley colours to victory at Epsom.

Ferry, ridden by the master horseman, 'Brownie' Carslake, won the One Thousand Guineas from My Dear, Herself, and five others, starting at the odds of 50 to 1 against, surprising her connections almost as much as she surprised the public. She ran again in the New Oaks, and was beaten by My Dear, she and Silver Bullet dead-heating for second place. The race was rather a tragedy, because Mrs. Arthur James's Stoney Ford, ridden by J. H. Martin, came in first, but Donoghue on My Dear objected for bumping and boring; the objection was sustained, and the race went to Manton. My Dear started favourite.

Lord Derby had left the Ministry and was now doing splendid work in Paris as our Ambassador. Incidentally, his colours began to appear on the French racecourses, for he is one of those who believe that there is no greater urge to affinity than a common interest in sport. The War was over and the peace muddle had begun. Possibly Lord Derby found his daily associations with professional politicians even more trying and more nerve-racking than his War work. His visits to England were few and far between, but he still maintained the closest connection with his stable, and the victories of his home-bred horses must have produced the sedative effect which was so necessary for a man living in the hectic atmosphere of the British Embassy.

There is one interesting thing which you cannot fail to notice, and to which I have already drawn attention, namely, the patience which Stanley House has ever shown with its two-year-olds. It is very rare that a good youngster is hurried, with the result that one so frequently finds that the first wins of his horses are as three-year-olds. In the early part of 1919 he brought out Beresina, a Swynford-Brig of Ayr filly, to win the West Derby Stakes, and followed this up by taking the inevitable Liverpool Spring Cup with Santa Cruz, a chestnut filly by Neil Gow out of Santa Brigida. The next day he won the Hylton Handicap with Crosstree, the Bridgeman Stakes with Mrs. Jawleyford, and the Bickerstaffe Stakes with Beresina!

Nor did this complete the total of his extraordinary successes, for on the Saturday Makepeace won the Maghull Plate. It was a wonderful Liverpool for Lord Derby, since he took six races with five horses.

The stable was now in form, and at the Derby Spring Meeting he brought out a beautifully bred three-year-old, Rothesay Bay, by Bayardo out of Anchora, to win the Quarndon Three-year-old Handicap. Beresina was a particularly fast filly: she won the Alexandra Handicap at Gatwick, but her finest performance was later in the year at Ayr, when she won the Gold Cup from Forest Guard and nine others. Santa Cruz won the Stewards' Three-year-old Maiden Plate at Chester.

I have never had a very high opinion of the Neil Gow blood, and neither Santa Cruz nor her progeny were ever favourites of mine.

The year 1919 saw the resumption of racing at Ascot, but here his lordship had a lean time, winning nothing.

A good filly of his by Harry of Hereford-Spean Bridge won the Warwickshire Breeders' Foal Plate at Birmingham. This was Princess Margaret, who won three races in succession before her defeat. She took the Stud Produce Stakes at Newmarket First July Meeting, the West Riding Produce Stakes at Pontefract, the Optional Selling Plate at Catterick Bridge, and the Friary Nursery at Derby, where she was ridden by Carslake. In all she won in her first season £2,055.

Rothesay Bay won the St. George Stakes at the Liverpool Summer Meeting, and another good winner that year was Keysoe, a brown filly by Swynford-Keystone II – the sire a St. Leger winner and the dam one who should certainly have won the same race. She was the most beautiful mare I have ever seen, being by Persimmon out of Lock and Key, and, although she won the Oaks, she failed in the St. Leger, though there were only heads between the first four, Troutbeck winning from Prince William, Beppo being third and Keystone II, fourth. She did indeed get a St. Leger winner in Keysoe. She started her winning career by taking the Gatwicke Stakes at Goodwood and the Nassau Stakes at the same venue, and won the St. Leger by six lengths from Dominion and Buchan, Carslake being the jockey. It was a very useful field, and not only Buchan, who started favourite in the race, but Dominion and that wonderful stayer, Pomme de Terre, were fancied. She won in all £8,087 in her first season – she did not run as a two-year-old, nor had her early performances been of note, for she had run unplaced in the One

Thousand Guineas and the Coronation Stakes, whilst in the Knowsley Dinner Stakes at Liverpool Summer Meeting she was beaten by African Star, a horse that will be remembered as having an extraordinary liking for the Liverpool course – so much so that he ran a 21lb. better horse on that track than on any other.

Rothesay Bay helped to swell the winnings total, taking the Great Yorkshire Handicap at Doncaster from Greek Scholar, Coriolanus, and five others, though here again the race was won in the objection-room, King John having finished first by a short head but was disqualified for boring.

At Alexandra Park, Harrier, by Harry of Hereford-Altcar, won the Mile Nursery, starting at 8 to 1, and afterwards won the Edgehill Nursery of a mile at Warwick. He was a good staying two-year-old.

Another two-year-old was Redhead, also by Harry of Hereford out of Hair Trigger II, who took the West of Scotland Foal Stakes on his first time out, starting at 7 to 2 on. He did not run again that year.

Santa Cruz won the Autumn Handicap over seven furlongs at Newmarket, and the Chaddesdon Plate at Derby in November; whilst a third Harry of Hereford colt in Great Seal won the Ditch Mile Nursery from ten others, Carslake being the jockey. The chestnut colt followed this up by taking the Witherslack Nursery, also over a mile at Liverpool.

Crevasse, the fourth Harry of Hereford two-year-old, also took a mile nursery at Manchester. Crevasse was out of Glacier. She was a dead stayer, as also was March Along, who won two races out of six, taking the Liverpool Nursery Stakes and the Wynyard Plate at Stockton. March Along was a horse for which I had a great liking. At a later age he won the Ebor Handicap, carrying a respectable weight.

Another three-year-old in Russel, by Chaucer-Princess Melton, was winner at the First Spring Newmarket Meeting, but did not win any other race during the year – a fate that befell a filly by Swynford-Marchetta (Tortona), who had one race to its credit in a big field, but did not run again this year with any success.

George Lambton sent out Canyon to win the One Thousand Guineas. She was, as I have said, a bay filly by Chaucer-Glassalt, and she had behind her a subsequent Derby winner in Fifinella and eight others.

Whitewash, a brown filly by White Eagle–Wife of Bath, won a race at Windsor, and another, the Bretby (Post) Stakes at Newmarket; while Hasta, a four-year-old by Spearmint–Santa Brigida, beat a big field for the Milton Welter Handicap at the First July Meeting.

It is history that Fifinella subsequently won the New Derby with Lord Derby's Canyon unplaced, and in consequence of this defeat Canyon was not pulled out for the New Oaks, which was also won by Fifinella.

Another fairly good filly, Serenissima, by Minoru out of Gondolette (the dam of Sansovino), won a race at Lingfield, and followed this up by winning the Haverhill Stakes at Newmarket at the Second Extra Meeting; while The Tabard gelding, which was afterwards known as Coq d'Or, won the Clearwell Stakes at Newmarket.

LORD DERBY AND BOGEY HORSES

How He Tackles the Problem of Breeding Thoroughbreds

THE thoroughbred racehorse is a mystery which even its most devoted student has never completely solved. How many yearlings come from the stud and raise the highest hopes in their trainers' minds, to flatter as two year-olds, to disappoint at the classic age, and to recover their early form when they are four and five years old?

'A horse never looks so much like a Derby winner as when he is a yearling,' said Lord Derby laughingly; 'and that is an experience which Lord Astor and the Aga Khan have also had.' Both these latter patrons of the Turf follow one rule which has been Lord Derby's ever since he gave his mind to the problem of breeding:

'Weed out the bad ones, and do not send a horse to stud unless his credentials are irreproachable.'

There is a great temptation, when one owns a good-class handicapper, to believe that he can reproduce the qualities of his more illustrious progenitors; but the stud manager who expects miracles, and who believes that great horses can come of the mating of mediocrities, however splendid their record be, is asking for a succession of lean seasons.

Lord Derby requires in all his sires three qualities – courage, honesty, and class. By 'class', I mean that quantity which enables a horse to set weight at defiance.

March Along was not a very high-class horse, although he had a fair number of successes to his credit. He ran nine times as a three-year-old, winning only the Royal Standard Stakes, at Manchester, over a mile; whilst Great Seal ran eleven times, with two victories to his credit – one in the Bickerstaffe Stakes, at the Liverpool Spring Meeting, and in the Royal Stakes, at Newbury.

The third of last year's two-year-olds, Crevasse, whom I have always regarded as an exceptionally good filly, won the Zetland Stakes at the Second July Newmarket Meeting, on her ninth outing the Duchy Stakes, at Liverpool, in the autumn.

A fairly moderate performer was Verbena, a filly by Spearmint-Wife of Bath, who also won two races – the Milverton Three-year-old Handicap at York, in August, out of nine attempts.

By the way, with a few exceptions (the most notable one in recent years being Selene) the horses from Stanley House seldom run more than eight or nine times – that is to say, on an average once a month, flat-racing occupying that period of the year.

A two-year-old exploited this year was a John o' Gaunt colt out of Port Sunlight. This colt, named Port Royal, won the Great Kingston Two-year-old Plate, at Sandown (the race which followed Buchan's successful Eclipse), and did not win again that year. Harrier, now a three-year-old, won the Liverpool Plate from Kentish Cob at this meeting, which was a typical Derby 'bean-feast'. Though March Along was beaten on the second day for the Knowsley Dinner Stakes, Lord Derby won a selling plate through the medium of Hawkshead, a Swynford colt, on the Friday, and took also the Jolliffe Two-year-old Plate with Spinney, the Liverpool Summer Cup with Redhead, and was only just beaten in the Atlantic Stakes by Archaic.

I think this was one of the first successes associated with Tommy Weston, who is now the Stanley House jockey. He rode Redhead, carrying 6 st. 9 lb., in the Cup, and the horse, starting at 8 to 1, won by four lengths, Tangier, who might have beaten him, being left.

Redhead was a particularly versatile performer, and was one of the money-getters for the stable that year. Although she was beaten by Most Beautiful for the Nassau Stakes at Goodwood, she won the Great Midland Breeders' Foal Plate at Nottingham, the Durham County Produce Plate at Stockton, and the Park Hill Stakes at Doncaster. She was afterwards beaten in an Apprentice Plate, but started favourite for the Derby Cup, which was won by Kerasos. In this race Redhead finished fourth.

Harrier added to the gains of the stable by taking the Round Course Handicap at the Kempton Summer Meeting, the Duke of York Stakes, at York, in August, and finished up by winning the Lancashire Handicap at the Liverpool Autumn Meeting. In all, Harrier won £2,882 this year.

Glaciale, another of Lord Derby's Glacier stock, was by no means a top-sawyer, being, in fact, two stone behind a really good one, as was proved when she ran a dead-heat with Pomme de Terre in the Redcar Handicap in the summer. Pomme de Terre was giving one pound short of two stone, and this sterling performer almost had his nose in front at the finish.

It was only by a short head that Crevasse was beaten by Grand Fleet, now a six-year-old, and though the difference in weight was twenty-six pounds in favour of the younger horse, it was something of a performance to run him to a short head.

The last Derby victory of the year was that of Princess Margaret, who beat a good field in the Flying Handicap at the Manchester November Meeting.

Crevasse, whose best performance the previous year had been to run Periosteum to a short head, giving the subsequent winner of the Ascot Cup seven pounds, improved with age, though she was still an uncertain creature, and only won one race in five attempts as a four-year-old. Time and time again she disappointed those who believed that in her Lord Derby had found a good, staying filly, destined to add lustre to the stud. But her victory was a distinguished one, for, carrying one pound overweight, she beat Blue Dun, who was giving her twelve pounds, Evander, who was receiving eight pounds, and nineteen others in the Liverpool Autumn Cup.

It was one of the finest fields ever seen out for that event, for it included Square Measure, Abbot's Trace, Leighton, Franklin, and Monarch. Crevasse had failed so dismally throughout the year that the bookmakers fielded against her, and she started at 100 to 8.

Like all Swynfords, March Along took some time to come to himself, and how the Swynford breed improves will be exemplified next year if Sansovino stands training. March Along ran four times as a four-year-old, starting the year a little ingloriously by running unplaced to Sprig of Orange in the Liverpool Spring Cup. The handicappers took a less exalted view of this prowess when they let him into the Manchester Cup with 7st. 10lb.

There were fifteen runners, and March Along was well backed, being second favourite to Pomme de Terre. Lord Derby's horse won, with Tangiers second, King's Idler third, and Pomme de Terre fourth. With this reminder that the horse was at his best, there was no doubt as to his favouritism when he came out of the Liverpool Stakes in July. He started at even money, and won in a canter, following this up two days later by taking the Atlantic Stakes, carrying 9st. 4lb., with Monarch second. On this occasion he started 11 to 8 on.

He was obviously a horse that required very resolute handling, and when he was given the steadier of 9st. 1lb. to carry in the Ebor Handicap, Carslake, the brainiest and physically the strongest jockey riding, was given the mount. It was a race with special interest for me, because I put March Along in a £2 double, which netted me £350!

Glorioso was something of a bogey. He also was a Swynford colt, and though he won the Union Jack Stakes and the Thomas Plate, at Kempton, these two victories were gained at the expense of a very moderate field, and subsequently this none-too-generous horse was weeded out of the stable.

Other horses to win for the stable were Stanislaus and Spinney, a brown filly by Great Sport-Russet, who won the Knowsley Stakes at the Liverpool Spring Meeting, the Quorndon Handicap, at Leicester, and was four times unplaced.

This year, however, saw the debut of two very high-class two-year-olds – Silurian, by Swynford out of Glacier, and Selene, by Chaucer out of Serenissima. Silurian only ran once as a two-year-old, the policy of patience being pursued by all animals of Lord Derby's breeding. But Selene, who was one of the sweetest fillies I have ever seen on a racecourse (and I do not except Verdict), was of the robust kind, and in eleven races her record was eight firsts, two seconds, and a third! What a glutton she was for a fight! Even-tempered, reliable, extraordinarily courageous, she cannot fail to add glory to Lord Derby's stud.

'She has a dear little colt,' Lord Derby told me some months ago, for she was retired to the stud at the end of her three-year-old career.

She started her racing career at the Second Spring Meeting at Newmarket, and was third for the Norfolk Stakes behind Lembach (now a selling plater!) and Kusu Bay. There were, I believe, twenty or twenty-one runners. So well did she perform, however, that the next time out she was made a hot favourite. It may be remarked, in passing, that when she was third, beaten two and a half lengths by Lembach, she had behind her St. Louis, the subsequent winner of the Two Thousand Guineas.

At Manchester, in the Lytham Stakes, her next outing, she had three very moderate horses behind her, and won by six lengths, starting at 7 to 1 on. She then came out at the Doncaster Spring Meeting in May, and this time the fielders were a little more generous, for they laid 2 to 1 that she would not beat the other five runners. She won, however, with consummate ease, and was unlucky in her next outing to run up against a particularly smart filly in Wild Mint.

This was in the Queen Mary Stakes, and although Wild Mint won fairly easily, it was my impression that Selene did not have the best of fortune in running.

All courses and all goings were alike to her. Having started well very early in the season, she continued to the end. At Haydock Park she took the July Plate, there being two runners. It is remarkable that against two moderate animals, only 2 to 1 should be laid on her.

Goodwood was her next outing and her most valuable race, the Rous Memorial Stakes being worth £1,037. Here, against nothing in particular, the field being moderate in the extreme, she won easily by three-quarters of a length, starting at 11 to 8 on. It was the greatest race certainty we have seen in our time.

She next came out against another moderate field in the Hardwicke Stakes, at Stockton, and beat them in a canter by four lengths, giving a stone to such a horse as Hidden Gun. She started at 9 to 4 on. In September she made the long journey to the North to win the Land of Burns Nursery Handicap, in which she carried 8st. 12lb., having Fodder and Hidden Gun behind her. She won by half a length without any great effort, and Donoghue, as usual, was the jockey.

In the Kempton Park Nursery Handicap she was set to give three pounds to Pondoland, and failed by half a length with an extraordinarily good field behind her. She was giving over a stone to Zoomp and twenty-two pounds to Hong Kong. She started at 7to 1 here, and was well fielded against. The next week, however, she came out at Newmarket, and gave a stone to Two Step, the subsequent winner of the Portland Plate, and beat that filly a length, the two being on the same mark at 6 to 4.

Selene made her last appearance that year at Newmarket in the Houghton Stakes over the Rowley Mile, and, with odds laid on her, dead-heated with Fodder, to whom she was giving one pound. The Rowley Mile was covered in the remarkably fast time of 1 min. 29 ⅕ secs., which is, I believe, the record for the course, unless the compilers of the time were in error. The dead-heaters were ridden, Selene by Donoghue, Fodder by Carslake. It was a remarkably good performance, for Selene met her masculine rival on four pounds less than weight-for-sex terms.

There is very little doubt that as a three-year-old Selene should have added the Gold Vase to her owner's trophies. As it happened, she ran unplaced at Ascot. In the race, which was won by Golden Myth, not only was Selene shut out at the start, but twice along the straight she was badly baulked. I haven't the slightest doubt in my mind that, had Selene been second instead of fourth, she would have won the race on an objection.

THE CAREER OF LORD DERBY'S PHAROS

Why He Failed in the Great Classic Event at Epsom

W E are now approaching the period of culmination in the history of Lord Derby's stud. That his fortune has already reached its zenith is doubtful, for old strains and new blood promise to continue his triumphs. One of the Cæsars said that all great triumphs are invariably preceded by successes which in themselves have the appearance of triumphs; and certainly Selene was a forerunner that indicated the upward tendency of the curve.

We have now reached the period of contemporary Turf history, when many of the horses with which we deal are running today.

Selene's three-year-old career was a succession of important victories, interlarded with at least one grevious disappointment.

Her last race, before she went to stud, was the Hampton Court Great Three-year-old Stakes of 1,450 sovs. This was over a mile and five furlongs, and she had behind her Simon Pure, Captain Fracasse, Lady Juror, Pondoland, and Diligence. When you remember that two of these – Simon Pure and Diligence – ran a dead-heat for the Jubilee, and that Lady Juror and Pondoland were both big race winners, this was a sterling performance. What the book does not show is the difficulties she had to overcome. Turning into the straight, she was shut in, and her position seemed a very precarious one three furlongs from home, till Gardner shot her through on the outside and came on, to score with the greatest ease.

Her total winnings in her second season were £9,452.

That year saw the debut of Pharos, a bay colt by Phalaris-Scapa

Flow. He started favourite in a field of eight runners, at the First Spring Meeting, and won easily by two lengths, following this up by winning the Bedford Two-year-old Stakes, at the Second Spring Meeting, at odds on. This he won comfortably from Vermena, with Town Guard (who was making his initial appearance) unplaced.

Pharos at Ascot beat Tetragon by six lengths, starting at odds on, in the Chesham Stakes; but at the Second July Meeting he had the misfortune to meet Legality, and that most disappointing grey was in one of his most generous moods and succeeded in beating the son of Phalaris.

At Liverpool Pharos resumed his winning account, taking the Mersey Stakes, and subsequently, at Stockton, the Lambton Two-year-old Stakes. He started in the Nunthorpe Sweepstakes, at York, in August – a race in which horses of varying age compete – but was unplaced to Two Step, and was subsequently beaten at Newmarket, in the Houghton Stakes, by three lengths, Twelve Pointer being his conqueror. He wound up his two-year-old career on the same day that Selene made her farewell bow to the Turf, by winning the Hurst Park Great Two-year-old Stakes, a race which is run over six furlongs and which has so far produced the best two-year-olds of the year. Pharos won by four lengths from Silver Grass, with Top Gallant third, Friar's Melody fourth, and Hurry Off last.

I told Lord Derby, at Hurst Park, that I thought he had the Derby winner, but he shook his head.

'I very much doubt it,' he said. 'What I am afraid of is that, like Phalaris, his sire, he will not stay more than a mile at top speed.'

The tradition of the non-staying sire has been largely exploded by the success of The Tetrarch stock in long-distance races, and I think there is no doubt at all that over middle distances Pharos is something of a champion. Nevertheless, I think that Lord Derby took a shrewd view of the situation when he expressed his doubt as to Pharos staying the gruelling mile and a half of the Derby.

There are some who believe that Pharos ran the race of his life at Epsom, and others who swear that, had different tactics been adopted, had Gardner waited before making his effort, he would have won. I am prepared, however, to accept the verdict of the shrewdest jockey riding – not only the shrewdest, but one of the most brilliant race-riders we have on the Turf today. When I suggested that Pharos could have won, he shook his head.

'You blame Gardner for coming too soon. You're wrong. I was in the race, and saw all that happened. I can tell you that Gardner had to push his mount well into it to keep within striking distance of Papyrus. After turning into the straight at Tattenham Corner, Pharos was fading away under Gardner, and he had to shake him up to keep close enough to Donoghue so that at the crucial moment he could come with his run. I think that Pharos ran, and Gardner rode, the race of his life, and that he extracted every ounce out of Lord Derby's horse. Put Papyrus and Pharos together over the same mile and a half, and I am satisfied in my mind that Papyrus would beat him every time.'

I am rather anticipating that historic race, however. In his first season Pharos won just short of £5,000. Other victories for the stable were gained by Spithead, Stanislaus, and the useful two-year-old Moabite, by Phalaris-Whitewash, who added £1,940 to the stable's winnings.

A newcomer of which reference must be made was Alienor, a chestnut filly, by Swynford-Eleanor M., who won one race in eleven attempts, but won that race at Ascot, beating Leighon Tor, and was perhaps a trifle lucky to do so.

Another was Dane's Voe, a chestnut colt by Swynford-Anchora who, in spite of his beautiful breeding, did not quite realise expectations. He won the Paddock Maiden Plate, at Haydock, a two-year-old plate, at Redcar, and the September Nursery, at Alexandra Park, in eight attempts, and was subsequently sold and went to the enrichment of the Australian stud.

An own sister was The Downs, who won the St. George's Stakes, at Liverpool Summer Meeting, and the August Maiden Plate, at Leicester – two wins in fourteen attempts.

Other minor victories of the year included that of Fordingbridge, a most disappointing filly and not too reliable, who took the Halnaker Plate at Goodwood, and was subsequently sold to Sir Charles Hyde, for whom, I believe, she won one race.

Highbrow, by Harry of Hereford-Collet Monte, also won three races – the Great National Breeders' Stakes, the Scottish Derby, the Haydock Autumn handicap, and the Lancashire Handicap, whilst Silurian took the Breeders' St. Leger, at the Derby Summer Meeting, was second to Royal Lancer, in the Doncaster St. Leger, and was subsequently exported.

It would be unfair not to mention the gallant fight which Silurian put up against Happy Man, in the Ascot Gold Cup of this year. He was receiving 4lb. from the old horse, and it was only by a short head that he was beaten.

Passing over the victories of such horses as Burnt Sienna, who won the Downe Nursery of 1,000 sovs., at Manchester, we come to the beginning of the 1923 racing season, which ended with his lordship at the head of the list of winning owners, though curiously enough, and for a reason which will be explained, George Lambton was only third in the list of winning trainers.

He was not only the winning owner but also the winning breeder, with £39,275 to his credit, of which that great sire Swynford put up a total of £37,897. A large slice of Lord Derby's winnings came through the medium of Tranquil, who started her three-year-old career by winning the Berkshire Three-year-old Handicap, at Newbury Spring Meeting, starting at 7 to 1. She next won the One Thousand Guineas from Cos, Shrove, and thirteen others, starting favourite. But at Epsom the failure of Pharos was accentuated by Tranquil's running unplaced to Brownhylda, Shrove and Teresina. For this race she was favourite.

Evidently she had gone off, for at Ascot she finished unplaced behind Paola, Teresina, and the King's Lady Feo, in the Coronation Stakes. All was not well with Tranquil, and George Lambton grew more and more worried as St. Leger day approached. Thinking the matter over, he decided that Tranquil was not thriving as she should on the Newmarket training ground, and he took the bold and generous step of advising Lord Derby to send Tranquil to Charles Morton, Jack Joel's trainer, at Wantage.

Lord Derby demurred, for he felt that if any credit was to be had out of a victory in the St. Leger, it should go to George Lambton; but his trainer insisted, and eventually Tranquil was sent off to Wantage, and on the new ground she shook off her staleness and progressed so favourably that when she was delivered at the post on St. Leger day, she represented nearer an even-money chance than the 100 to 9 that was offered against her.

Papyrus, Parth, and Teresina were opposed to her, whilst in the beaten division were Twelve Pointer, Ellangowan – the winner of the Two Thousand Guineas, and Eastern Monarch. Papyrus started a very hot favourite, but Tranquil, after making most of the running, won comfortably by two lengths.

Though she was subsequently beaten for the Jockey Club Stakes, at the First October Meeting, Tranquil won the Newmarket Oaks, the Jockey Club Cup, the Liverpool St. Leger, giving Twelve Pointer two pounds and a head beating, and starting at 11 to 10 against.

She won in stakes in her second season £20,807 including the £100 which goes to the third in the Jockey Club Stakes. It was a good St. Leger week for Lord Derby, for Silurian took the Doncaster Cup, after winning the Queen's Handicap, at Kempton Park, and subsequently won the Seventy-fourth Triennial Produce Stakes, at the First October Newmarket Meeting. With his second to Happy Man I have already dealt.

The course of Pharos this year was not as smooth as it might have been. He commenced badly by being beaten by Darrach and Portumna, for the Pontefract Plate, in the spring. The course was a quagmire.

He won the Hastings Plate, and the March Stakes, at Newmarket, and after his second in the Derby took the Royal Stakes, at Newbury Summer Meeting, and probably ran the finest race of his three-year-old career in the Cambridgeshire, which was won by Verdict.

In all, Pharos won £3,173 in stakes during his second season, and the luck of racing was never better exemplified than by the fact that his stable companion, Moabite, who was infinitely inferior, totalled up in the same season the important sum of £4,491.

LORD DERBY'S RACING TRIUMPH

A Memorable Day on Epsom Downs

THOUGH the year 1924 was not to see Lord Derby at the head of the winning owners, it saw the fulfilment of his ambition, and, indeed, as the King very rightly said in his telegram to the Press Club, 'the ambition of every owner' – in winning the Derby Stakes.

Sansovino is one of those horses that appeared in the bookmakers' winter lists on the 20 to 1 mark. He had certainly won the Gimcrack Stakes, and his only other race as a two-year-old; but, then, so many horses of his age go into winter quarters with an unbeaten certificate, but are not regarded with any confidence in relation to their classic engagements.

Sansovino had won at Goodwood unexpectedly when he was not ready – it is an open secret that Mr. Lambton expected to win the race with Sunstone, Mrs. Arthur James' horse, which subsequently developed into a first-class sprinter. Nor, in the early part of the year, did Sansovino shape like a 'smasher'. He was obviously a useful horse, but it was not until the spring that the most astute of the horse-watchers at Newmarket, seeing him galloping, recognised that in this horse Lord Derby had something out of the ordinary.

Mr. Lambton would not hurry any kind of animal, but a son of Swynford least of all. He is one of those who believe that the best course to take is to allow a horse to develop naturally, and not by any artifice or trick of training to bring him to a 'false best' before his time. Sansovino, however, is one of the early Swynfords. His success as a two-year-old was a little unusual in progeny of that stock, and it was not long before the master of Stanley House saw that he had got something very much out of the ordinary.

Sansovino, contrary to general expectation, made his three-year-old debut at Birmingham, in a £176 sweepstakes. He had against him Rugeley, who was giving him eleven pounds, and Vaudricourt, on the same mark as himself, and the field was considered so mediocre that the fielders asked for 5 to 1, in spite of the fact that Rugeley had only a week before won the Thatcham Long Distance Handicap, at Newbury, beating such horses as Brisl – a good winner, although disqualified, of the Newbury Cup – Boddam, who was second in the Metropolitan, and Forseti. Forseti finished second in a bumping race, and was giving Rugeley twenty-four pounds. Vaudricourt subsequently developed into a very good second-class handicapper.

Sansovino only won by a head, and on this performance some of his staunchest friends wavered in their allegiance. There were others, however, who thought that Sansovino had done remarkably well, and this view was supported when, later, Rugeley came out and cantered away in the Chester Cup.

'Lord Derby's horse did not run in the Guineas, and made his next appearance in the Newmarket Stakes – a race which he should undoubtedly have won. Hurstwood finished a neck in front of Salmon Trout, the subsequent winner of the St. Leger, and Sansovino was a head behind. The fourth horse was Bright Night, who was unlucky not to win the Two Thousand Guineas, and the fifth Polyphontes, the subsequent winner of the Eclipse Stakes.

When he had beaten Rugeley, Sansovino had alienated many of his friends. His defeat by Hurstwood brought them back to his standard. Nevertheless, Sansovino drifted a little in the betting, and a week before the Derby was decided 100 to 7 could have been had about him.

The spring and the early summer brought terrible weather to the training fields. Rain fell incessantly, and the Spring Meeting at Epsom, especially on City and Suburban day, will long be remembered by racegoers as the worst that Epsom races have known. It most effectively stopped Pharos winning the City and Suburban, and probably had a lot to do with Sierra Leone's failure in the Great Metropolitan Stakes.

For those owners who had a Derby candidate, the months preceding the race must have been a time of trial and agony. Mr. Alec Taylor has some of the best gallops in the world at Manton, and even these were at times waterlogged; and probably the only stables which were indifferent to the weather were those in Sussex, where the gallops are usually along the top of the downs, and are, in consequence, naturally drained.

Mr. Lambton was fortunate in having in his stable, and in training, Tranquil, the winner of the previous year's St. Leger, but, good a mare as she was, Sansovino was going just as well as she at exercise, and in all the sharp gallops the filly had her work cut out to shake off the attentions of the big-boned son of Swynford.

Tranquil was brought out at Haydock Park in a little race, presumably to discover whether she was in form and was capable of trying Lord Derby's hope. She came out at Haydock Park, in the Copeland Sweepstakes of 197 sovs., and although she was only opposed by rags – with the exception of Gyroscope – she won in a hack canter by five lengths from Goldsmith, to whom she was giving thirty-three pounds, with Tudor King five lengths farther off, and Gyroscope last. In all circumstances the Ring was unusually generous in asking no more than 9 to 4. It was her only race of 1924, and after the preparation of Sansovino she was, I believe, retired to stud.

Mr. Lambton was not dependent alone on this 'line'. He had a useful horse in Live Wire, the property of Lord Wolverton, who had won a three-year-old handicap at Alexandra Park, and the Union Jack Stakes, at Liverpool. He had another Liverpool winner in Dunmow, one of Lord Derby's; whilst Sierra Leone was in a position to confirm the form with Rugeley, Lord Derby's gelding having finished second three lengths behind that horse in the Chester Cup, with a number of good stayers in the rear.

The actual details of Sansovino's Derby trial are not for the moment available, nor is it desirable that they should be, since the horse is still in training; but I believe I am correct in saying that he carried only a few pounds less than Tranquil and beat the mare cleverly. The owner who is satisfied with his trials, or who attaches too much importance to the wonderful things which his horse does on the Rowley Mile trial-ground, is asking for many disappointments, and at least one shock. Neither Lord Derby nor the genius who trains for him thought, as a result of Sansovino's gallop, that the Derby Stakes were practically in the coffers of Stanley House. Two wise men, experienced in the vicissitudes of the Turf, they did no more than express a confident hope that the luck of the Earls of Derby in this race would be at last broken.

They did not, however, keep their hopes to themselves. Lord Derby told his friends that he thought he had one of the best, if not the best, horse he had ever owned in his stable; and wherever opportunity offered he was very open and frank about the success of Sansovino.

He himself does not bet, and he is usually so anxious to prevent people who cannot afford to lose money from reckless wagering, that he never failed, when he expressed his hope, to draw attention to the condition of the ground and the unfavourable prospects of the weather. This latter was going from bad to worse. Run your eyes back through the record of the racing of 1924, and under almost every meeting you will find the word 'soft' or 'heavy', which indicates the state of the course.

The Epsom Spring Meeting was merely an intelligent anticipation of what the weather would be like on Derby Day.

'I have the best trainer in England, but he has not taught Sansovino how to swim,' said Lord Derby. And really it looked as though this accomplishment must be mastered by any horse who hoped to swim past the judge. Monday of Derby week was wet. Tuesday, when the meeting opened, was even wetter. It rained during the evening, and the dawn of Derby Day was grey and moist. I saw his Highness the Aga Khan in the early morning, gloomily surveying the quagmire through which the horses must run.

'Diophon will never get through this!' he said despairingly; and most of the other owners had the same view.

There was, however, some encouragement for the Stanley House party. On the Tuesday, the last race of the day, the Molesey Handicap, over one and a half miles, had been won by Dunmow from this stable, in fairly good time, remembering the heavy condition of the going. Curiously enough, this useful handicapper, who was a stone and more behind Sansovino, had covered the Derby course in the time that it took Baltimore to win the Derby of 1897, and only a little less time than the distance covered by such good performers as Flying Fox, Orby, Ard Patrick, and Diamond Jubilee. It was, in fact, more than two seconds faster than Sansovino's time on the following day.

Remembering the character of the day, and the immense physical discomfort which surely awaited the crowd on the hill, the attendance was phenomenal. It was as though England had decided that the Derby luck was to be broken, and that they must be there to participate in and cheer the triumph.

It was a day of great anxiety for those responsible for the upkeep of the Epsom track. The Downs are common land; there are rights of way across the course in several places, and the heavily laden charabancs had already begun to churn up the turf long before the bell rang for the first race.

The hill was covered with people; big London omnibuses stood in phalanx along the course; and by the time the first race was set for decision the appearance of the course where the buses had passed was a little alarming. I went and had a look at Sansovino before the race, and if ever there was a horse designed for mudlarking, it was he.

'He is more like a Grand National than a Derby horse,' was the comment one heard. But my own view then, as it is now, was that in his strong frame were reproduced, sometimes with a coarse touch, all the finest qualities of his sire. And if he is not the champion stallion of his time, I shall be very much surprised.

It was raining when the horses went to the post, and the condition of the turf was incomparably worse than ever it had been on Epsom Downs.

All the morning money had been coming to the Ring for Sansovino, and he shrank gradually in price until he was a firm favourite at 9 to 2, and that difficult to back. In spite of the going, Diophon was also expected; whilst that rather disappointing horse, Tom Pinch, Lord Woolavington's hope, had a great following.

After a breakaway, the field was despatched to a good start, Dawson City going ahead of Arausio (a sprinter), Defiance (a bad horse), and Polyphontes (who was by no means at his best), with Sansovino in the middle-rear division. Weston's orders were simple: 'Don't get shut in,' said Mr. Lambton laconically; and it was probably his anxiety to carry out these orders which made him ride what, in my opinion, was not the best race of his life.

At the top of the hill he rushed Sansovino to within striking distance of the leader, which was still Dawson City. Coming down to Tattenham Corner, Sansovino lay second, with St. Germans, Polyphontes, Hurstwood, and Salmon Trout in attendance.

The moment the field turned into the straight, the white cap was distinguished through the drizzle, ahead of the beaten Dawson City, and thence onwards to the winning-post, Sansovino galloping like a lion, drew away from his field to win in a hack canter from St. Germans.

It was an hour of triumph for the Stanleys. After more than a hundred years an Earl of Derby had won the race that his ancestor had initiated. It is fitting that these recollections of Lord Derby's racing career should end upon this triumphant note. He is, for the moment, relieved of the cares of office; but he is the type of man who is superior to the caprices and intrigues of the political underworld. To him the letters '1924' will not be associated with the success of one political party or another, but with the victory of Sansovino, and the magnificent justification of his racing policy. In our great world of sport he will find a loyalty which is unknown in the field of political endeavour; and Sansovino and his owner will be remembered when the little-part men who loom so largely now are forgotten.

THE SHORT
STORIES

WHITE STOCKINGS

JOHN TREVOR was not a jealous man. He told himself this a dozen times; he told Marjorie Banning only once.

'Jealous!' she flamed, and then gaining control of her anger; 'I don't quite understand you. What do you mean by jealous?'

Jack felt and looked uncomfortable.

'Jealous, of course, is a silly word to use, but,' he blundered, 'what I mean is suspicious – '

He checked himself again.

They were sitting in the park under an expansive elm, and though not far from the madding crowd, the crowd was sufficiently removed for its madding qualities to be minimised to a negligible quantity. There were within sight exactly three courting couples, a nurse with a perambulator, a policeman, and a few playing children.

'What I mean to say is,' said Jack desperately, 'I trust you, dear, and well, I don't want to know your secrets, but – '

'But –?' she repeated coldly.

'Well, I merely remark that I have seen you three times driving in a swagger motorcar – '

'A client's car,' she said quietly.

'But surely the dressing of people's hair does not occupy all the afternoon and evening,' he persisted. 'Really, I'm awfully sorry if I'm bothering you, but it is a fact that whenever I've seen you it has been on the days when you have told me you could not come to me in the evening.'

She did not answer immediately.

He was making it very hard for her, and she resented, bitterly resented, not only his doubt and the knowledge that in his eyes her movements were suspicious, but that she could offer no explanation.

She resented most of all the justification which her silence gave to him.

'Who has been putting those ideas into your head?' she asked. 'Lennox Mayne?'

'Lennox!' he snorted. 'How ridiculous you are, Marjorie! Lennox would not dream of saying anything against you, to me or anybody else. Lennox is very fond of you – why, Lennox introduced me to you.'

She bit her lips thoughtfully. She had excellent reasons for knowing that Lennox was very fond of her, fond in the way that Lennox had been of so many chance-met shop-girls, and that she also was a shop-girl brought that young man's admiration into a too-familiar category.

She was employed at a great West End hairdresser's, and hated the work; indeed, hated the work more than the necessity for working. Her father, a small provincial doctor, had died a few years before, leaving her and her mother penniless. A friend of the family had known the proprietor of Fennett's and old Fennett was in need of a secretary. She had come to what Lennox Mayne crudely described as the 'woman's barbers' in that capacity. From secretary she had passed to a more practical side of the business, for the old man, a master of his craft, had initiated her into the mysteries of 'colour culture' – an artless euphemism.

'I'm awfully sorry that I've annoyed you,' she said primly, as she got up, 'but we shop-girls have our duties, Jack.'

'For heaven's sake, don't call yourself a shop-girl,' he snapped. 'Of course, dear, I quite accept your explanation, only why make a mystery of it?'

Suddenly she slipped her arm in his.

'Because I am paid to make a mystery of it,' she said, with a smile. 'Now take me to Fragiana's, for I'm starving.'

Over the meal they returned to the subject of Lennox.

'I know you don't like him,' said Jack. 'He really is a good fellow, and, what is more, he is very useful to me, and I cannot afford to lose useful friends. We were at Rugby together, but, of course, he was always a smarter chap than I. He has made a fortune, while I am struggling to get together the necessary thousand that will enable me to introduce you to the dinkiest little suburban home – '

She put her hand under the table and squeezed his.

'You're a darling,' she said, 'but I hope you will never make your money as Lennox has made his.'

He protested indignantly, but she went on, with a shake of her head: 'We hear queer stories, we dyers of ladies' faded locks,' she said, 'and Lennox is awfully well known in London as a man who lives by his wits.'

'But his uncle – ' he began.

'His uncle is very rich, but hates Lennox. Everybody says so.'

'That is where you're wrong,' said Jack triumphantly. 'They have been bad friends, but now they are reconciled. I was dining with Lennox last night, when you were gadding around in your expensive motor-car – I didn't mean that unpleasantly, dear – anyway, I was dining with him, and he told me that the old man was most friendly now. And what is more,' he lowered his voice confidentially, 'he is putting me in the way of making a fortune.'

'Lennox?' said the girl incredulously, and shook her head. 'I can imagine Lennox making a fortune for himself, or even dazzling unsophisticated maidens with golden prospects, but I cannot imagine him making a fortune for you.'

He laughed.

'Has he ever tried to dazzle you with golden prospects?' he bantered, but she avoided the question.

She and Lennox Mayne had met at the house of a mutual friend, and then they had met again in the park, as she and Jack were meeting, and Lennox had discovered a future for her which had certain material advantages and definite spiritual drawbacks. And then one Sunday, when he had taken her on the river, they had met Jack Trevor, and she had found it increasingly easy to hold at bay the philanthropist.

They strolled back to the park as the dusk was falling, and, entering the Marble Arch gate, they passed an untidy, horsey little man, who touched his hat to Jack and grinned broadly.

'That is Willie Jeans,' said Jack, with a smile. 'His father was our groom in the old Royston days. I wonder what he is doing in London?'

'What is he?' she asked curiously.

'He is a tout.'

'A tout?'

'Yes; a tout is a man who watches racehorses. Willie is a very clever watcher. He works for one of the sporting papers, and, I believe, makes quite a lot of money.'

'How queer!' she said, and laughed.

'What amuses you?' he asked in surprise, but she did not tell him.

*   *   *

The man who sprawled motionless along the top of the wall had certain strange, chameleon-like characteristics. His mottled green coat and his dingy-yellow breeches and gaiters so completely harmonised with the ancient wall and its overhanging trees, that nine passers-by out of ten would have failed to notice him. Happily for his peace of mind, there were no passers-by, the hour being seven o'clock on a sunny May morning. His elbows were propped on a patch of crumbling mortar, a pair of prismatic glasses were glued to his eyes, and on his face was a painful grimace of concentrated attention.

For twenty minutes he had waited in this attitude, and the stout man who sat in the car drawn up some distance along the road sighed patiently. He turned is head as he heard the descent of the watcher.

'Finished?' he asked.

'Huh,' replied the other.

The stout man sighed again and set the rattling machine running towards the village.

Not until they were on the outskirts of Baldock did the dingy watcher regain his speech.

'Yamen's lame,' he said.

The stout man, in his agitation, nearly drove the car on to the sidewalk.

'Lame?' he repeated incredulously.

Willie nodded.

'He went lame when the gallop was halfway through,' he said. 'He'll win no Derby.'

The fat man breathed heavily.

They were brothers, Willie the younger, and Paul the elder, though there was no greater family resemblance between the pair than there is between a rat and a comfortable hen.

The car jerked to a stop before the Baldock post office, and Willie got out thoughtfully. He stood for some time meditating upon the broad pavement, scratching his chin and exhibiting unexpected signs of indecision. Presently he climbed back into the car.

'Let's go down to the garage and get some juice on board,' he said.

'Why?' asked the astounded brother. 'I thought you were going to wire – '

'Never mind what you thought,' said the other impatiently; 'go and load up with petrol. You can take me to London. The post office won't be open for half an hour.'

His stout relation uttered gurgling noises intended to convey his astonishment and annoyance.

As the rattling car came back to the Stevenage road, Willie condescended to explain.

'If I send a wire from here, it might be all over the town in a few minutes,' he said libellously. 'You know what these little places are, and Mr. Mayne would never forgive me.'

Lennox Mayne was the principal source of the tout's income. Though he had a few other clients, Willie Jeans depended chiefly upon the honorarium which he received from his opulent patron.

Mr. Jeans' profession was a curious one. He was what is described in the sporting press as a 'man of observation', and he had his headquarters at Newmarket. But there are great racing establishments outside of the headquarters of the Turf, and when his chief patron required information which could not be otherwise secured, Mr. Jeans travelled afar to the Wiltshire Downs, to Epsom, and elsewhere, in order to gain at first hand knowledge of certain horses' well-being.

'It was a bit of luck,' he mused as he went along. I don't suppose there is another man in England who could have touted old Greyman's horses. He usually has half a dozen men patrolling along the road to see that nobody sneaks over the wall.'

Stuart Greyman owned a large estate on the Royston road, which was peculiarly adapted for so furtive and secretive a man, for a high wall surrounded the big park wherein his horses were trained, and his staff was loyalty itself.

From the other stables it is possible to secure valuable information through the judicious acquaintance of a stable-lad, but Greyman either payed his staff too well to allow of that kind of leakage, or he showed a remarkable discrimination in employing his servants. And in consequence the old man was something of a terror to the ring. He produced unexpected winners, and so well kept was his secret that until the race was over, and the money began to roll back from the starting-price offices, there was not the slightest hint that the winner was 'expected'. In consequence, he enjoyed the luxury of long prices, and every attempt that had been made to tout his horses had hitherto been unsuccessful.

Willie's gratification was, therefore, natural, and his success a little short of miraculous.

The dust-stained car came to a stop in a decorous London square, and an outraged butler who answered the door hesitated for some considerable time before he announced the visitors.

Lennox Mayne was at breakfast, a sleek-looking young man, who was less disconcerted than his butler at the spectacle of the untidy Mr. Jeans.

'Sit down,' he said curtly, and when the visitors obeyed and the butler had closed the door – 'Well?'

Willie poured forth his story, and Lennox Mayne listened with a thoughtful frown.

'The old devil!' he said softly, and not without admiration; 'the wicked old devil!'

Willie agreed on principle that Stuart Greyman was all and more than his loving nephew had described him, but was puzzled to know why Mr. Greyman was more particularly devilish that morning than any other.

Lennox sat for a moment deep in thought, and then –

'Now, Jeans, you understand that this is a secret. Not a whisper of Yamen's lameness must leak out. I might tell you that ten minutes ago my uncle rang me up from Baldock to say that he had galloped Yamen and he had pulled up fit.'

'What!' said the indignant Willie. 'Why, that horse is as lame – '

'I don't doubt it,' interrupted his employer, 'but Mr. Greyman has a good reason for putting it about that Yamen is sound. He has heavily backed the horse to win the Derby, and he wants time to save his money. What other horses were in the gallop?'

'I don't know his horses very well,' explained Willie, 'but the colt that made all the running was a smasher, if ever there was one. He simply carried the rest of the horses off their feet. I couldn't put the clock on him, but I know they were going a racing gallop.'

'You're sure it was Yamen that pulled up lame?'

'Sure, sir,' said the other emphatically. 'I saw him run at Ascot and at Newmarket last year, and there is no mistaking his white legs. You don't often see a brown horse with four white stockings.'

The other meditated.

'What kind of horse was it that won the gallop?'

'He was brown all over, not a speck of white on him.'

'H'm,' mused Mr. Mayne; 'that must be Fairyland. I must remember him. Thank you for coming,' he said, as he dismissed his visitors with a nod, 'and remember – '

'Mum's the word,' said Willie, as he folded up the two banknotes which his employer had pushed across the table.

Left alone, Mr. Lennox Mayne did some quick, intensive thinking. He had in his mind no thought of blaming his uncle. Lennox Mayne could not afford to condemn trickery or treachery in others, for he had not amassed a comfortable fortune by paying too strict an attention to the niceties of any known code of conduct. He was a gambler, and a successful gambler. He gambled on stocks, on horses, but in the main his success was due to backing and laying against human beings. In this latter respect he had made two *faux pas*. He had gambled not only upon the tolerance, but also upon the inferior intelligence of his maternal uncle, Stuart Greyman. He had used information given to him in secret by that reticent man, and, to his consternation, had been detected, and there had been an estrangement which had lasted five years, and had apparently ended when old Greyman met him one day at lunch at the Carlton Grill and had gruffly notified his forgiveness.

'The old devil!' he murmured admiringly; 'he nearly sold me.'

For old Greyman had told him, again in confidence, to back Yamen for the Derby.

Lennox Mayne trusted no man, least of all the uncle whom he suspected of harbouring a grudge against him. Therefore, he had sent his tout to confirm the exalted story of the dark Yamen's amazing speed. Yamen had only run twice as a two-year-old. He had been carefully nursed for his classic engagements, and, at least, the story which the old man had told him was plausible.

So the old man was trying to catch him! Luckily, Lennox had not wagered a penny on the information which his uncle had brought him.

If Greyman had been one of his failures, no less had Marjorie Banning. There were times when Lennox Mayne irritably admitted that she had been the greatest failure of all. She had seemed so easy. She was just so circumstanced that the way seemed simple.

It was a coincidence that, as his mind dwelt upon her, the telephone bell rang shrilly and the voice of John Trevor greeted him.

He heard the name and made a wry face, but his voice was pleasant enough.

'Hallo, Jack! Certainly, come round. Aren't you working today? Good.'

He hung up the receiver and returned to his table. Jack Trevor! His eyes narrowed. He had not forgotten this innocent friend of his, and for ten minutes his mind was very busy.

Jack had a fairly good post in a City office, and just at that time the rubber trade was one of England's decaying industries, and his time was very much his own.

Lennox received him in his study, and pushed a silver box of cigarettes toward his visitor.

'What brings you west at this hour?' he asked. 'You'll stay to lunch?'

Jack shook his head.

'The fact is,' he blurted, 'I'm a bit worried, Lennox. It is about Marjorie.'

Lennox raised his eyebrows.

'What has Marjorie been doing?' he asked. 'Does she want to turn your hair a flaming gold?'

Jack smiled.

'Not so bad as that,' he said; 'but I know you are very fond of Marjorie. Lennox, you're a man of the world, whose advice is worth having, and – the fact is, I am worried like the devil about her.' He was silent for a long time, and Lennox watched him curiously. 'Either she has a mysterious friend or she has a mysterious job,' said Jack at last. 'Four times she has passed me in the street, in a most swagger car.'

'Alone?'

Jack nodded.

'Perhaps she was going to see a client,' suggested the other carelessly. 'You know, even women who own luxurious motor-cars need the service of a trained perruquier.'

'Even females who own luxurious motor-cars do not require the service of a perruquier from three in the afternoon until eleven at night,' said Jack grimly; 'and that is the time Marjorie has returned to her diggings. I know it was hateful to spy on her, but that is just what I've done. She is getting a lot of money. I had a chat with her landlady. I called in on the pretence that I called in to see Marjorie, and got her to talk about her, and she told me that she had recently changed a hundred-pound cheque.'

'H'm,' said Lennox. He was as puzzled as his friend. His agile brain was busy, and presently he said:

'There is certain to be a simple explanation, my dear chap, so don't worry. Marjorie is not flighty, whatever else she is. When are you going to get married?'

Jack shrugged his shoulders.

'Heaven knows,' he said. 'It is all very well for you to talk about marriage, because you're a rich man, but for me it means another twelve months of saving.'

'Have you fixed the sum on which you can get married?' asked Lennox, with a smile.

'A thousand pounds,' replied Jack, 'and I've got about six hundred towards it.'

'Then, my dear chap, I'll put you in the way of getting not a thousand, but ten thousand.'

Jack stared at him.

'What the dickens are you talking about?'

'I'm talking about the dark Yamen,' said Lennox, 'my uncle's horse. I told you the other day that I would make your fortune – I am going to do it.'

He got up, went to a table, and took up the morning paper, turning its pages.

'Here is the betting,' he said. 'One hundred to six, Yamen – and Yamen is as certain to win the Derby as you are to marry your nice little girl. I can get you ten thousand to six hundred, today – to-morrow the price may he shorter.'

'Good lord! I couldn't lose six hundred pounds,' gasped Jack, and the other laughed.

'If you knew how small a risk it was you wouldn't yammer like a sheep. I tell you this is money for nothing.'

'Suppose I had sixty pounds on it – '

'Sixty pounds?' sneered the other. 'My dear chap, what is the use of making money in pennies? Here is the chance of your lifetime, and, unless you are a lunatic, you will not miss it. Tomorrow the horse will be nearer six to one than sixteen, and you can lay out your money and stand to win a fortune at practically no risk to yourself.'

He spoke for half an hour on horses – of Yamen, its speed, its breeding – and Jack listened, fascinated.

'I'll ring up a bookmaker and put it on for you.'

'Wait, wait,' said Jack hoarsely, as the other reached for the telephone; 'it is a fearful lot of money to risk, Lennox.'

'And a fearful lot of money to win,' said the tempter. If he had had more time, he would have arranged the bet so that the six hundred pounds fell into his pocket, but that was impossible. Jack Trevor must be caught immediately or not at all – must be given no time to reflect or seek advice, and certainly no time to discover that Yamen was a cripple. The secret might leak out at any moment; a disgruntled stable-boy, a chance spy, a too-talkative veterinary surgeon – any of these might talk and the stable's secret would be revealed. The loss of six hundred might not prevent a contemptuous little hairdressing girl from marrying – it would certainly postpone the event.

'I'll do it,' said Jack, with a gasp, and listened as in a dream to his placid companion's voice.

'Put it to the account of Mr. John Trevor, Castlemaine Gardens . . . yes, I'll be responsible. Thank you.'

He hung up the receiver, and looked round at the other with a queer smile.

'I congratulate you,' he said softly, and Jack went back to the City, his head in a whirl, even the mystery of his fiancée's movements obscured by the tremendous realisation of his own recklessness.

Marjorie Banning heard the news and dropped into a twopenny park chair. Happily, the chair was there.

'You've put all the money on a horse?' she said hollowly. 'Oh, Jack!'

'But, my dear,' said Jack stoutly, 'the money is as good as mine, and all that Lennox said is true. The horse was one hundred to six yesterday and it is only eight to one today.'

'Oh, Jack!' was all she could say.

He had to find conviction for himself. He was miserably conscious of his own folly, and had cursed himself that he had ever listened to the voice of temptation.

'It is all right, Marjorie,' he said, with poorly simulated cheerfulness; 'the horse belongs to Lennox Mayne's uncle. He told Lennox that it is certain to win. Think what ten thousand pounds means, Marjorie, dear . . .'

She listened, unconvinced. She, who knew with what labour and sacrifice his little nest-egg had been gathered, who understood even more clearly than he what its loss would entail, could only sit with a blank sense of despair at her heart.

At that moment Mr. Lennox Mayne was experiencing something of her dismay, though the cause was a little different. Summoned by telegram, he who had been described as the 'Prince of Touts' – though a more untidy, unshaven, and uncomfortable prince had never borne such a title – had come poste-haste to Manchester Square, and whilst the grimy Ford, with its stout, hen-like driver, stood at the door, Mr. Willie Jeans fidgeted uneasily and endured, with such patience as he could command, the flow of his employer's abuse.

'You're a blundering jackass, and I was a fool to hire you,' stormed Lennox Mayne. 'What is the use of touting a horse if you're seen touting? I told you that you were not to let anybody know that you were connected with me, you drivelling fool, and you've been talking.'

'No, I ain't,' said the other indignantly. 'I never talk. Do you think I should be able to earn a living if I – '

'You've been talking. Listen to this.'

Lennox snatched up a letter from the table. 'This is from my uncle. Listen to this, you darned fool:

' "You are not satisfied with my information, it seems, but employ your tout to spy on my training. You can tell Mr. Willie Jeans from me that if ever he is again seen in or near my estate, he will get the biggest flogging he has ever had in his life." '

The following paragraph, which gave Stuart Greyman's opinion of his nephew, Lennox did not read.

'I never knew anybody saw me; there was nobody about when I was on the wall,' grumbled Mr. Jeans. 'I've earned my fifty, if ever a man has earned it.'

'You'll get no fifty from me,' said Lennox. 'I've given you as much money as you're entitled to and don't come near me again.'

When Mr. Willie Jeans joined his brother, he was in no amiable frame of mind.

'Where are we going now?' asked that placid man.

Willie suggested a place which has the easiest and most varied of routes, and his brother, who was not unused to these temperamental outbursts, held on his way, for their original destination had been Epsom. A policeman at Hyde Park raised a warning hand at the sight of the ramshackle machine, but Mr. Willie Jean's flivver was a 'private car' within the meaning of the Act, and they joined the resplendent procession of machines that were moving slowly through the park.

It was Fate that made the oil lubrication choke within a dozen paces of where two disconsolate lovers were sitting.

'What a queer car!' said the girl; 'and isn't that the man you saw the other day – the tout, did you call him?'

'Yes,' said Jack gloomily; 'that's the tout,' and then suddenly, 'I wonder if he knows?'

He rose and walked across to the man, and Willie touched his cap.

'Good-evening, Mr. Trevor.'

'Where are you going?' asked Jack.

'I'm going to Epsom, to watch the Derby gallops. Most of the horses are there now, but,' he grinned unpleasantly, 'not Yamen.'

'Why isn't he there?' asked Jack, with a sickening of heart, for he instinctively recognised the hostility which the little man displayed toward the horse on whose well-being so much depended.

'Because he'll never see a racecourse – that's why,' said the other savagely.

'He'll never see a racecourse? What do you mean?' asked Jack slowly.

'He is lame,' said the little man. I hope you haven't backed him?' he asked suddenly.

Jack nodded.

'Come over here,' he said. 'This is pretty bad news I've heard, Marjorie,' he said. 'Jeans says that Yamen is lame.'

'That's right,' nodded the tout, 'as lame as old Junket. That is another one of Mr. Greyman's. You remember him, sir, he always looked as if he was winning in a canter and then went lame in the last hundred yards.'

'I don't know much about horses,' said Jack. 'I want you to tell me about Yamen. How long has he been lame?'

'Three days,' said the little man. 'I have been touting him for a week. It broke down in the winding-up gallop.'

'But does Mr. Greyman know?'

'Mr. Greyman!' said the little man scornfully; 'why, of course he knows. He didn't let on to Lennox Mayne but I told Lennox Mayne and a fat lot of thanks I got for it.'

'When did you tell him?' asked Jack, going white.

'The day before yesterday.'

'Then Lennox Mayne knew!'

Jack was bewildered, shocked beyond expression.

'It can't be true,' he said. 'Lennox would never – '

'Lennox Mayne would give away his own aunt.' said Willie Jeans contemptuously.

'Was it Lennox Mayne who persuaded you to back this horse?' asked the girl.

Jack nodded.

'You are sure Yamen is lame?'

'I swear to it. I know Yamen as I know the back of my hand,' said the little man emphatically. 'The only horse with four white stockings in the Baldock stables – '

'Baldock!' The girl was on her feet, staring. 'Baldock, did you say?'

'That's right, miss.'

'Who lives there?' she asked quickly. 'What is his name?'

'Greyman.'

'What sort of man is he?'

'He is an old man, about sixty, grey-haired, and as hard as a nail. A cunning old devil he is, too; I'll bet he's too cunning for Lennox Mayne.'

She was silent a long time after the little man had gone on his shaky way, and then most unexpectedly, most surprisingly, she asked:

'Will you take me to see the Derby, Jack?'

'Good lord! I didn't expect you'd be interested,' he said, 'and it will be an awful crush.'

'Will you take me? You can hire a car for the day, and we would see the race from the roof. Will you take me?'

He nodded, too dumbfounded to speak. She had never before evinced the slightest interest in a horse-race.

★ ★ ★

Some rumour of the dark Yamen's infirmity must have crept out, for on the morning of the race the horse was quoted amongst the twenty-five-to-one brigade, and hints of a mishap appeared in the morning Press.

'We hear,' said the *Sporting Post*, 'that all is not well with Mr. Greyman's dark candidate, Yamen. Perhaps it is wrong to described him as 'dark', since he has already run twice in public, but until his name appeared prominently in the betting list, very few had the slightest idea that the colt by Mandarin–Ettabell had any pretensions to classic events. We hope for the sake of that good sportsman, Mr. Stuart Greyman, that rumour has been exaggerated.'

Marjorie had never been to a race-meeting before, and possibly even the more sedate meetings would have astonished her, but Epsom was a revelation. It was not so much a race-meeting as a great festival and fair. The people frightened her. She tried, as she stood on the roof of the car, to calculate their number. They blackened the hills, they formed a deep phalanx from one end of the course to the other, they packed the stands and crowded the rings, and between races filled the course. The thunderous noise of them, their ceaseless movement, the kaleidoscope of colour, the booths and placards, even more than the horses, held her interest.

'There are all sorts of rumours about,' said Jack, returning from his tour of discovery. 'They say that Yamen doesn't run. The papers prepared us for that. I am horribly afraid, dear, I've been a fool.'

She bent down over the edge of the roof and took his hand, and to his amazement he discovered she had left a paper in it.

'What's this – a banknote? Are you going to have a bet?'

She nodded.

'I want you to make a bet for me,' she said.

'What are you backing?'

'Yamen,' she replied.

'Yamen!' he repeated incredulously, and then looked at the note. It was for a hundred pounds. He could only stare helplessly at her.

'But you mustn't do this, you really mustn't.'

'Please,' she insisted firmly.

He made his way to Tattersall's ring and after the race preliminary to the Derby had been run, he approached a bookmaker whose name he knew. The numbers were going up when he got back to her.

'I got two thousand to a hundred for you,' he said – 'and I nearly didn't.'

'I should have been very angry with you if you hadn't,' said Marjorie.

'But why – ' he began, and then broke off as the frame of the number board went up. 'Yamen is running,' he said.

Nobody knew better than the girl that Yamen was running. She watched the powder-blue jacket in the preliminary parade and caught a glimpse of the famous white stockings of Mandarin's son as he cantered down to the post. Her arm was aching with the labour of holding the glasses, but she never took them off the powder-blue jacket until the white tape flew upward, and the roar of two hundred thousand voices cried in unison:

'They're off!'

The blue jacket was third as the horses climbed the hill, fourth on the level by the railway turn, third again as the huge field ran round Tattenham Corner into the straight and then a strident voice from a nearby bookmaker shouted:

'Yamen wins for a pony!' as the dark Yamen took the lead and won, hard held, by three lengths.

★ ★ ★

'I don't know how to begin the story,' she said that night. They were dining together, but Marjorie was hostess.

'It really began about a month ago, when an old gentleman came into the shop and saw Mr. Fennett, the proprietor. They were together about ten minutes, and then I was sent for to the private office. Mr. Fennett told me that the gentleman had a special commission, and he wanted an expert to undertake some dying work. I thought at first it was for himself, and I was rather sorry that a nice-looking old gentleman should want to interfere with his beautiful white hair. I didn't actually know for what purpose I was required until the next week, when his car came for me, and I was driven to Baldock. And then he told me. He asked me if I had brought the bleaching and dyeing material with me, and when I told him that I had, he let me into the secret. He said he was very fussy about the colour of his horses and he had a wonderful horse with white legs, and that he objected to white legs. He wanted me to dye his legs a beautiful brown. Of course, I laughed at first, it was so amusing, but he was very serious and then I was introduced to this beautiful horse – who was the most docile client I have ever treated,' she smiled.

'And you dyed his legs brown?'

She nodded.

'But that was not all. There was another horse whose legs had to be bleached. Poor dear, they will be bleached permanently, unless he dyes them again. I know now, but I didn't know then, that it was a horse called Junket. Every few days I had to go to Baldock and renew the dye and the bleach. Mr. Greyman made it a condition with Mr. Fennet that my commission should be kept a secret even from the firm, and, of course, I never spoke about it, not even to you.'

'Then when I saw you in the car – '

'I was on my way to Baldock to dye and bleach my two beautiful clients,' she laughed. 'I know nothing about racehorses, and I hadn't the slightest idea that the horse I had dyed was Yamen. In fact, until Willie Jeans mentioned the word 'Baldock', I had not connected the stable with the Derby.

'The morning after I left you I had an engagement to go to Baldock to remove the dye. Mr. Greyman had told me that he had changed his mind, and that he wanted the horse to have white legs again. And then I determined to speak to him and tell him just how you were situated. He told me the truth, and he swore me to secrecy. He was reconciled with Lennox, and had told him all about Yamen. And then he discovered that Lennox did not believe him, and was having the horses watched. He was so angry that, in order to deceive his nephew's watcher, he had the horse's legs dyed, and gave the tout a chance of seeing poor old Junket with his bleached legs break down – as he knew he would. He told me he had backed Yamen to win him a great fortune.'

'So you, of all people on Epsom Downs, knew that Yamen would win?'

'Didn't I back him?' asked the dyer of legs.

THE GIRL WHO WON
AT EPSOM

WHEN Alicia Penton entered the chaste establishment of Max Brabazin in Holland Park Gardens, she did so after consultation with Tressa.

'Uncle is wholly impossible, and I wouldn't stay at Penton Court, not if I were the heiress to millions – which, as a matter of fact, my dear Tressa, I'm not.'

'You're rather young to be a governess,' murmured Tressa who, knowing all the circumstances, could not honestly advise her against the step. 'And besides, Ralph really isn't too bad.'

'Uncle Ralph is a smug,' said Alicia hotly. 'He hates everything I like and the other day he turned out a gardener who had worked for him for twenty years because he had a bet on the Lincolnshire Handicap! And when I told him I had a bet on every big race, he nearly threw a fit. He said that people who betted were either thieves or fools; they were people who were trying to get money for nothing. He said that cupidity and stupidity were the basis of all gambling, and then he said some horrible things about father – poor daddy did rather overrun the constable, as we know, but there's no reason why his own brother should sneer about his slow racehorses. But anyway, I'm going to this creature's perfectly awful house to teach. Brabazin and his wife are most impossible people, and the little boy has the manners of a pig – '

'It looks as though you're going to have quite a good time,' said Tressa. 'Don't you think it would be better if you stayed on at Penton Court and endured Ralph?'

Alicia shook her head.

'I can't,' she said emphatically. 'When he isn't talking about the evils of betting, he's talking about the excessive taxation which made him so poor that he'd have been obliged to leave Penton Court only, with his usual luck, somebody induced him to put five thousand pounds into an agency business – or at least he answered an advertisement or something of the sort – and he's been drawing fat dividends ever since. No, Tressa, I'm going to earn my living. The only thing I ask of you is that, when I am fired, or I hit the oleaginous Mr. Brabazin over the head, you give me a bed for two or three nights, until I find something better.'

She shivered. 'Penton Court is a palace of gloom at any time, but at the present moment it is a palace of horror.'

Since Penton Court went Methodist, for reasons best known to itself, in the enthusiastic days of Wesley's ministry, it had observed an attitude – no less – of personal conduct which may best be described as serious. Sir Ralph Penton had absorbed all the gloom religion had to impart, pictured hell in detail with the assurance of one who himself would never secure a closer inspection than the lofty crags of heaven afforded, revelled in the Book of Revelations, and found sheer joy in the Mysteries of Vessels which would be unsealed out of the Angel's Trump. He spoke familiarly of the great and sacred figures of Christianity; was, so you might think from his diction, much in God's confidence, moving his mind on even trivial matters.

Thus Sir Ralph knew positively that God did not like bridge at anything over 5d. a hundred. He did not approve of the Socialist Party. He abhorred strikes and the Sunday opening of cinemas. Aviation was directly contrary to the wisdom of providence; 'For,' said Sir Ralph with the emphasis of one who was enunciating an original theme, 'if it had been intended that man should fly, God would have given him wings.'

This was too excellent an illustration to devote to one unnatural habit. Sir Ralph also remarked on many occasions that, if men had been intended to smoke, God would have given him a chimney-pot instead of a head.

In what manner the deity would have acted on any occasion, however trifling, was no secret to Sir Ralph, and rightly, for he justified Voltaire's cynicism in that he had created God after his own image.

Sir Ralph was a tall man, broad of shoulder, bushy of beard. He stood well above six feet four. His conception of the saints, of apostles, of the big and bloodthirsty, holy figures of the Old Testament, was that they too were men of six feet odd, broad of shoulder, heavily bearded. He confessed that he had no desire to live contrary to their precepts and examples, and accordingly laid to their charge and upon them the responsibility for his own eccentricities of charity.

Twenty shillings in one pound – and not a penny more. His justice was depressing. He did that which was right in God's eyes, he said, and inferred that he shared vision with the Divinity.

He hated gambling, drinking, dancing and horse-racing, and found no hope of grace in the exponents of either vice.

Sir Ralph did not often come to the flat in Piccadilly Circus – it is a remarkable tribute to Tressa's catholicity of tastes and the wide range of her acquaintanceships that he came at all. Alicia Penton had been installed in the Brabazin household for two months when he called one afternoon, in time for tea, and had the good fortune to find Tressa alone. He grumbled over his cup at the high cost of living, at iniquitous taxations, at the extraordinary demands of agricultural workers: he complained bitterly of the Labour Government, and when he had finished, he asked gruffly:

'Have you any news of Alicia?'

'I believe she's very comfortable,' said Tressa. 'I had a note from her the other day, saying that she was getting on well.'

Sir Ralph grunted.

'It was no wish of mine that she should be earning her living,' he said. 'London to me is the very pit of the devil. It is filled with temptation for young and old. I find it difficult to walk along Piccadilly without meeting leering and wanton eyes – '

Tressa sighed wearily.

'My dear Ralph,' she said, with admirable patience, 'are you in the category of those curiously archaic individuals who believe that Piccadilly is the haunt of vice, and Leicester Square the breeding place of sin? You are twenty years behind the times! I think you must have been reading books on the subject, and I rather guess the book is out of print and was bought from one of the secondhand stalls. I have such a large circle of acquaintances that I can almost tell you the real haunts. Do you know that girls who are arrested in Leicester Square are taken to Bow Street and get a month, and that girls arrested in Lisle Street, which is just behind Leicester Square, go to Marlborough Street and are fined? In those circumstances do you imagine that Leicester Square would be filled with these undesirable creatures?'

'Happily, I know nothing about it,' said Sir Ralph hastily, getting off a subject which he regarded as so delicate that it might not be discussed except in the clouded privacy of a smoking-room and a respectable smoking-room at that. 'Anyway, London is horrible.'

'London is beautiful,' said Tressa calmly. 'Have you walked through Hyde Park when the daffodils are out, or when the rhododendron bushes are in bloom? If you haven't, you've missed something. Or have you looked southward across the lake in Green Park? Or driven down Kingsway in the early hours of the morning?'

'I haven't,' said Sir Ralph, and added: 'I have no desire to. I'm worried about Alicia,' he went on. 'I fear that her father's vices are inherited by that unfortunate girl. Do you know that I discovered that she was making surreptitious bets on a horse-race and, when I questioned her, she told me she always backed the horse in the Derby that ran fourth in the Guineas? Do you know that she won thirty pounds on an animal called Captain Kettle, or something of the sort?'

'She was lucky,' said Tressa wilfully. 'I backed the second!'

Sir Ralph made a little noise of disapproval.

'Is there a possibility of my seeing her?' he said at last. 'I shall be up next Wednesday.'

Tressa shook her head.

'I don't know,' she said, 'but I'll ask her to come.'

It so happened that the invitation was unnecessary, for things were happening in Holland Park Gardens. One bright spring morning Mr. Brabazin pushed back his chair from the desk. Incidentally he also pushed himself back for, at the moment, he was occupying the chair.

This feat constituted no small exhibition of what Mr. Brabazin described as his 'latent strength'; he was on the wrong side of sixteen stone. He was of middle height and hotly dressed. His purple tie, his claret socks and his russet shoes were all on the sultry side. His head was big and his hair well seccotined and brushed. As to his face, it was red and stout – he was one of those men who invariably perspire on the chin; his short, thick nose was retroussé and his sharp, dark eyes set close together under a somewhat blank and unnecessarily expansive forehead.

The 'den' – so described by him – in which he sat had been furnished by him 'to his taste'. These are the exact terms of his boast, so that the responsibility was all his. The carpet that covered the floor was an expensive Axminster, and the scheme of colour was comprehended in two shades of red, four of yellow, with a peacock-blue motif. The furniture was dark red leather. The walls were covered with a red and gold paper, the mantelpiece was of dark mahogany, the desk of varnished pine and that, I think, is a fairly charitable description of the den in which Brabazin sat when he was not occupying an even more beautiful office in Cockspur Street.

Photographs of beautiful actresses adorned the walls – each signed hilariously, familiarly or coyly, according to the temperament or the contract of the signer. There were two telephones in the den, a large painting of Ormonde, and a weedy girl who wore glasses was Mr. Brabazin's secretary, and was invariably addressed as 'Miss O.'

It is possible that she had another name, but in Mr. Brabazin's records there was no evidence of the fact.

'Miss O.,' snapped Max Brabazin.

The apologetic girl at the door clutched her notebook and pencil nervously and said in a pale voice:

'The young lady has come down, sir.'

Mr. Brabazin nibbled the forefinger of his clenched hand in thought.

'Show her in, Miss O.'

Mr. Brabazin settled back in his chair and waited the advent of 'the young lady' with that placid contentment which is the common property of gods and employers of labour who are about to discharge dispensable hands.

The door opened and Alicia came in. She was slim and pretty, plainly but neatly dressed, and she bore on her face that look of superiority which was very annoying to Mr. Brabazin.

'Well, Miss Penton,' he said briskly, 'so here you are! Will you
sit down? I shan't keep you long.'

He looked at his watch, for no valid reason, since the morning
was all his and he had no appointments within the next hour.
Possibly he wished her to appreciate the fact that he could give her
any time at all.

The girl seated herself on the edge of one of the chairs which
were ranged with geometrical precision all round the walls, and
waited.

'You have been with us for six months,' said Mr. Brabazin, 'and
I admit, Miss Penton, that I have nothing against you, your erudition
or your general conduct. It grieves me to part with you, but the
fact is, Miss Penton, my kid can't stand you any longer.'

He added this with a frank and hearty smile, accompanied by the
expressive out-throw of hands which was intended to neutralise the
undoubted offensiveness of his remarks.

'I'm very sorry, Mr. Brabazin,' said Alicia mildly, 'but Willie has
been rather trying.'

'All children are trying,' said Mr. Brabazin sententiously. 'I was
trying as a child, and probably you were too. Boys will be boys.'

'Some boys can be little fiends, Mr. Brabazin,' said the girl, and
Brabazin raised a pained and arresting hand.

'I will hear no word against my child,' he said, and his voice rose
to a bellow. 'Not a word, I tell you – you're simply the wrong kind
of governess, and my wife says – however, we won't quarrel.'

'I hope we won't,' said Alicia. 'But on the whole, I prefer you
more in a quarrelsome mood than in those tender moments when
you have invited me to spend my evening out with you at a little
Soho restaurant.'

Mr. Brabazin's neck went red, but before he could frame an
indignant retort, she went on:

'Certainly I have no quarrel with your child, who merely inherits
the peculiar qualities of his parent,' she said outrageously. 'Most of
the bookmakers I have known have been gentlemen.'

Mr. Brabazin was apoplectic with anger. He could pass over the
charge of not being a gentleman, but that his calling could be so
vulgarly described was beyond forgiveness.

'Let me tell you, miss,' he spluttered, 'that when you call me a
bookmaker you are going a bit too far. I am connected with an

eminent firm of commission agents, I admit, but that is neither here
nor there. We lay and we pay. Nobody can ever raise the finger of
scorn' – here he became incoherent, thrust a cheque towards her,
and pointed to the door. 'You are an ill-mannered young woman,'
he said, 'and if you apply to me for a reference – '

'Is it likely?' said the scornful Alicia and, going upstairs, super-
intended the removal of her trunk.

'I'm fired,' she announced as she came into Tressa's bedroom.
'And oh, Tressa, I'm a Christian martyr! What I've endured! I'm
going to stay a week with you, and I'll be able to go to the theatre,
and could you, like an angel, persuade the Olivers to let me have a
seat in their box at Epsom? I'm told Greek Bachelor is a certainty
for the City and Suburban!'

Tressa took off her horn-rimmed glasses – she had been reading
when the interruption came.

'I'm afraid there's one drawback to staying here: you can't very
well miss seeing your admirable relative. He's calling this afternoon.'

Alicia's face fell.

'Uncle Ralph?' she asked.

Tressa nodded.

'He's very anxious for you to go back to Penton Court.'

'I will do many things, but not that,' said the girl. 'I'll let him
take me to dinner at the Savoy – I'll even let him take me to see a
play. But go back to Penton Court I won't!'

This was the spirit which Sir Ralph encountered when he called
in the afternoon. He listened, his tight lips set, his virtuous eyes
half-closed, his immaculate finger-tips touching. When she finished
a little breathlessly:

'Alicia, I will put the matter to you plainly,' he said. 'I am, as
you know, childless, and you are my sole relative. Penton Court
will be yours, and an income, largely curtailed by the wretched
and inefficient government and reaching almost the vanishing point
under the present abominable administration. Providing you return
and take your place in county society, and promise never again to
indulge in the pernicious practices which – er – marred our relation-
ship. Quite by accident, I met Sir Bertram Oliver at my club, and
was appalled to learn that you intended going to a race-meeting on
Wednesday, that you had, in fact, begged a place in his box. That,
of course, I cannot allow.'

'My dear Uncle Ralph' – her tone was calm and decisive – 'I am going to Epsom on Wednesday and I am going to win a lot of money.'

'Ridiculous!' snorted Sir Ralph, and a light gleamed in the girl's eyes.

'If you think I am going to back the favourite, I agree it is ridiculous to take 7 to 4 about a horse that may not get more than a mile at racing pace. I've been talking to Johnnie Boulter, who's got a stable of horses at Newmarket, and he says that he's never known a Phalaris that could stay more than a mile. Now Greek Bachelor – '

'Greek grandmothers!' snapped Sir Ralph. 'Now listen to me, Alicia! Whether you win or lose at Epsom – '

'I shall win,' murmured his niece.

'Whether you win or lose at Epsom is wholly immaterial. I, happily, shall neither win nor lose. If you insist on working for your living, I will find you an opportunity. As you know, I have a large interest in the firm of Elvert, Card, Rice & Co., and I'll endeavour to secure a position for you, providing you agree to drop your ridiculous gambling – '

Alicia was staring at him.

'Uncle, do you ever bet?' she asked.

'Certainly not,' he replied scornfully. 'You know I don't. If I won or lost money by racing, I should certainly not be such a hypocrite as to object to your indulging in that disgraceful practice!'

Solemnly she put out her hand and grasped his warmly.

'Thank you,' she said.

Epsom Downs, with its banners, its mass movement, its roaring rings and queer air of unreality, was in a condition of hectic excitement when Alicia slipped out of the box and made her way down to the crowded Tattersall's ring. The crowd here was thick, for the runners in the City and Suburban were on their way to the post, and it was with some difficulty that she sidled up to a tall, saturnine man, who stood silently by the rails, a small betting book in his hand. He recognised her almost at once and lifted his hat.

'Good afternoon, Miss Penton,' he said, 'I hear you've left the governor?'

She nodded.

'I want to have a bet,' she said, and he frowned.

'I didn't know you went in for that sort of thing, miss,' he said. 'What do you want to back?'

'Can you tell me a horse that can't possibly win?'

He frowned at her again.

'Yes, I can tell you that,' he said, and named an outsider.

'I want ten pounds on that, please.'

'But you'll lose your money.'

'I want to lose my money, Mr. Rice. You *are* the senior partner of your firm, aren't you?'

The bookmaker shook his head.

'No, Miss Penton, the senior partner is Brabazin. We still keep the name of Elvert, Card, Rice & Co., for old associations' sake. Besides it is much more respectable. Very few people know that we are bookmakers at all. As a matter of fact, we'd have been out of business a few years ago, we had such a bad time, only Mr. Card managed to raise a little capital from some gentlemen in the country, which put us on our feet. Brabazin must have told you that?'

He took her ten pounds and put it in his pocket.

'You'll lose,' he warned her.

She shook her head.

'Whatever happens, I shall win,' said Alicia Penton.

She telephoned Penton Court that night and explained to the agonised Sir Ralph the exact character of the firm he had been financing.

'And didn't you know that a commission agent is a bookmaker?' she asked sweetly. 'Poor dear! And to think that all these years you have been drawing dividends from poor, deluded punters! What will you do, uncle – will you send the money back?'

'I must consider my position,' said Sir Ralph shakily.

'Will you consider mine?' she asked, in the same dulcet tone. 'You said if you won money over the City and Suburban you'd change your point of view. Well, you've won ten pounds of mine!'

When Alicia went back to Penton Court, the subject of Sir Ralph's investment was tacitly avoided. Until, one day, going into the study, she found him reading *The Sporting Life*, which he hastily concealed under his chair. And when, later that day, he asked her casually which was the best of the Aga Khan's three, she knew that the largest shareholder in the firm of Elvert, Card, Rice & Co., had not severed his connections with the firm.

THE CHRISTMAS CUP

OLONEL DESBORO was an easy-going man and, for himself,
did not greatly object to patched carpets, an odd-handled
knife or two, and chintz covers that had faded and thinned
through over-much washing. But he had no desire that Joan should
go through life in an environment of patches and make-shifts.

'He's a very nice fellow, Martin, but – ' He shook his head.

The big 'but' was put more definitely by Miss Æthel Bainton
later in the day, when Joan Desboro called at Matte Hall, a little too
early for the 'club' but in nice time to absorb from experienced 26,
the wisdom so vitally necessary to 21 and three months.

'Men,' said Æthel, with an air of finality, 'are naturally children.
They boast and they lie, and they mean no harm by it. Children.
They never grow up.' She said this in the manner of one who had
wrapped a clever thought in a gossamer of paradox.

The girl who was perched on the fender in Æthel Bainton's
sitting-room, sighed and knit her forehead in a tremendous frown.
She was more than pretty even in the searching light of a March
morning. Her figure was slim, every movement revealed a new and
pleasing grace; but she was no philosopher, and her views about
men were too concentrated to be of any use in a broad and general
conspectus of their merits.

To rich people like Æthel, philosophy comes as natural as purring
to a cat, but with the poor, philosophy is a painful exercise. And
the Desboros were so poor that they could not afford to hide the
fact.

'Mark is a little difficult,' she admitted reluctantly, 'but I don't
think you quite understand him, Æthel.'

'He's American,' said Æthel significantly, and when Joan murmured, 'Canadian', she ignored the distinction.

'He's a boaster and, of course, quite impossible,' said Æthel. 'We don't even know that he has any money. And he's not "county". We'd better be very careful.' She nodded ominously.

'Why?'

But the warning obliquely flung was not amplified, and there was really no reason why it should have been.

'Martin must be well off – he paid a thousand pounds for a horse,' said Joan with some spirit. A thousand pounds was an awful lot of money.

'Money for horses means nothing,' said the practical Æthel. 'Quite dreadful people buy horses. Of course he must have money – he does no work. Papa says he's probably living on his capital. And that can end only in bankruptcy.'

Not by candlelight or moonlight could Æthel Bainton be described as pretty. She had been 'Ethel' in the baptismal register, and 'Ethel' she would have been to the end of her days but for the advent of Ælfred Burdenlast, a young man of considerable musical attainments, but with no particular gift for earning his daily bread.

The association was of a transitory kind. He came, made love with a certain delicacy, was figuratively thrown on to the ash-pit by Mr. Bainton, and faded from human ken. Some say that he went to Hollywood and became a film star. He left an additional vowel in Æthel's name, and a heart which never again glowed to the music and banners of romance.

The Baintons were the Baintons of Braystone, in the county of Westshire. There was another branch in Northumberland, but nobody knew anything about them; how they ever got to Northumberland is a mystery.

Arthur Persimmin Bainton was very rich, an owner of 10,000 acres, a deer forest, a trout stream, a tract of territory in Angola, a ranch in Canada and a flat in Park Lane.

He was a large pink man, who rode to hounds with the greatest care, and knew every gate and safety path in Westshire. He had never seen a live fox, except at the Zoo, for he was rather shortsighted. Nevertheless, his picture appeared in certain illustrated weeklies with great regularity as 'Mr. Bainton, the well-known huntsman'. Thus he was depicted on his horse and off, or else with a very black face – flashlight photographs produce that effect sometimes – in a very white shirt and his pink jacket – which also photographed black – at the annual hunt ball.

It is a copybook axiom that riches do not necessarily bring content, and this was the case with Mr. Bainton. He was a hard bargainer and a shrewd buyer; the sight of money flowing past his golden reservoir, untrapped by the many channels which maintained its height, made him a very unhappy man. And money came easily to him: his luck was phenomenal. He invariably returned from Monte Carlo with an addition to his capital; he never played at the Paddock of which exclusive club he was one of the most respected – or, at least, one of the oldest members – without rising from the table a winner, though it was uncharitably suggested that he chose his table judiciously, preferring the society of callow and monied youth to the competition of hard-faced men to whom the playing of poker was a natural instinct. And when he had a house-party at Matte Hall the male guests were chosen as carefully.

He once won £4,000 at a sitting from a youth named Jones, and derived great satisfaction from his coup, for, by so doing, as he said, he 'knocked the infernal nonsense out of the young cub'.

All foolish young men were 'young cubs' to Mr. Bainton, just as all gentlemen who never went beyond half-crown bridge were 'old foxes'.

Jones is a very usual name, sometimes borne by unusual people. Bill Jones, for example, was an unusual youth. He had been desperately in love with Æthel, and had advanced the impossible suggestion that with the £4,000 left over from his patrimony he should turn Sunna Lodge into a poultry farm, marry Æthel, and live happily ever after.

Long days had passed since Æthel lost her heart to an impecunious violinist. She had acquired balance and a sense of what was due to wealth. Important people had looked wistfully at her, a rickety peer had once kissed her. She consulted her father about Bill. Mr. Bainton frowned at his cigar and invited Bill to spend a week-end at the Hall.

It was a fair game, if anything is fair when one player of poker had learnt the game only a few weeks before, and the other could draw cards in his sleep.

So Bill Jones went away, and Sunna Lodge appeared in the back page of *The Times* as:

A desirable hunting box in a good hunting district. Two packs. Company's water, own electric plant. A bargain . . .

Once a week during the winter it was the usual thing to drop in at Matte Hall for tea. Nobody knew how the practice started, but Matte Hall on Thursday afternoons became a sort of county club.

The big oak-lined banqueting hall, with its huge fireplace piled with blazing logs in the colder weather, was crowded with people between the hours of five and six-thirty. They sat on the ancient settles, or they perched on the window seats or leant against the panelled walls, adding new lustre to the polish.

And everybody talked at once.

'We got on to a new scent at Figgerty Farm – a vixen, and she gave us a run for two and a half hours, my boy! Killed at Reverly Copse . . . went to earth near Crawford's place . . . He's a half-brother to Bachelor's Fancy – a fine "lepper" with legs as sound as a bell of brass . . . You can't do better than go to Critchfords; the breeches I bought there four years ago are like new . . .'

They all talked at once – all except Mark Martin, who drifted from group to group, listening, with a smile on his good-looking face.

Nobody took much notice of Mark. They were too polite to pull his leg, too satisfied with the possession of his guilty secret to pursue enquiries any further. And when he found an opening, as he sometimes did, they listened with extraordinary courtesy.

'You don't get hunting in this county that any way approaches the sport we have in Canada. I remember an old hunter of mine . . .'

They listened, not looking at one another, interjecting in the proper places a conventional expression of their surprise and wonder. But everybody knew that he couldn't ride.

Whether Mark Martin was an American, a Canadian, or plain English, he was certainly an amiable man. His age was something under 30 but not very far under, and it was he who purchased, from the agents of the departed Jones, that desirable residence, Sunna Lodge.

He was not considered to be 'county'. You could not be 'county' unless you had an immediate interest in a family vault, or could claim part proprietorship in one of those commemorative tablets which adorn the walls of so many parish churches, and which usually start off with a coat-of-arms and end with:

Also, the wife of the above
Sir. Thos. Smithington, Kt.

But hunting breeds a sort of democracy. Stout men and women, hard-riding and wind-bitten – as they are described by local reporters – grow tender towards one another in the common bond which unites all who go forth on horses to the destruction of *Vulpes alopex*.

Mr. Martin had a stable of horses in training, was a member of the hunt, and he had often appeared in the field, but generally afoot. Sometimes he would come to a meet in his expensive car, but never had he appeared on horseback. It was regrettable, he explained, but he had kicked an ankle, or he had bruised a knee, or he had one of those fearful headaches which made riding a positive torture.

He had also been photographed in hunting pink and his picture had appeared alongside of Mr. Bainton's. He had been photographed at the hunt ball sitting side by side with Lady Mary Seprals – that hard-riding, wind-bitten woman. But nobody had ever seen him riding a horse.

There was an occasion when he turned up at the Highcliffe Races wearing jockey's breeches and top boots, and it had been announced, not only in the local newspaper, but in those stately metropolitan organs devoted to the sport of kings, that he would ride his own horse, Ripple Along, in the Highcliffe Handicap.

But this time he had a sprained shoulder, and with great regret handed over his mount to a professional rider, who won. Indeed, many of Mr. Martin's horses won races, though in other hands than his.

When it was given out that he would ride Lumber in the Hunt Gold Cup, people remembered the sprain and gave him another chance. But this time he cut his finger – and there was the hugely bandaged digit in proof. Some talk there was of asking him to resign from the hunt, but nothing came of it.

And then came the supreme bluff. He entered Lumber in the Christmas Cup at Wolverston Races. The Christmas Cup is to hunting the blue ribbon of steeplechasing. It is the 'paramount and Olympic Prize' which brings the shires in full force to Wolverston.

Moreover, it was publicly announced that Lumber would be ridden by Mark Martin himself. Colonel Desboro heard this news at first hand, and wriggled uncomfortably in the deep and none too comfortable armchair.

'What a weird beggar you are, Martin!' he said, becoming frank in his irritation. 'Enter the horse by all means, but why tell people you're going to ride it!'

Mark looked at him thoughtfully. 'I don't know. I thought I would,' he said. He tapped his long riding-boots with his hunting-crop – he never went abroad without this evidence of his horseman-ship. 'I rather like to see fellows riding their own horses.'

'But Mark, is it necessary you should ride at all?' broke in Joan. Her voice was troubled, and that frown of hers had become almost immovable in the past few days. 'People are so horrid about – things.'

His look of astonishment was badly simulated.

'And the Wolverston course wants an awful lot of riding, Mark. Captain Burnley, who won the race last year, told me there wasn't a course in England, not even the National course, that took so much out of a horse and a rider.'

'In Canada – ' began Mark.

'This isn't Canada,' interrupted the Colonel shortly. 'This is Wol-verston, and the Christmas Cup isn't a point-to-point affair. You'll have to compete against men like Ridley and Burnley and other fellows who are as good as the best professionals. I think your horse has a good chance – I was telling Joan just before you came – and I suppose in the end it will win. But why on earth commit yourself to the statement that you'll ride?'

He glanced across at his daughter and signalled her to leave the room, and when they were alone he said: 'I'm going to talk straight to you, Martin. Joan and you have developed rather a friendship in the past six months. What is there in it?'

The younger man eyed him steadily. 'There's a lot in it, Colonel,' he said quietly. 'I love Joan and I'm hoping that you'll let me marry her – one of these days.'

Colonel Desboro filled his pipe with great deliberation. 'It comes down to a question of your prospects, my young friend,' he said gruffly.

It required a physical and spiritual effort on his part to mention as mundane a subject as money, but he braced himself.

'You have an income, I suppose?'

Mark Martin nodded. 'I have five thousand a year,' he said.

The Colonel looked up quickly in surprise and fingered his chin. 'That's a pretty good income,' he admitted.

'So Mr. Bainton seems to think,' replied the other gravely.

'Bainton? What has he to do with it?'

The young man studied the bone crook of his crop as though he had only just discovered its use.

'He's been making enquiries about my position, fortunately through a friend of mine in London. He happens to be a commercial agent, and enquiries of that character come to him.'

The Colonel sat upright, pipe in hand. 'The devil he has!' he said softly. 'Do you play cards, Martin?'

Mark Martin shook his head. 'No,' he said. 'I like an occasional gamble, but not on cards. Why do you ask, Colonel?'

But Colonel Desboro was too charitable to give expression to his thoughts. Instead:

'Do you mind if I speak plainly to you, my friend?'

Mark shook his head, guessing what was coming.

'You're not really a very good rider, are you?'

Gently as the question was put, it was blunt enough, and the young man resumed his study of the hunting-crop.

'I'm one of the best riders in Canada,' he said doggedly, and the Colonel smiled.

'We've all got our weaknesses, my boy,' he said kindly. 'I remember when I was a kid I upset my mother – who'd rather have died than tell a lie – by describing a dog-fight that I hadn't seen!'

He waited.

'I've never seen a dog-fight, either,' said Mark simply. 'If you want me to say that I'm a bad rider, I'm afraid I must disappoint you. I'm really awfully good. And, Colonel – I'm very fond of Joan and everything, but I've not asked her to marry me – yet.'

Colonel Desboro looked at him sharply. 'Is there any special reason?'

The other nodded. 'A very good reason. Nothing discreditable to me, but – well, I don't know. Would you mind very much if nothing was definitely settled until after the Christmas Cup?'

Colonel Desboro considered this matter.

'No,' he said slowly, 'there's no desperate hurry. But why the Christmas Cup?'

'Until after I've won it.'

Mark was avoiding the questioning eyes of the older man.

'Till after you've won it, eh?' The Colonel pursed his lips, and then: 'All right, let it go at that. Jackson trains the horse, doesn't he?'

Mark nodded.

'I'll come over one morning and see you do an exercise gallop,' said the Colonel, not without malice, and had the satisfaction of seeing the young man start.

'I'd rather you didn't,' he said; 'I'm really fearfully nervous – that's my only weakness. If I knew anybody was looking on, I should feel terrible. It's sort of a stage-fright,' he explained lamely. 'I don't know whether you've ever had it?'

'I've never been on the stage.' The Colonel was unusually blunt that morning. 'In fact, I've never pretended to be anything else but what I am, and I think other people would be happier if they followed my example.'

'I must tell Bainton then,' said Mark innocently, 'because he's pretending that he has taken a violent liking to me!'

Arthur Persimmin Bainton was a gentleman who had many of the attributes of the eagle. He could hover on extended pinions and, to the uninitiated eye, appear to be motionless, when in reality he was planning a devastating swoop.

It was the news in *The Westshire Gazette* that made him hover a little more tensely.

> Lumber is a certain runner in the Christmas Cup. He will be ridden by his owner, Mr. Mark Martin, the wealthy young Canadian who a year ago purchased Sunna Lodge, which has been unoccupied since Mr. William Jones went abroad. Mr. Martin is an enthusiastic huntsman and is certain to take a lot of beating in the Cup.

Amongst the many channels which drained into the golden pit of Mr. Bainton was one labelled *Westshire Gazette*, of which he was the principal shareholder and chairman of directors. He rang up the editor, a civil and obliging man.

'Where did you get the paragraph about Martin?' he asked.

The editor begged him to wait one moment whilst he interviewed the chief reporter, who was also the chief sub-editor and all the other sub-editors there were. After a while he came back.

'It was written by Mr. Martin himself,' he said.

Bainton smiled into his trim white moustache. 'I thought so,' he said.

The training of Lumber for the Christmas Cup was taken in hand during the month of November. Every morning Mr. Martin could be seen driving in the direction of his trainer's stables, and invariably was attired in riding breeches. And every day, a few hours later, he would alight from his car at the end of the village, and come walking briskly up the street, his boots splashed with mud.

And at that hour there were quite a number of people to be met with in the village. Joan met him twice. Mr. Bainton saw him on several occasions and was rather amused. To Æthel one evening he said:

'What are you doing about Christmas, my dear?'

Æthel was doing nothing about Christmas.

'You might ask the Desboros to dinner, and ask that fellow Martin over. And, in case I forget it, I'd like you to put the Desboro girl next to this young cub.'

'Good heavens – why?' asked Æthel.

Mr. Bainton was lighting a cigar, and she had to wait till he stopped to breathe. 'A whim of mine.'

'Is he really training his horse?' asked Æthel. 'The vicar told me that he had seen him come in, his boots and breeches splashed with mud.'

'He does that half-way between here and Jackson's place,' said Mr. Bainton without smiling. 'Breaks off a twig, dips it into the nearest puddle and flicks it around. I've had a man watching him for a week.'

'But has he been riding the horse?' insisted Æthel.

'He hasn't been near the horse,' replied her father. 'All the riding has been done by Jenkins, the stable jockey.'

'Is he mad?' demanded Æthel, who could find no other explanation.

'No, my dear – vanity, just vanity. Not a bad fellow apart from that infernal nonsense of his. I suppose these Americans like to be thought well of, and cut a dash with their money. Don't forget the

Christmas Eve dinner. Write pretty soon in case they make another engagement.'

It was Bainton's practice to go to London once a week to a board meeting. He was methodical in his habits. He usually walked from the terminus to Piccadilly, where his London car was waiting for him. This walk supplied the constitutional which was denied him by his early departure from Matte Hall. He knew Priggins' Riding School very well, and passed its gates every morning he came to London. Indeed, he had a friendly feeling for Priggins' Riding School, because over the office entrance, by the side of the gate, was a small sign, supported on wrought-iron brackets, depicting a noble-looking huntsman in a beautifully fitting pink coat, jumping a huge fence with a confident smile on his handsome face. Once he had taken Æthel that way and had pointed out the curious resemblance between the handsome, smiling gentleman and himself.

He had turned into the street which holds Priggins' establishment, when ahead of him he saw a familiar figure. It was Mark Martin, and he was hurrying along, evidently having left the taxi which was turning as Bainton came into the street. He moved furtively and, with a nervous glance round, disappeared through the gates of the riding school. Mr. Bainton's jaw dropped in astonishment, and then a curious gleam came into his eyes. He stopped opposite the open gates and looked into the sand-covered courtyard. It was empty. Without hesitation he turned into the little office, and gathered that the gentleman in riding breeches and highly polished boots who was writing a letter as he came in was either Mr. Priggins himself or someone in authority. It proved to be both.

'Oh yes, Mr. Bainton,' said Priggins respectfully, when the visitor had cautiously revealed himself, with a request that the object of his call should be treated confidentially. 'I know your name very well, sir; I saw a photograph of you in *County Sport* the other day.'

'Very likely, very likely,' said Bainton, with a great air of indifference. 'Now I want you to tell me, Mr. Priggins, in the strictest confidence, do you know that young man who came into your yard a few minutes ago.'

There was a small window above the desk which commanded a view of the courtyard, and Mr. Priggins had duly noted the arrival.

'Oh, him.' He chuckled as at a good joke. 'He's a gentleman from the country – Martin by name.'

'What does he do here?'

Again Mr. Priggins smiled. 'Well, to tell you the truth, he's rather a source of income to me, Mr. Bainton. He's been taking riding lessons off and on for the past month, but I've never been able to get him out of the school.'

A slow smile dawned on Mr. Bainton's pink face.

'A good rider, is he?' he asked almost joyfully.

'Good rider! If only I could get him to sit on a horse properly, I'd be happy! I've given up trying, and I've handed him over to one of my assistants. There are some people you can never teach to ride: they haven't the gift for it.'

Bainton considered. 'Is is possible to take a look at him?' he suggested.

Mr. Priggins nodded, took down a key from the board-lined wall and, leading the way through a door, traversed a harness-room and conducted the enquirer up a steep and narrow flight of dark stairs. At the top he paused, his hand on a door.

'If you don't want him to know you're here, you'd better not speak,' he said, and Bainton nodded.

The riding-master opened the door cautiously. They were on a small wooden balcony overlooking the school, which was a fairly large hall, its floor covered deep with peat moss. Riding at a jog-trot was Mark Martin. His back was towards the observer, but even if he had faced the other way it seemed doubtful whether he would have noticed anything but the extreme unsteadiness of the large roan horse he was riding. He swayed in the saddle like a drunken man, and bumped up and down at the psychologically wrong moment in a manner which was curious to see. And all the time there was an exchange of instruction and protest between the rider and a sad young man in gaiters who directed the lesson.

'Keep your elbows down, sir. Your toes in, sir. Put your shoulders back, sir. No, sir, don't hold him by the mane. Walk!'

'Can't walk! Beastly thing jolts. Whoa, you brute! Am I doing any better today?'

Even the riding instructor, inured as he was to the habit of praise, would not answer in the affirmative. Bainton shook with laughter and his face grew purple.

'Now, sir, just try trotting again. Keep your elbows down by your side. Your hands up – that's right, sir. Now, sir. . . .'

The indignant horse broke into a steady trot. Mark Martin rolled like a ship in a heavy gale. He lost an iron and clutched at the mane. He slipped forward on the horse's withers, he pushed himself back on to the horse's quarters, and finally slipped ungracefully from the horse's neck to the tanned floor.

'Good heavens! Phew!'

A touch on Bainton's elbow and he withdrew through the door and down the stairs. A few minutes later he was walking away, swinging his umbrella, a beatific smile upon his face.

Christmas Eve at Matte Hall: the countryside still white with the heavy snows that had fallen on the Monday; cedar logs burning in the great fireplace; holly wreaths decorously hung on the panelled walls; and a gay company about the generous board of Mr. Persimmin Bainton.

And everybody – except one – was happy, for the very season was as a vintage wine, and Mark found himself, to his comfort, placed next to Joan Desboro. There was a whisper that Æthel's engagement to Lord Winderley was to be announced but this proved to be premature, though his lordship – who was a fawn-coloured man with a heavy yellow moustache – was seated next to her, and from time to time they looked at one another understandingly.

There was no talk but of the Wolverston races and the Cup. The redoubtable Captain Burnley was there, an apple-faced man who regarded all public meals as tiresome preliminaries to the consumption of old brandy, and Lady Mary, who had bought a new hunter at Tattersalls and had discovered unsuspected values in her purchase. There also was the Rev. Walter Affelow, the famous hunting parson who was famous rather for his prowess over the country than for his other Christian qualities, and Connington-Drake, one of the leading lights of the Paddock Club; even Boultby Malcolm, the hunting banker and, facing Mark, Colonel Desboro, a very uneasy man, but not quite so uneasy as the nervous girl who sat by Mark's side.

'Oh, there'll be racing all right,' said Burnley confidently. 'The course dries up easily and gets most of the sun that's going. I went round the track this morning. By God, those fences will take some jumping! A horse has only got to touch them and you're down – stiff as a park wall!'

'The water kills them,' said the Rev. Walter Affelow complacently. 'After weather like this the take-off will be like batter pudding!'

'Riding yours?'

It was Bainton's careless enquiry that cut through the conversation.

Mark nodded with a smile. 'Yes, I shall be riding mine. What is more, I shall win. Don't any of you people miss Lumber! I went down into Wolverston yesterday and had a look at the Cup – it's a beauty! Of course, I've got dozens of 'em,' he went on, and with one accord the whole table stopped talking, 'but curiously enough, I've never had a gold cup.'

'I don't remember seeing them on your sideboard,' said the vicar.

'I've got a packing-case full of 'em. I haven't troubled to get them out,' said Mark carelessly.

'How's the horse?' asked Burnley.

'Never better,' replied Mark complacently, as he sipped his wine. 'He gave me a wonderful ride this morning. I'm a little worried about the water jump, too, but I think I can get over that. The wretched people who bet at Wolverston would scream if you asked them for the odds to fifty pounds.'

Everybody agreed about this, for the poverty, or parsimony, of Wolverston bookmakers was notorious.

The girl by his side was groaning inwardly. She tried ineffectually to turn the conversation in another direction.

'I thought of keeping Lumber for the National,' Mark rattled on. 'One could win a fortune there.'

'You can win a fortune at Wolverston,' said Bainton slowly. 'Come now, Martin, to oblige you I'll turn bookmaker for your special benefit!'

There were eight people at that table who saw the fly thrown and waited breathlessly for the fish to rise. And he rose nobly.

'Good Lord! Would you?' said Mark.

'He'll be at least six to one against,' said Bainton, 'especially if you ride him yourself. Now, I'll make you an offer. I'll lay you twelve thousand to two that Lumber doesn't win the Cup.'

'I'll take you,' said Mark, half rising from his seat.

'Wait a moment. This is the only condition – *that you are the rider.*'

They saw the change that came to the young man's face. The girl was looking at him appealingly, and her heart sank as she saw the smile fade.

'That – er – that isn't necessary, is it?' he asked. 'I mean, suppose anything happened to me – and I had rather a twinge of rheumatism this morning.'

'You say you're going to ride the horse, you're the best rider in Canada, and I'm offering you a wager that you couldn't get and will not get on the course.'

And the company knew just why Mark Martin had been invited to dinner, and why the girl had been placed by him. He must either refuse, humiliate her hopelessly, and be completely and finally exposed, or he must save his face at the cost of £2,000. He looked left and right as though seeking a way of escape.

'I'll take your wager, Mr. Bainton,' he said loudly.

'You can make it eighteen thousand to three thousand, if you like,' suggested Bainton.

He leaned back in his chair, his eyes never moving from the face of the Great Sham.

'I'll take that!'

'There you are,' Bainton beamed, 'there you are, my boy! You've made eighteen thousand pounds! If I don't pay you,' he said jovially, 'you can post me at the Paddock Club!'

And that, for the girl, was the tragedy of the evening.

Mark drove her back in his car to the little cottage. Colonel Desboro sat in the back and brooded on the vanity of youth. As for Joan, she did not speak until he helped her out of the car.

'Why did you do it, Mark?' she asked, and he knew from her voice that she was really hurt.

'I'm awfully sorry, but I had to do it, Joan.'

When Colonel Desboro had gone in, she lingered.

'Mark, why did you tell father – ' She did not finish the sentence.

'About not asking you until the Cup was run?'

She nodded: her face in the moonlight was very pale, and he thought he had never seen her look so eerily beautiful.

'Is there some reason – why I shouldn't – bear your name?' she asked.

'There is – yes,' he answered awkwardly. 'But I think that reason will not exist after Boxing Day.'

The authorities invariably drafted large forces of police to Wolverston for Boxing Day, and they were needed to control the crowd which flocked up to Knight's Field, where the races were held. An unclouded blue sky, an invigorating, frosty morning, and the little stands and paddock were crowded; the field where the cars were parked was black with shining roofs.

Joan did not see Mark until after the second race, and then with a groan she noted that, although he was wearing his breeches and boots, he walked with a limp.

'It's nothing,' he said almost savagely. 'I knocked my knee getting into the car.'

'You won't be able to ride?'

'I think so.' He was almost brusque.

Mr. Bainton in his big tweed coat was also an amused observer of the limp. He saw Mark disappear into the stewards' room, and laughed softly.

Æthel was never at her best on a cold day – her nose had a tendency to redden in the northern breezes – but there was a very good reason why she, who never went even to point-to-point meetings because of this disability, which even make-up would not overcome, should have an interest in the Christmas Cup. For Mark Martin was to give her an additional wedding present. It was true that he did not know that his £3,000 would be invested in a most luxurious car, but that, indeed, was its destination. Moreover, she had a very natural and proper desire to be present on the occasion of the great exposure.

'He has gone in to tell the stewards he can't ride and, by God, he's only just in time!' said Bainton, for already the riders were coming from the weighing-room, their gaudy caps showing incongruously above heavy overcoats and turned-up collars.

'It's too late to alter it on the card or even on the number-board. You'll have to go out as you are,' said the senior steward. 'Have you notified the change, in accordance with the rules, to the Hunt Committee?'

'Yes,' said Mark and showed the letter he had received from the august secretary of National Hunt Racing.

'That's all right,' said the steward. 'You'd better hurry up: the saddling bell will be ringing in a few minutes. Have you weighed out?'

Mark smiled. 'Yes, I've weighed out,' he said and, to the everlasting amazement of Mr. Bainton, he came out from the weighing-room swinging his whip, limping a little, but showing no other sign of perturbation.

Mr. Bainton watched like a man in a dream, and saw him get up on the back of the big chestnut. He cantered down to the post and did not fall off. When the flag fell he was the first away, heading his field by half a length. The preliminary fence was an easy one, but it was sufficiently difficult to make an inexperienced rider fall. So far from falling, Mark seemed part of the horse. He overleapt his antagonists at every fence, and took the water jump in his stride.

Joan stood by her father on a farm waggon, open-mouthed, amazed, dreaming, she thought, so that she pinched herself. But she was wide awake. Lumber was leading by a field. He hopped the two last fences like a bird and cantered up the straight, an easy winner by a distance.

Mr. Bainton said nothing. He was incapable of speech. He could only stare in a mad kind of way as, with a smile on his brown face, Martin touched his hat to the applauding huntsmen, and then he said hollowly:

'I've been caught.'

But he sent his cheque that night. The cheque had been cleared when he met Mark Martin, and he would have passed him with a glare, but Mark stopped him.

'I think you ought to know, Mr. Bainton,' he said, 'that I raced in an assumed name.'

'Eh?' said Bainton suddenly alert. 'That isn't allowed under the rules.'

'The horse was not nominated in my name, but in the name of my trainer,' said Mark quietly, 'and at the last minute I notified the Hunt Committee that I was not Mark Martin, but Mark Martin Jones, and received permission to ride.'

'Jones!' The name had a familiar ring.

'You knew a brother of mine – Bill. He's on my ranch now in Canada, Bainton. He had the effrontery to fall in love with your daughter, and you cleared up that entanglement by taking four thousand pounds from him at a card game he knew nothing about. I'm not saying it wasn't a straight game: I'm merely stating a bald fact. I'm sending him four thousand out of the eighteen thousand you so kindly gave me.' He emphasised 'gave'. 'And it was a gift, Mr. Bainton.' There was a smile in the eyes that met the glare of the infuriated man. 'You see, I *am* the best amateur rider in Canada. By the way, did you enjoy the morning in the riding school? That was the fourth occasion on which I tried to lure you in – you hadn't noticed me before. Four is my lucky number!'

Mr. Bainton waved his hands wildly, gurgled something and passed on.

'I still don't know,' said Joan that night, 'what was the dreadful secret you had to tell me. Why shouldn't I bear your name?'

He shook his head with gentle melancholy.

'Jones!' he said.

'And a very nice name,' she said with conviction.

TONY NEWTON – BOOKMAKER

'HUMAN nature,' said Tony, 'is dominated by two vices – credulity and stupidity. It is said that a fool is born every minute, which is true, but it takes a long time for him to grow up, and the chances are that somebody will skin him before you meet him.'

'Spoken like a heartless criminal!' said Big Bill Farrel lazily.

They were at dinner at the Empress Hotel, and they were dining on the fat of the land.

'I make these few remarks,' said Tony, looking at his cigar thoughtfully, 'because I have just come from an interview with the amiable Inspector Parrit, of Scotland Yard. Something of an exploit, carried out apparently by persons with no particular regard for the law, has come to the ears of the police. In other words, the story is going around official circles that an unofficial police force raided two gambling houses, got away with £8,000, and added to the infamy of their conduct by robbing Mr. Jepburn, the proprietor, of certain objects of art to which they took their fancy when they visited him in his flat.'

'I didn't take the gold snuff-box,' said Bill Farrel.

'I did,' admitted Tony calmly. 'I have a passion for gold snuff-boxes set with rubies. Besides, it has an historical interest. I believe it came down from one of the Czars. It was a gift of Peter the Great to Mr. Jepburn's ancestor. Not that Mr. Jepburn ever had an ancestor worth mentioning, but it is a weakness of rich men to acquire ancestry at his time of life.'

'What did the police say?' asked Farrel, interested.

'They knew I was the villain,' said Tony coolly, 'and that they hoped I wouldn't make a practice of impersonating the constabulary. I asked whether it had been stated that the raiders had described themselves as police at all, and he admitted that they hadn't and that it was the guilty consciences of ladies and gentlemen who patronised Mr. Jepburn's establishments which led them to believe that the eight stalwart and good-looking ex-officers of infantry, who had marched in so sternly and had interrupted their little game, had some association with Scotland Yard .'

He chuckled softly.

'It isn't a laughing matter,' said the serious Bill. 'I'm sure that that crazy Greek who attacked you the other night in the street was set on to the job by Jepburn.'

'You are not surer than I am,' said Tony, carefully removing the ashes of his cigar. 'In fact I saw Jepburn this morning, and told him that if it happened again that a lunatic foreigner tried to knife me on the King's highway, I should come round to his flat with my confederates, tie him to a bed and tickle the soles of his feet with feathers until he went mad.'

Farrel gasped.

'That's a pretty bloodthirsty threat.'

'He wouldn't understand any other,' said Tony. 'These Eastern people are not to be dealt with in any other way. Where is the gang?'

Bill grinned.

'The gang is enjoying its ill-gotten gain according to its several temperaments. Dinky Brown is opening a hat shop off Regent Street; Tommy Barlow is working a new racing system; Foreman, the fellow who used to be colonel of the 112th, has bought a poultry farm – '

Tony nodded.

'You didn't make much out of the job yourself?' said Farrel.

'I got my whack,' replied Tony, 'and quite enough for my little investment.'

'Your investment?' repeated the puzzled Bill.

Tony nodded, felt in his waistcoat pocket, and produced a small newspaper cutting.

Bill took it from his hand and read:

'Sleeping partner wanted with a thousand pounds. Huge profit. No risks – Apply Box 943, *Daily Magaphone*.'

'The gentleman's name is Yarrow,' explained Tony, between puffs at his cigar, 'and he is a bookmaker – '

'A bookmaker!' said Bill.

Tony nodded.

'A bookmaker with a fairly strange record. He has had other partners who have put in a thousand pounds, only this time he is not going to get a sleeping partner.'

'But what sense is there in investing a thousand pounds in a shady bookmaker's business?' said Bill. 'Besides, he won't have any clients.'

'Oh, yes, he will,' said Tony. 'He will have at least one client. Yarrow's father,' he explained, 'is something big on the Stock Exchange. He's big, but he's a crook. In fact, he is as much of a rascal as his son. But don't forget that, Bill' – he emphasised his point with his cigar – 'that Yarrow senior is a man of substance.'

'Mind you don't get stung,' warned Bill, and Mr. Anthony Newton smiled.

★ ★ ★

Tony had his interview with Mr. Silvester Yarrow the following morning. Mr. Yarrow occupied two rooms on the third floor of a building off Piccadilly. It was handsomely furnished and equipped with the usual tape machine and telephone.

Mr. Yarrow himself was a sleek, perfectly dressed young man, whose hair was pomaded until it shone. He brought to the outer office, when he came to meet the newcomer, a delicate fragrance of some exotic scent which he favoured, and he offered a white, well-manicured hand to his caller.

'Good-morning, Mr. Newton,' he said with a smile. 'Will you come into my office?'

Tony followed him into a room which might more fittingly and accurately have been described as a boudoir. Mr. Yarrow liked pretty things, art hangings, heavy carpets of a peculiarly aesthetic hue, heavy notepaper and purple sealing-wax.

He was a thin, sallow-faced young man, with bright black eyes, and his voice was gentle, even languorous.

'I don't keep a clerk. One can never trust those fellows,' he explained. 'Now, Mr. Newton, you have read my proposition. Will you come into the business?'

'That is my intention,' said Tony, 'except' – Mr. Yarrow shot a swift glance at him – 'except that I do not like the idea of being a sleeping partner. I should like to play some active part.'

Mr. Yarrow's eyes went down to the desk.

'Do you know anything about bookmaking? It is a perfectly horrid profession, and I'm awfully ashamed of being associated with it,' he said; 'but one must live.'

'I don't know anything about it at all,' said Tony, 'except that people wire you money to put on horses. If they win, you pay them, and if they lose, they pay you.'

Mr. Yarrow's smile was beatific.

'Very well,' he said, 'if you wish to work and if you do not mind taking the desk at the outer office, I shall be happy for you to play an active part. As I say, I have no clerk, and you will be able to answer the telephone, open the telegrams and make a note upon a voucher-form of all the bets which are made.'

It seemed a rather dull business to Tony. The whole of the afternoon nobody telephoned, no telegrams came.

'It is the first day of Newmarket,' explained Mr. Yarrow; 'there is very little betting.' He looked at his watch. 'Go out and have a cup of tea, like a good chap, and when you come back I'll go.'

Tony thought it a excellent idea. He was gone a quarter of an hour, and when he returned the face of Mr. Yarrow was long and lugubrious.

'A very vexing thing has happened,' he said. 'Just after you went a fellow named Bertie Feener rang up and had fifty on Merriboy, and the infernal thing has won at six to one.'

'Ah!' said Tony, watching him rise and disappear.

The next afternoon was much busier. Strange people called on the telephone, made bets of a very small amount, which were duly recorded and reported to the head of the business, who sat at ease in his scented room, polishing his nails incessantly. At four o'clock Tony went out for a cup of tea, and was met by Mr. Yarrow on his return.

'That fellow Feener has got the devil's own luck,' he said. 'He has just had a hundred on a horse that started at four to one.'

'Good business!' said Tony heartily. 'I suppose you have these runs of luck?'

'Oh, yes,' said the other, palpably relieved that his partner had taken the matter so calmly. 'And then, of course, we get a run of luck the other way, and thousands simply roll into the office.'

On the following afternoon Tony did not go out to tea.

'It is too expensive,' he said: 'and besides, I'd like to talk to Bertie Feener.'

Mr. Yarrow seemed a little uncomfortable.

'Hang the fellow!' he said. 'I wish he'd have a thousand on a horse that wasn't trying; but that's the sort of thing he'll never do.'

Apparently Bertie was not betting that day, for he did not ring up, and the few bets which were made over the telephone showed a profit to the firm.

The fourth day was a Friday. About three o'clock in the afternoon the bell rang, and Yarrow went hurriedly to the telephone. Tony pretended to be very busy at his desk, but he paid particular attention to the monosyllabic answers which the usually voluble and polite Mr. Yarrow was returning to the person at the other end of the wire. Presently Mr. Yarrow grew more genial.

'Yes, old thing,' he said, 'certainly, old thing. I'll do so with pleasure. Two hundred pounds, you say? Three hundred? Good!'

The tape at Tony's elbow began to whirr, then to tick furiously. The result of the two-thirty race was coming through.

'Yes, yes. I'll lay it to you – three hundred pounds – certainly.' Mr. Yarrow glanced across at Tony and whispered: 'What has won?'

'Black Emperor,' said Tony, and a look of pain crept into Mr. Yarrow's face.

'Now isn't that annoying? The devil's backed another winner,' he said.

'Ask him if he's sure he meant Black Emperor!' hissed Tony, with an agonised expression, and the obliging Mr. Yarrow nodded.

'Is that you, Bertie?' he said. 'What was that horse you wanted to back for three hundred? Black Emperor? You're sure? You are certain that is the horse? Well you lucky devil, it has won!'

He hung up the receiver and came disconsolately across to the tape.

'Isn't that exasperating?' he asked. His tone suggested enthusiasm rather than sorrow. 'Just my luck to have him back the horse a minute before the message came through.'

He glanced at the tape, and his face changed.

'Black Emperor didn't win,' he said sharply. 'Rarebell won.'

'My mistake,' said Tony coolly.

By Mr. Yarrow's annoyance it almost seemed that he was sorry the firm of Yarrow had won three hundred pounds.

'Deuced careless of you, old fellow,' he said, trying hard to recover some of his natural politeness. 'I told Bertie it had won. He may take away his business from us.'

'That would break my heart,' said Tony.

He saw Bill Farrel that night.

'How's it going?' asked Bill.

'Fine?' said Tony with enthusiasm. 'But really' – Tony smiled – 'Yarrow has no clients at all,' he said. 'He fakes them while I'm out. The whole thing is deliciously simple. As soon as my back turns some mythical person telephones through a winner which takes four or five hundred out of my pocket. When my funds are exhausted, friend Yarrow will get another partner.'

'Who is this Bertie Feener?'

'There is no Bertie Feener. He's like Mrs. Harris. When Yarrow was having that delightful conversation which resulted in his friend backing Black Emperor his finger was on the hook. He had finished the real conversation with whoever it was three minutes before.'

★ ★ ★

The next afternoon, to Mr. Yarrow's surprise, as it was a big race day, Tony went out to tea. Before he went he asked a rather important question.

'Have you a limit to the bets you lay to Mr. Feener?' he asked.

'No,' said the other with a smile. 'It wouldn't be advisable, would it, old boy, when he is so much in our debt? No, give the jolly old rascal enough rope and he'll hang himself.'

On Tony's return Mr. Yarrow had a tale of sorrow to relate. He was stalking up and down the office, giving evidence of great mental distress.

'Confound that beastly chap!' he moaned. 'I wish to Heaven I'd never had his name on the books!'

'Bertie Feener?' asked Tony innocently. 'What has he done?'

'Had two hundred on a four-to-one chance. You had hardly got down the stairs before the begger rang up. At first I thought of turning him down, and then like a fool I laid him the bet.'

'So we lost eight hundred pounds?' asked Tony thoughtfully.

Mr. Yarrow nodded.

'It is beastly hard luck on you, old boy,' he said. 'Such a thing has never happened in this office before. Why we've practically lost over a thousand pounds this week.'

'It can't be helped,' said Tony cheerfully. 'Go and get your tea, Yarrow. I'll make the cheque out to Mr. Feener if you will give me his address when you come back.'

Mr. Yarrow bounced forth gaily.

The last race had been run and the result had been through twenty minutes when he returned.

'Well, old boy, anything happened?' he asked cheerfully as he hung up his hat.

'Yes,' said Tony. 'Bertie Feener came through and had twelve hundred pounds on Blue Diamond. We are square with Bertie now.'

Mr. Yarrow looked at him open-mouthed.

'Bertie Feener did what?' he asked hollowly. It was as though he could not believe his ears.

'He had twelve hundred pounds on Blue Diamond. It was beaten in the last race but one,' said Tony confidentially. 'As a matter of fact he rang up just as you were going down the stairs, and for a moment I hesitated as to whether I should lay him the bet, but then realising that you have no limit, I thought we'd take a chance. Congratulations, partner.'

He put out his hand, but Mr. Yarrow did not take it.

'But Bernie Feener went away to the country; he caught the four o'clock train. In fact, he told me so when I was talking to him this afternoon on the telephone.'

'He telephoned from the railway-station,' said Tony calmly.

Mr. Yarrow's sallow face was white.

'Very good,' he said shortly.

'I don't think,' said Tony, 'we'll have these telephone bets. It is much more satisfactory if our clients wire.'

'Very good,' said Mr. Yarrow again.

'How profidential it was,' mused Tony, 'that I was here when

Bertie rang through. May I call him Bertie? You don't think he'd be very much annoyed, do you?'

Mr. Yarrow, at his desk, did not raise his eyes.

'If you'd been here you might have hesitated about laying such a huge wager,' said Tony. 'Happily we are all square on the week.'

'I don't see how you can do a telegraph business,' Mr. Yarrow was stung into saying. 'No starting-price offices accept more than fifty up to the time the race starts, and very few accept that!'

'Let us be the exception,' said Tony, and he saw a glad light come into his partner's eyes. 'Why not,' he went on recklessly, 'give them an option of putting a thousand or two thousand up to the "off" as long as they sign their names to their telegrams and we know them. Why, Yarrow, we might get a tremendous business that way.'

'So we might,' said Mr. Yarrow with a return to his own cheerfulness. 'I'll think it out and let you know on Monday morning.'

On Monday morning Mr. Yarrow was almost gay.

'You are a deuced clever fellow, Newton,' he said. 'I've been thinking it out, and your scheme is a jolly good one. I consulted my governor, who doesn't approve of this business, as you can well understand, and he says it is an excellent notion. He does a bit of racing himself, Newton; in fact, he owns half a dozen horses, and he says that if we are willing to make those terms he is quite willing to put all his business in our hands. We'll have a new code typewritten and sent to our clients, so that they can wire to the fullest extent without exciting comment. What do you say to that?'

To judge by Tony Newton's attitude, facial expression and gurgling speech he was beside himself with delight.

'We'll try it anyway for a week,' he said. 'On Wednesday I have to go down into Gloucestershire, but there is nothing much happening on Wednesday.'

'There is racing at Hurst Park,' said the other, breathing heavily, and trying to appear wholly indifferent. 'But we shan't have any heavy betting on that day. There is nothing to bet on. To what part of Gloucestershire are you going?'

'To Gloucester itself. I shall be back by night. Will you send me a wire if anything unusual happens?'

★ ★ ★

Tony left by the ten o'clock train, which had the advantage of stopping at Reading. Mr. Yarrow who, to make absolutely sure, had come down to Paddington to see his partner safely out of London, did not know about the stop at Reading.

'It is deuced curious my being here,' he said at the carriage door, 'but I've got to meet an aunt who is coming up from Cardiff in a quarter of an hour, so I thought I'd stroll round and have a look at you. What time will you be back?'

'About six o'clock tonight,' said Tony. 'I shall only be an hour in the town.'

At Reading he chartered a taxicab to carry him the not very considerable distance which separates Reading from Hurst Park.

Mr. Yarrow senior did not know Tony, but Tony knew Mr. Yarrow senior. A tallish, bent man, with a loose lip and a pendulous nose, Mr. Yarrow had in his day many chance adventures which, were he writing the recollection of his racing career, he would never have put into print. A justice of the peace, a prospective candidate for Parliament, his wealth was held to atone for the method by which it was secured. Not that Mr. Yarrow was ever guilty now-adays of the indiscretion which had made his name a term of reproach in the best sporting and bookmaking circles.

The third race of the day was one of those events which are frequently found on the card at most big meetings – a Foal Plate for horses which had been entered as yearlings by the optimistic owners. Three years after their entry, all that had survived the severe test of the racecourse met to do battle for a thousand-pound trophy. There remained exactly three horses of the original ninety-five entered, and it was on this race, as Tony had guessed when he searched the programme, that Mr. Yarrow would help to assist his son to the fulfilment of his heart's desire – the acquirement of Tony's thousand pounds.

Of the three horses left, obviously only two had a chance. The third, as had been proved on every racecourse in England, might have won a selling race if the class had been extremely poor, but Mr. Yarrow was taking no chances.

Tony, watching him, with his back to the unsaddling enclosure, saw him take down three telegraph forms and write on each. He wormed his way to a position immediately behind Yarrow, and saw the old man pass the three forms into the cubby-hole where the telegraph clerk sat. They were all addressed to 'Yoxi, London', Mr. Yarrow junior's telegraphic address, and they each had a name of a different horse with a code-word 'Yail', which young Yarrow and he had agreed should stand for two thousand pounds.

There is no sin in backing three horses in one race. Many sportsmen have done this and are still walking about, though sadly deficient in bootleather. There was nothing exactly criminal in backing three horses in a race where there were only three runners. It is, to put it mildly, foolish, but it is not sinful.

Tony strolled into the ring.

Bird's Eye was favourite and an odds-on favourite; Morton's Pride was second favourite, two to one against; and the third horse was quoted at twenty to one.

He stood in the ring and watched the race being run. It was less of a race than a procession, for Bird's Eye led from start to finish, and won in a canter.

Satisfied, Tony went back to London, and at a quarter-past six strolled into his office.

Mr. Yarrow made no attempt to conceal his gratification.

'Old boy, we are done in the eye!' he said.

'What has happened?' asked Tony.

'My governor had two thousand on Bird's Eye. It is unfortunate, old chap; but there, what can you do? Here is the telegram, time all correct.'

Tony took the telegram.

'Yes,' he said, 'that's in order.'

'We've lost a thousand, and that's just about burst the till, unless you can get a little more capital,' said Mr. Yarrow stroking his smear of a moustache.

'On the contrary, I reckon that we've made three thousand,' said Tony thoughtfully.

'What do you mean?' gasped Yarrow.

'Where are the other two telegrams your father sent? asked Tony.

Mr. Yarrow flushed red.

'What the devil do you mean?' he demanded, but Tony stopped him with a gesture.

'Your father sent three wires, one backing each horse. The only chance of his winning from us would have been if an outsider had come in first. As a matter of fact, that outsider finished so far last that I doubt if he has passed the winning post yet. You will greatly oblige me, Yarrow, if you call on your parent this evening and tell him that unless three thousand pounds is placed in my hands by to-morrow morning I will have you both arrested for conspiracy to defraud. I am well aware, and you need not tell me, that it is in itself a felony to demand money by threats of prosecution, but there it is, Yarrow. I am sinning with my eyes open.'

'I tell you there were no other telegrams,' screamed the young man.

'There are two others,' said Tony patiently, 'but you have burnt them or got rid of them in some way. They are probably in your trouser pocket, crumpled up. Anyway that's an easy thing to find out, because the post office would give me copies of all the telegrams your father sent from Hurst Park. Now be a good lad and see the old man, and tell him I give him till twelve o'clock, failing which I will go to Scotland Yard and swear an information. And,' he added, standing at the door as he walked out, 'tell your fond parent that I prefer banknotes of small denomination.'

THE BURGLARY AT GOODWOOD

Bob Brewer, temporary chief of the Federated Assurance Corporation's Detective Department, loved to roll forth this string of adjectives, and for the mystification of his friends he had added to his visiting card the cryptic initials – T.C.F.A.C.D.D. Now he paused on the second marble step which led to the imposing entrance of Federated Building, and fixed his interested gaze upon a young man, the sole passenger of a car which was passing at that moment.

The young man wore a grey hat and smoked a long cigar, and he lolled back in the interior of the machine with an air of unspeakable boredom.

'Neatly and nicely posed,' said Bob, took a note of the car's number and passed into the interior of the building.

A clerk recognised him with a nod and showed him straight into the general manager's room.

'Mr. Campbell is expecting you, sir,' he said. 'You got our telegram?'

'I always get telegrams,' smiled Bob. 'What's the hurry?'

The clerk hesitated.

'I think you had better see Mr. Campbell,' he said.

Douglas Campbell, after the manner of very busy men, seemed to be doing nothing when Bob came into his office.

'Hello!' he growled. 'Shut the door. What – '

'I got your telegram. I had a good crossing. The weather in France was perfect. I posted my expense account, and I have no money,' said Bob rapidly, 'and after these preliminary pleasantries, I repeat, what's the hurry?'

'Sit down,' said Campbell. 'Society, Bob,' he began, preparing to emphasise his points with a paper-knife, 'is chiefly remarkable by its adherence to convention.'

'Listen,' interrupted Bob; 'do I get this lecture on society every time I come to see you?'

'Nearly every time you will get it,' said Campbell, 'because I want to impress upon you this one fact, that robbing the truly rich is a simpler matter than taking toffee out of a baby's mouth. It is because it is so simple that our work's so hard. By the way,' he said suddenly, 'I hear that your friend Reddy escaped from the French police.'

Bob nodded.

'He got away into Spain through no fault of mine,' he said. 'He is in Spain still. You are not suggesting that he is laying for me in London?'

'No. I didn't ask you to come here to warn you. I think we can cut Reddy out for a month or two.'

'Quite right,' said Bob. 'Reddy's more concerned about Reddy than he is about me, and, anyway, he is not so dangerous a man as, say, Soapy Wilkins.'

Douglas Campbell sat bolt upright in surprise.

'Soapy Wilkins?' he repeated. 'Who the devil has been talking to you? It was Soapy I wanted to see you about.'

Bob Brewer laughed.

'There's no mystery about Soapy,' he said, 'and less about my reference to him. I saw him exactly two minutes ago, riding, so to speak, in the lap of luxury and a hired car and a grand outfit which was probably his own.'

Campbell looked troubled.

'That's a curious coincidence,' he said; 'Soapy's staying at the Hotel Magnificent, and Bob – Soapy is a standing menace to capital, mostly our capital.'

'Why don't you get the real police to pull him in?' asked Bob. 'He's a well-known crook. Everybody knows Soapy in America; and I suppose the police know him here. He's one of the cleverest crooks in the world and one of the most dangerous, because, like lightning, he never strikes twice in the same place. Most criminals are specialists and stick to one type of crime. Soapy is so infernally clever that he can pass from commonplace burglary to the artistic forgery of bonds without turning a hair, and get away with both jobs. I admire Soapy – so named, I believe, because of his exceptionally pleasant conversational powers. He is a genius. That fellow has ideas – '

'I didn't send for you to listen to an eulogy of Soapy Wilkins,' snarled Campbell, 'and I deplore your taste that you can admire a man who, at any moment, may reduce the dividends of Federated Assurance. As to pulling him in, that's impossible. We are not working in the dear old days, when you could deport without trouble any undesirable person who was not of British nationality. The police have nothing against him, and cannot move. They are watching him – '

'Ha! ha!' Bob said.

'I say they are watching him, and your ironic laughter exactly expresses my feelings in the matter.'

He took a paper out of a basket and laid it on the desk before him.

'Now, I'll tell you why I am worried about Soapy, although my anxiety may be groundless. Do you know Windhever Castle?'

Bob nodded.

'It's the Sussex residence of the Duchess of Manton,' he said promptly, 'a great dame, entirely surrounded by money and social influence.'

Campbell nodded.

'Windhever Castle is exactly five miles from Goodwood,' he said. 'Next week we have Goodwood races, at which all the right people in Britain will be present. Society goes to Goodwood because it lies on the weary road which society tramps from Christmas Day to Christmas Eve. Society goes there because it's the thing to do.'

'Cut out all that society stuff,' said Bob, 'and come to the dramatic climax of your interesting story.'

Campbell gulped.

'I'll put it within your comprehension,' he said. 'Next week Windhever Castle will be filled with exclusive ladies and gentlemen who will bring for their adornment bright and beautiful jewels, all of which are insured by us. Now, what is worrying me is this. A month ago, there was a burglary at Windhever Castle.'

Bob nodded.

'Did they get anything?' he asked.

'Nothing,' replied Mr. Campbell. 'As a matter of fact, there were no guests there, the Duchess being at Ascot with the flock. There were only a few servants in the house and practically no portable property. Nevertheless, an entrance was effected in the night, the Duke's safe was opened, three or four locks leading from the garden to the study were picked and, in fact, it was a clean job and the burglars got away.'

'That's strange,' said Bob thoughtfully. 'Give me some details of the work these enterprising fellows performed.'

Campbell sketched the work of destruction briefly.

'It took them three hours, did it?' said the thoughtful Bob. 'Of course, it was easy; because, as you said, there were only three servants in the house and they had all the time they needed. The burglary sounds like the work of real fellows – men who knew their game, and they must have known there was no money in the house. Now, what the devil did they expect to find? The job must have cost them two or three hundred pounds; and professional burglars are thrifty souls, who don't waste money.'

'That's what is puzzling me,' said Campbell; 'as a matter of fact, the burglary was not reported to us, because the Duke himself does not insure with our companies, and I only found it out in a round-about way. However, forewarned is forearmed. The Duke has had new locks fixed to all the doors, a new burglar-proof safe of one of the best makes installed; and I understand that the library, where the safe is situated, is to be guarded by patrols whilst the house party is in residence.'

'Do you connect Soapy with this business?'

'I'm bound to,' said Campbell. 'He's the only big man in London at the present moment. I want you to go down and see the Duke – I have a letter of introduction to him from one of our clients – and offer him any assistance which you can. Look over the servants and see if you can recognise any; and be on hand on the night of the Goodwood Cup, when the Duchess gives a big dance and that safe will contain the Penson emeralds. Lady Penson is one of the guests; and I have reason to know that her jewels will be sent down for the occasion. Above all, don't forget that society – '

'There's nothing you've ever said about society that I'm likely to forget,' said Bob, and made his escape.

Windhever Castle is a building in the Georgian style, standing in beautiful grounds on the Chichester road. The Duke was a gentleman whose portrait was familiar to every newspaper reader. He was a small, thin man, with a small, thin face. His expression was somewhat vacant; and he had probably gained his reputation for profound thinking by the extent and rarity of his library, and his habit of never speaking save to disagree with every view which was expressed to him.

He received Bob in that same library and offered a limp hand.

'I don't think it is necessary that you should interest yourself in the safety of my guests' jewellery,' he said; 'but as Lord What's-his-name' – he looked at the letter of introduction – he made a point of never remembering names, or, if he did remember, of never committing himself to their pronunciation – 'as Lord What's-his-name wishes you to look after his missus' property, of course, you can go anywhere you like, except into her Grace's bedroom.'

'I quite understand. Your Grace has taken every precaution?'

'Of course I have,' said the Duke. 'I have told you so, haven't I? I have a new safe here' – he pointed to a great steel cupboard bearing the name-plate of the best maker. 'I am having a patrol outside the window, changed every hour, and I think you will agree it will take more than an hour to open that safe.'

Bob did agree. He knew the make; and in the most favourable circumstances it could not be opened in one hour or in six.

'If Lord What's-his-name doesn't think his missus' jewels are safe, there's no need for him to come,' his Grace went on. 'What the deuce have I spent two hundred in getting the house fitted with burglar alarms, buying a new safe, fixing new locks, for, hey?'

He again held out his limp hand.

'Well, Mr. What's-ye-may-call-it, don't make yourself an infernal nuisance. Go and see my house-steward and he will do anything he can for you.'

Bob found the house-steward and interviewed him, though the interview did not take the form which the Duke might have expected. He also had an opportunity of seeing, one by one, the various male servants who were to be on guard outside the library on the night of the ball.

'There's only one way into the library from the ground,' said the house-steward, 'and that's through the little door his Grace uses, and through two other doors, all of which are fitted with new locks, and one of the doors is sheeted with steel.'

'Could a burglar get in from the house?'

'That's more difficult still,' said the house-steward. 'He would have to go through the main corridor, where I shall be on duty throughout the night.'

Bob scratched his chin.

'I suppose you have known all the footmen for years?' he said.

'Every one of them,' said the house-steward promptly. 'They've all lived in this neighbourhood since they were children, and, with one or two exceptions, they've been here all the time.'

That the appearance of a stranger in a little country village should fail to excite interest and attention was not to be expected, Bob knew. In a few hours his business was known, as he expected it would be known; and the landlord of the little inn at which he lodged had even tried to get his views on the recent burglary, which was still the topic of conversation.

'There will be a lot of ladies and gentlemen down here for the races next week, sir,' he said. He was attending personally upon Bob at his solitary dinner. 'And I suppose you're down here to see there are no more burglaries?'

'Something like that,' said Bob.

'By all accounts,' said the garrulous landlord, 'there won't be much chance for them this time. The young gentleman who came down from the safe company said that he defied any burglar to open their safe.'

'I think it will be difficult,' agreed Bob good-humouredly.

'It's a mystery to me,' the landlord went on, 'why they burgled the castle. Why, everybody in the village knew that his Grace was away – even the silver was at the bank, by all accounts. I was talking to Mr. Coles, the Duke's valet, about it and he said they must've been mad. That's him, sir,' he said, nodding to the window.

Bob looked, and saw one of the manservants he had observed that morning. He was a man of thirty, soberly dressed and expressionless of face, as befitted a gentleman's gentleman.

'He often comes in here for a glass of sherry,' explained the landlord. 'Of course, he is, practically speaking, his Grace's right-hand man. He was born here and used to be one of the footmen. Then he went to Australia for six years. His brother died suddenly and he had to go out and look after his property. It wasn't much, by all accounts,' continued the landlord, 'and when he came back to Windhever he had no money; and it was a bit of luck that his Grace wanted a valet.'

Bob rose, strolled through the stone-flagged entrance hall into the yard outside. The valet recognised him and touched his hat; and Bob got into conversation with him. It was a curious conversation, for it was all about English hills and their heights; and the conversation flagged until Bob brought up the question of the great Tors of Derbyshire.

'No, sir; you're wrong,' said the valet in answer to one statement Bob made; 'Hay Tor is the highest. Why, you can see it for miles!'

'There's a wonderful view from the top,' agreed Bob.

The man hesitated.

'I've never been on top,' he said, 'but I should say you are right, sir.'

He seemed willing to continue the conversation which, again at Bob's instigation, took a curious turn, being mainly about horses, and particularly ponies, and wild ponies at that. Here again the man's knowledge was extensive. It was a random shot of Bob's, but he had struck his target.

'You must have a drink with me, Mr. Cole,' he said, and led the way to the private sitting-room he had engaged. It was Bob who, with his hands, and despite the protests of the landlord, bore the glasses and the bottle. He paused outside the door of the sitting-room to give one of the glasses an extra polish with his silk handkerchief, for he wanted it very clean.

'Here's very good health, sir,' said Cole, and drank his wine at a gulp.

Bob took the glass from him, placed it carefully on the table, and led the way into the open again. Then, when he had said good-night to the valet, he sat down and wrote a letter to Douglas Campbell:

I think I have smelt out the plot and can explain the abortive burglary almost as easily as I shall be able to describe the burglary which will be committed on the night of the Goodwood Cup. I hope to send you tomorrow a finger print which I have taken off a glass and which, I believe, will reveal the identity of an old lag. The man's name is Cole. He had a mysterious absence from the village for six years, which immediately followed the arrest of the Perrers gang. Apparently Cole's identity is not known to the Duke, and his crime is unknown to the villagers. At any rate, from his knowledge of the hills of Dartmoor and his acquaintance with Dartmoor ponies, I should say that he had seen the interior of the Princetown prison. The rest as they say in books, looks like being easy.

Bob Brewer went to the Goodwood Races for his own pleasure and profit. Though there might be minor rogues about, he could afford to concentrate upon the bigger gang; and the bigger gang would not begin operations before the night. On his return from the races on the day of the Goodwood Cup, he found a telegram awaiting him. It ran:

Have made important discovery. Your theories are wrong. Am going Portsmouth by 7.53 tonight. Drive over and meet me Grand Hotel 10.15.

Bob folded up the telegram and sent for the landlord.

'I want you to get through to Chichester to any garage you know and hire me a car,' he said. 'I have to go to Portsmouth.'

There was some little difficulty about hiring a car in Goodwood week, but the hour favoured him.

At eight o'clock a serviceable vehicle was at the door. He left instructions that any message which came through to him by telephone, or any telegrams which might arrive should be repeated to him at Portsmouth.

'I'm sorry you're going, sir,' said the landlord. 'I thought you would be here until after the ball.'

'I don't think my presence is necessary,' laughed Bob. 'In fact, I don't mind making to you, Mr. Landlord, a confession which few detectives make; I have been working on the wrong track.'

He had to wait a little while because he had put through a call to London to the residence of Douglas Campbell. It came a few minutes before he left, and it was Mrs Campbell who answered him.

'I've had a telegram from your husband telling me to meet him at Portsmouth. I suppose that is all right?' he asked.

'He is going to Portsmouth by the 7.53,' replied Mrs. Campbell.

Bob hung up the receiver. A few minutes later his car was disappearing along the road to Chichester.

It was the Duke of Manton's boast that he went to bed early and, fortunately for him, he had as his guest a royal visitor who shared the same views, so that before midnight the big Georgian house was in darkness; and there was no sound but the occasional cough of one of the servants guarding the entrance to the library. At a quarter past twelve the coughing sentry was relieved. Scarcely had his footsteps died away on the gravel when a man came noiselessly from the shrubbery, crossed the gravel path with scarcely a sound and approached the sentry.

'Is that you, Cole?' he said in a low voice.

'Yes,' was the reply. 'You'd better get a move on. They're relieving me in half an hour.'

'Gee!' said the man, 'being a Duke's valet gives you a pull.'

He moved past the sentry on the way to the door, but not very far past. An arm was flung round his neck, a deft hand slipped the revolver from his hip pocket and a voice in his ear said:

'Are you going rough or going quiet, Soapy?'

'Quiet,' said Soapy philosophically and put up his right hand mechanically for the handcuff. 'So you're not Cole; you're Brewer, aren't you?' he asked.

'That's so,' said Bob. 'I will relieve you of all those keys you have in your pocket, the key of the safe and the keys of the doors.'

'I thought you were in Portsmouth,' said Soapy.

'Come off it!' scoffed Bob. 'You didn't think a fake like that would do, did you?'

'But you got Mrs. Campbell on the phone?'

'Yes; but I happened to know he was going to Portsmouth anyway, and I suppose you found it out, too. Come on, Soapy, it's the long, long trail for you.'

'It was one of the easiest tricks, and it had been worked before,' explained Bob to the gratified Campbell. 'The first burglary was a fake and was intended to draw attention to the insecurity of the locks and the poor quality of the safe. On top of this, down comes Soapy as an agent for a safe company, and talks old man Duke into putting in a new outfit.

'The Duke is as mean as the devil. When Soapy offered to install safe and locks and burglar alarms for two hundred pounds, it was the fact that the Duke casually mentioned he had paid two hundred for a four-hundred-pound job which put me on to it – the old man fell for the bargain. Soapy kept a set of keys, he had an old friend in the house, and all he had to do was to walk in, unlock the doors, unlock the safe, and walk off with the swag. Nobody would know when or how the burglary was committed. Of course, it was only accident that Cole had got a job as valet. He would have been just as useful if he had been a plain under-footman.'

'What did the Duke say?' asked Campbell.

Bob laughed.

'He cursed me. He said he'd lost the best valet he'd ever had.'

That's what I say about society,' said Douglas Campbell; 'they are thick-headed and heavy – '

'What do you say about my expenses?' said Bob. 'They are a bit thick and heavy, too!'

THE MAN WHO SHOT THE 'FAVOURITE'

'THERE always will be a certain percentage of mysteries turnin' up, that simply won't untwist themselves, but the mystery that I'm thinkin' of particularly is the Wexford Brothers' Industrial Society, which unravelled itself in a curious fashion,' said P. C. Lee.

'If you don't happen to know the Wexford Brothers, I can tell you that you haven't missed much. It was a sort of religious sect, only more so, because these chaps didn't smoke, an' didn't drink, or eat meat, or enjoy themselves like ordinary human bein's, an' they belonged to the anti-gamblin', anti-Imperial, anti-life-worth-livin' folks.

'The chief chap was Brother Samsin, a white-faced gentleman with black whiskers. He was a sort of class leader, an' it was through him that the Duke started his Wexford Brothers' Industrial Society.

'The Duke wasn't a bad character, in spite of his name, which was given to him by the lads of Nottin' Dale. He was a bright, talkative, an' plausible young feller, who'd spent a lot of time in the Colonies, an' had come back to London broke to the world owin' to speculation.

'Why I know so much about him is that he used to lodge in my house. He was a gentleman with very nice manners, an' when Brother Samsin called on me one afternoon an' met the Duke, the brother was so impressed with the respect an' reverence with which the Duke treated him that he asked him home to tea.

'To cut a long story short, this bright young man came to

know all the brothers and sisters of the society an' became quite a favourite.

'I thought at first he had thoughts of joinin' the Brotherhood, but he soon corrected that.

' "No, Lee," ses he, "that would spoil the whole thing. At present I'm attracted to them because I'm worldly and wicked. If I became a brother, I'd be like one of them. At present they've no standard to measure me by, an' so I'm unique." '

'What interested the brothers most was the Duke's stories of his speculations in the Colonies, of how you can make a thousand pounds in the morning, lose two thousand in the evening, an wake up next mornin' to find that you've still got a chance of makin' all you've lost an' a thousand besides.

'Well, anyway, he got the brothers interested, an' after a lot of palaver an' all sorts of secret meetin's, it was decided to start the Industrial Society, an' make the Duke chief organiser an' secretary.

'The idea was to subscribe a big sum of money, an allow the Duke to use it to the best of his ability "on legitimate enterprises" – those were the words in the contract.

'The Duke took a little office over a barber's shop near the Nottin' Hill Gate Station, an' started work. Nothin' happened for a month. There were directors' meetin's an' money was voted, but in the second week of April, two months after the society was formed, the Duke said the society was now flourishin' an' declared a dividend of 20 per cent. What is more, the money was paid, an' you may be sure the brothers were delighted.

'A fortnight later, he declared another dividend of 30 per cent., an' the next week a dividend of 50 per cent., an' the brothers had a solemn meetin' an' raised his salary. Throughout that year hardly a week passed without a dividend bein' declared and paid.

'Accordin' to his agreement the Duke didn't have to state where the money came from. On the books of the society were two assets:

Gold mine . . . £1,000
Silver mine . . . £500

an' from one or the other the dividends came.

'All went well to the beginning of this year. You would think that the brothers, havin' got their capital back three times over, would be satisfied to sit down an' take their "divvies", but of all true sayin's in this world the truest is that "the more you get, the more you want".

'From what I hear, the Duke paid no more dividends at all from the end of November to the end of February, an' only a beggarly 10 per cent. in March. So the directors had a meetin' an' passed a vote of censure on the secretary.

'He wasn't the kind of man to get worried over a little affair like that, but he was annoyed.

"What these perishers don't understand,' he ses to me, 'is that the gold mine doesn't work in the winter.'

' "Where is it?" I asked.

'He thought a bit. "In the Klondike," he ses, thoughtful.

' "An' where's the silver mine?"

' "In never-never land," he ses, very glib.

' "He got the brothers quiet again by the end of March, for he declared a dividend of 20 per cent., but somehow or other all those weeks of non-payment got their backs up, an' they wasn't so friendly with him as they used to be.

'Mr. Samsin asked me to call round an' see him, an' I went.

'When I got to his house, I was shown into the parlour, an' to my surprise, I found about a dozen of the brothers all sittin' round a table very solemn an' stern.

' "We've asked you to come, Mr. Lee," ses Samsin, "because bein' a constable, an' acquainted with law, an' moreover," he ses with a cough, "acquainted with our dear young friend who's actin' as secretary to our society, you may be able to give us advice. You must know," he ses, mysteriously, "that for three months no dividends have been forthcomin' to our society."

'I nodded.

' "We have wondered why," he ses, "but have never suspected one whom we thought was above suspicion."

' "Meanin', the Duke?" I ses.

' "Meanin' Mr. Tiptree," ses Brother Samsin. Tiptree was the Duke's private name.

' "We have made a discovery," ses Samsin, impressively, "an' when I say 'we' I mean our dear Brother Lawley."

'A very pale gent in spectacles nodded his head.

' "Brother Lawley," ses Samsin, "was addressin' a meetin' on Lincoln racecourse – he bein' the vice-president of the Anti-Race-

course League – an' whilst runnin' away from a number of misguided sinners, who pursued him with contumely—"

' "An' bricks," ses Brother Lawley.

' "An' bricks," Samsin went on, "he saw Tiptree!"

'He paused, and there was a hushed silence.

' "He was bettin!" ' ses Brother Samsin.

' "Now," he adds, "I don't want to be uncharitable, but I've got
an idea where our dividends have gone to."

' "Stolen," ses I.

' "Stolen an' betted," ses the brother, solemnly.

' "Well," ses I, "if you report the matter to me, an' you've got
proof, an' you'll lay information, I'll take it to my superior, but if
you ask me anythin' I'll tell you that you haven't much of a case.
It's no offence to bet—"

' "It's an offence against our sacred principles," ses Brother
Samsin.

'The upshot of this conversation was – they asked me to watch
the Duke an' report any suspicious movement, an' this I flatly
refused to do.

'An' with that I left 'em. I don't know what they would have
done, only suddenly the society began to pay dividends. Especially
the gold mine, which paid a bigger dividend every week.

'So the brothers decided to overlook the Duke's disgraceful conduct, especially in view of the fact that Brother Lawley was preparin'
for one of the most terrible attacks on horse-racin' that had ever
been known.

'I got to hear about it afterwards. Brother Lawley was all for bein'
a martyr to the cause. He said he wanted to draw attention to the
horrible gamblin' habits of the nation, but there were lots of people
who said that the main idea was to call attention to Brother Lawley.

'Be that as it may, he thought out a great plan an' he put it into
execution on the day before Derby Day.

'A number of our fellows were drafted down for the races and I
went with them.

'On the Monday, as I went down on the Tuesday, I saw the Duke.
He still lodged in my house, although he was fairly prosperous, an'
happenin' to want to borrow the evenin' paper to see what young
Harry Bigge got for a larceny I was interested in, I went to his
room.

'He was sittin' in front of a table, an' was polishin' up the lenses of a pair of race-glasses, an' I stopped dead when I remembered my conversation with the brothers.

' "Hullo!" I ses, "you an' me are apparently goin' to the same place."

' "Epsom? Yes," ses he, coolly. "An' if you take my tip you'll back Belle of Maida Vale in the second race."

' "I never bet," I ses, "an' I take no interest in horse-racin' an', moreover," I ses, "she can't give Bountiful Boy seven pounds over a mile an' a quarter."

'When I got downstairs I went over her "form". She was a consistent winner. The year before she'd won eight races at nice prices, an' I decided to overcome my aversion to bettin' an back her, although I'd made up my mind to have my week's salary on Bountiful Boy.

'There was the usual Tuesday crowd at Epsom, an' I got a glimpse of Brother Lawley holdin' his little meetin'. He was on his own. It wasn't like the racecourse Mission, that does its work without offence, but Lawley's mission was all brimstone an' heat.

'We cleared the course for the first race, an' after it was over I casually mentioned to Big Joe France, the Bookmaker, that if Belle of Maida Vale was 20 to 1 I'd back her.

' "I'm very sorry, Mr. Lee," he ses, "but you'll have to take a shorter price – I'll lay you sixes."

'I took the odds to 30s. and laid half of it off with Issy Jacobs a few minutes later at threes.

'The course was cleared again for the second race, an' it was whilst the horses were at the post that I saw Brother Lawley leanin' over the rails near the winnin' post. He looked very white an' excited, but I didn't take much notice of him, because that was his natural condition.

'In the rings the bookies were shoutin' "Even money on Belle of Maida Vale", an' it looked as if somebody was havin' a rare gamble on her.

'The bell rang, an' there was a yell. "They're off!"

'I was on the course, near the judge's box, an' could see nothin' of the race till the field came round Tattenham Corner with one horse leadin' – and that one the Belle.

'Well out by herself she was, an' there she kept right along the straight to the distance. There was no chance of the others catchin' her an' they were easin' up when suddenly from the rails came a report like the snap of a whip, an' the Belle staggered, swerved, an' went down all of a heap.

'For a moment there was a dead silence, an' then such a yell as I've never heard before.

'They would have lynched Brother Lawley, with his smokin' pistol in his hand, but the police were round him in a minute.

"I've done it!" he yelled. "I've drawn attention to the curse —"

' "Shut up!" I said, "an' come along before the people get you."

'Next day there was a special meetin' of the Wexford Brothers' Industrial Society, an' the Duke attended by request.

'Brother Samsin was in the chair.

' "We are gathered," he ses, "to consider what can be done for the defence of our sainted Brother Lawley, who's in the hands of the myrmidons of the law. I propose that we vote a sum out of the society —"

' "Hold hard," ses the Duke, roughly, "you can't vote any money – because there ain't any."

' "Explain yourself," ses Brother Samsin. "What of the gold mine?"

' "The gold mine," ses the Duke sadly, "was a horse called Belle of Maida Vale, that I bought out of the society's funds – she's dead."

' "An' the silver mine?" faltered Samsin.

' "That was the Belle of Maida Vale, too," ses the Duke. "A good filly, she was. She won regularly every month at a nice price – but she won't win any more dividends." '

THE DERBY FAVOURITE

'LIKELY enough,' said P.C. Lee, 'you've heard me tell about Captain Kintock. He wasn't the sort of man you'd expect a police constable to have much to do with, because he was of the higher class of bad lot, but owin' to his livin' on my ground – a very fine house he had in Ladbroke Gardens – an' owin' to my knowin' Baine, that did most of his dirty work, I got a fair inside knowledge of what happened at Epsom.

'In a sense, this story I'm goin' to tell you is a racin' story, though I don't want you to run away with the idea that I know much about it.

'When people tell you that racin' is a game that is only followed by thieves an' blackguards, by sharps an' flats, do not believe them. Some of the worst men in England go racin', but then, again, some of the best go, too.

'The bulk lie between the two extremes, an' are sane, decent citizens, who love the sport for the sport's sake.

'But the bad men are very bad, because they are clever, an' a clever bad man is a dangerous animal.

'Kintock was one the "Heads". He'd had money enough to sink a ship, at one time or another. A gambler born an' bred, he would bet on anything from horses to windmills.

'But Kintock was a crook, it was against his nature to go straight, an' when it was a question of an easy honest way of doin' a thing, an' a hard, dishonest way, he always chose the latter for the sheer devilry of it.

'Rumly enough, he never took to horses till he'd run through every other form of gamblin', but when he did, he took to it on a colossal scale. He bought bloodstock in every direction, bought horses at the sales, an' out of sellin' races, an' took a lease of an old trainin' establishment down in Wiltshire, an' spent half his time between there an' Kensin'ton. Everybody knew he was a crook, but nobody knew enough about him to point to any definite act he had committed, an' so, somehow, he managed to get the Jockey Club to give him a licence to train.

'He was an extraordinarily fascinatin' man. Tall, lean-limbed, with a face like one of those Greek gods you see at the British Museum, an' a head of brown, curly hair that was goin' grey.

'So far as I could find out, he'd come into a lot of money – somethin' well into six figures – when he was twenty-one. He lived for a year at the rate of £500 a day, went into bankruptcy, an' was sent abroad. He made a fortune in the Argentine an' lost it in South Africa, floated a bogus company in Egypt, got concessions from the Turkish Government in Syria, an' turned up smilin' in England a rich man for the second time.

'Then he disappeared suddenly, an' about the same time a lot of excited shareholders made the discovery that the concession in Syria wasn't worth the paper it was written on, an' the assets of the Egyptian company were just worth the market value of a roller-top desk an' an easy chair, which formed the furniture of the company's office in Mincin' Lane. I don't know how they settled it, but I rather think that some of his rich relations paid up an' liquidated the company, an' a year later Kintock was in Monte Carlo with enough banknotes to stuff a portmanteau. Soon after this it was that he came to England to work the horses.

'I don't know how he froze on to Baine, but I can guess. Baine used to call himself a commission agent, had a house in Nottin' Dale, an' was a wrong 'un through an' through. A little bullet-headed man with an enormous slit of a mouth an' bow legs that were always done up in horsey-lookin' gaiters, he was well known at small meetin's an' made his livin' by chummin' up to inexperienced young men an' "tellin' the tale". His *modus operandi* was to get them to invest a few sovereigns on a horse that hadn't got an earthly chance of winnin'. He would take the few sovereigns an' "invest" them by puttin' the money in his pocket. When the horse lost he'd come back to the "mug" an' spin a beautiful yarn about how the horse would have won if he hadn't been interfered with at the start.

'Just about this time there was a young chap livin' in Kensin'ton Gardens by the name of Hite. He was one of those fellows who suffer from havin' too much money, an' naturally he turned to racin' as a cure for the disease. His father was one of them scientific fellows who don't take any notice of money, but spend their lives lookin' through a microscope to see the little bugs in the blood. A professor at Oxford he was, an' so young Sanderson Hite, who wasn't scientific, except with a book of form, got into touch with Baine.

'Baine noticed him at one or two race meetins, an' particularly noticed that he was always alone, an' so he struck up a sort of acquaintance with him, an' told him "the tale".

'It was about the winner of the Newbury Spring Cup, an' Sandy took it all in, very eagerly.

'Only when it came to the question of partin' with five pounds he hesitated an' said he'd put the money on himself.

'To Baine's annoyance he went into the ring an' backed the horse which hadn't a hundred to one chance – for £250!

'Baine absolutely gnashed his teeth when he saw all this good money goin' into the bookmaker's pocket, but he nearly died with amazement when this "dead" horse he'd recommended won the race by a short head, beatin' a hot favourite.

'Two thousand pounds young Sandy cleared, an' he handed over a hundred to Baine for his information. After that, Baine couldn't do wrong so far as Sandy Hite was concerned. Seein' that he'd got hold of the original golden egg-layin' goose, Baine clamped himself on to it, an' laid himself out to get *bona fide* information, an' for weeks these two reaped in a fine harvest.

'The Captain was beginnin' to win a few races just then, but was bettin' very light, for him, so that when Baine mentioned "Sandy" an' asked if he could put him "on" to a good thing that the Captain was runnin', he said he didn't mind.

'Now, the most curious feature of the whole business was this, that Kintock never met Sandy, not even when he marked the boy down for pluckin'. He preferred to do it through Baine, an' what is more, he never touched Sandy for a penny until the great Highbury Boy bet.

'Highbury Boy was a two-year-old, the property of Lord Horling.

Entered for all the classic races an' tried, almost as a yearlin', to be well above the average, Kintock purchased the colt, with his engagements, for ten thousand pounds.

'If ever there was a man who knew a horse, that man was the Captain, an' when he said that Highbury Boy would win the Derby, Baine believed him.

'He ran him in a couple of his engagements an' ran a "bye". The colt could have won on both occasions, but the jockey, ridin' to orders, contrived to get himself shut in.

'Then he brought him out for the Champagne Stakes at Doncaster, an' the Captain betted. He went into the ring, an' threw the money about as though he were bettin' on the most certain of certainties, an' Highbury Boy startin' at 2 to 1 a strong favourite, won in a common canter.

'That was the last race of his two-year-old days, an' when, just before Christmas of that year, bettin' on the next year's Derby began to creep into the papers, he would have been installed a hot favourite but for the disquietin' news published in the sportin' press, that he had trained off, accordin' to the papers.

'Baine was very prosperous in those days – I think he was on the Captain's pension list – an' I don't doubt that some of the exclusive information published in the London sportin' papers came from him.

'I saw him one day – Highbury Boy bein' at 20 to 1 an' me havin' backed him at sixes I was a bit upset.

' "What about this horse of yours, Baine?" I ses.

' "Highbury Boy?" ses he, innocent, "oh, he's trained off accordin' to the papers."

' "I know all about the papers," I ses; "are you their special correspondent?"

' "Without the word of a lie," he ses, very frank, "I am."

'The Craven Stakes, the first race in which Highbury Boy was entered as a three-year-old, came, an' the "Boy" was scratched; the Two Thousand Guineas, won by Bel Mere (who also won the Craven), passed without the colt's puttin' in an appearance. He ran at Kempton for the Jubilee Handicap an' finished tenth, an' he went right out of the Derby list an' was spoken of as a doubtful starter.

'On public form it looked a thousand pounds to an orange pip on Bel Mere, an' money was laid on him, an' the first an' most enthusiastic of his supporters was Sandy.

'He was very jubilant, an' very confident, because he'd had a good season the year before, an' he'd come into somethin' like £40,000 by the death of an aunt.

' "Baine," ses he one day when we were all in the tea-room at Newbury, "if these were the old days when one could bet in ten thousands, I could double my fortune on Bel Mere."

' "What do you mean by old days, Mr. Hite?" ses Baine. "It is just as easy to get a bet on for ten thousand, or one of even twenty thousand for the matter of that, as it ever was."

'Then he went on to tell him of Captain Kintock, of what a fine, generous "better" he was, an' how, even though Highbury Boy was a physical wreck, he was so cocksure that it would beat Bel Mere that he'd stake his life on it.

'Sandy bit at the bait quicker than Baine thought possible.

' "Would he?" he said eagerly. "What! After the Jubilee runnin'? I wish to goodness he would!"

'If you wonder why this young man was prepared to make such a huge bet, you have got to remember that Bel Mere was extraordinarily superior to any other horse in that race except Highbury Boy, an' that Highbury Boy was popularly supposed to be a cripple on crutches. Well, the long an' the short of the discussion was that Baine promised to see the Captain an' ask him if he was prepared to back Highbury Boy against Bel Mere, an' after a lot of palaver an' an exchange of polite letters, the Captain expressed himself as willin' to lay one bet of £15,000 against Bel Mere beatin' Highbury Boy.

'I heard all this afterwards.

'Derby Day came nearer, an' then I believe there was some more correspondence, an' the £15,000 bet was increased to £25,000, an' then the Captain had a bit of bad luck, for the story of this wager got into the papers, an' the first thing that happened was old Mr. Sanderson Hite got to hear of the foolish tricks that his son was playin', an' puttin' aside his microscope an' his test-tubes an' his electric batteries, he came down to see Kintock, one simple old man with no worldly knowledge worth speakin' about – an' Kintock so wise an' cunnin' an' glib.

'It was a gorgeous spring mornin' when he arrived at Epsom.

Kintock had rented a house just outside the town, an' Highbury Boy was in the stable, guarded day an' night by a couple of men.

'They were sittin' out on the lawn takin' eleven o'clock tea – he was a very abstemious man was the Captain – when old Mr. Hite was announced.

'He came up the garden path, by Baine's account, a neat old figure dressed with scrupulous care. Spotless linen, perfectly fittin' frock coat, an' a big old-fashioned satin bow to his wing collar. His fashion was the fashion of forty years ago, he might have stepped out of an 1874 fashion plate.

'He got straight to business with Kintock with an old-fashioned quietness of speech an' courtesy that was very puzzlin' to Baine. Without any preliminary he started in about Highbury Boy.

' "I have taken the trouble," he ses, "to study the form – is that the word? – of Highbury Boy, an' to my surprise I find that it is quite possible to anticipate winners from the study of a horse's performances. If Highbury Boy were in good health, would he win the Derby, Mr. Kintock?"

'The Captain hesitated.

' "Yes," he admitted after a pause.

' "Is he well?"

'The old man sat bolt upright in his chair, his thin white hands crossed upon his stick, an' the question was hurled at Kintock with a sudden ferocity that was surprisin'.

'Baine saw the Captain shift uneasily at the directness of the attack.

'Then the old man went on.

' "You have told me all I want to know," he ses. "I have made diligent search for the origin of the stories of your horse's illness, an' I have traced the rumours an' head shakin's an' whispered reports. Now, I ask you, sir," he went on, "to do me a favour."

' "I shall be happy to do anythin' in reason," said Kintock.

' "I ask you to take your bettin' book an' run your pen through the bets my son has made with you concernin' your horse."

'Kintock laughed.

' "That I shall not do," he said calmly.

'The old man rose with a little inclination of his head.

' "Then your horse will not win," he said with such an air of confidence that the Captain was startled. "I have given you a chance, an' you have refused to take it. I do not care a straw how much money you may make from your other dupes, I am satisfied that the foolish young man who is my son shall be saved from his folly."

'Then Kintock got wild at the old man's confidence, an' did a foolish thing, for he lost his temper an' spoke frankly.

' "My horse will win," he said angrily, "that's the truth, an' you might as well know it. Win! Why, Bel Mere will not see the way the Boy will go! An' as for your son, I hold him to his bargain. If he doesn't pay I'll post him, yes, by —"

'The old man turned to go; then he hesitated an' came back.

' "Would it be askin' too much if I asked your permission to see this wonderful horse of yours?" Then, as a suspicious frown gathered on Kintock's face, he went on, with a wry smile, "My interest is not an unnatural one, is it?"

'But Kintock's suspicions were aroused.

' "You may see the horse," he said, "but at a distance."

'He called Baine aside, an' told him to watch the old man closely, an' if he made any movement that threatened the horse's safety to grip him.

'He went to the stables himself, an' by an' bye came back to invite the professor into the little meadow that adjoined the house, an' after a while the two grooms come in leadin' Highbury Boy.

'The old man stood with his 'ands behind him watchin' the beautiful bay as they led him up an' down.

'There never was a more perfect-lookin' colt than the Boy, an' somethin' like pride came into Kintock's face as he watched the horse movin'.

'Then the old man spoke.

' "Once more, Mr. Kintock, will you cancel my son's bet?"

' "No," said Mr. Kintock briefly, an' the old man nodded.

'Baine was watchin' him as a cat watches a mouse, but he made no sign. Still, with his hands clasped behind him, he stood like one lost in thought. Then he roused himself.

' "Very well," was all he said, an' with bent head an' knitted brows he accompanied us back to the garden.

' "I have one thing to say to you," he said to Kintock, "have you ever heard of a sayin', falsely ascribed to the Jesuits, that a man may do harm that good may come?"

' "I have heard that very frequently," said Kintock. "Moreover, that has been my creed."

' "Suppose," the old man said slowly, "suppose somebody got into the stable of this fine horse of yours, an' —"

' "Nobbled it?" smiled Kintock.

' "I think that is the word I have read in connection with similar occurrences," said Mr. Hite; "suppose this happened – suppose I sent my friends —"

' "Try," said Kintock with an ugly smile; "if you or they succeed in gettin' at Highbury Boy they're welcome. I shall not complain. If that is your hope of preventin' him winnin', you are buildin' upon sand. Good-morning."

' "We shall see," said old Mr. Sanderson Hite, an' he walked down the path to the gate.

'Baine went round to see the Boy boxed for the day, an' after Kintock had issued his orders to the grooms, who were devoted to him body an' soul, he walked back across the meadow.

'The Captain had already shaken off his annoyance, an' was laughin' quietly at the old man an' his threat.

' "He is certainly an original, an' if young Sandy had half his brains – hullo!"

'He stopped suddenly an' picked up a matchbox – he was the tidiest man I ever knew.

' "Who dropped this?" he said. Then he looked at the box an' whistled. On the outside was printed in red letters – Tompkins, Tobacconist, Cambridge. "The old man dropped that," he said with a frown, "he was standin' close to this spot. He is not the sort of man to carry an empty matchbox about for fun, he didn't look like a smoker; now, what is the meanin' of this?"

'Somehow old Mr. Hite's threat had a depressin' effect upon Kintock, an' he must have taken him more seriously than did Baine, for he ordered his bed to be taken to the room above the stables, an' had a square hole cut in the floor immediately over Highbury Boy's box, an' a pane of glass fitted. He was thus able to see all that was happenin' in the stable from the room above. He went farther than this, for he went to the police an' got a couple of officers specially detailed to watch the outside of the stable for the two nights that intervened between Mr. Hite's visit an' Derby Day. I was one of 'em, an' that's how I come to know all about this story.

'The Epsom summer meetin' begins on the Tuesday, an' it was on the Tuesday that Kintock started to bet. Highbury Boy stood at 50 to 1 in the list when Kintock started operations. He was a clever gambler, for he never showed his hand thoroughly. He had an agent in Holland backin' the horse, whilst he was simultaneously gettin' the odds from the biggest bookmakers on the course, an' by night Highbury Boy had been "backed down" to 4 to 1 an' was co-favourite with Bel Mere.

'Kintock's great fear had been that his foolish outburst might have been taken advantage of by old Hite; that he would spoil his market, an' he put a man on to watch the old fellow.

'The Captain came home to dinner the night before the Derby jubilant.

' "He's gone back to Cambridge," he said, with a triumphant laugh, "an' to think I was worryin' about him!"

' "He's thrown up the sponge," said Baine.

' "Capitulated without firin' a shot," smiled Kintock, "but it may be a ruse to throw us off our guard. The Boy must not be left out of our sight."

'Nothin' happened that night so far as I know, an' Derby Day dawned with me sittin' on a chair outside the favourite's stable smokin' a pipe.

'It was a glorious May day, with bright sunshine, an' a fleck or two of white cloud in the sky, an' the Downs were crowded. The people stood in a solid black mass up the hill, an' ten deep from the startin' gate, round Tattenham Corner, to the winnin' post. In the paddock, big as it is, there was scarcely room to walk about, but we found a corner where the crowd was thin, an' there we saddled Highbury Boy an' gave him his final preparation.

'Kerslake was the jockey, a lad who had won two Derbies, an' knew exactly every inch of the course.

'The bell rang, an' Kerslake mounted.

'Kintock had a few words with him, an' what the jockey said, I think, restored some of the Captain's assurance.

' "I stand to win £60,000," he said to me, as he an' Baine walked back to the rings, me an' Baine to Tattersalls, an' he to the Members' enclosure, "an' that old man got on my nerves."

' "Is he still at Cambridge?" says Baine, an' Kintock nodded.

' "I've had a man watchin' him there, an' I received a wire from him only half an hour ago, sayin' that Hite was lecturin' this mornin' at eleven, an' he had seen him a few minutes before he sent the wire."

'There was the usual parade an' canter, the usual string of horses pickin' a slow way across the Downs to the startin' gate, the usual delay, an' then —

' "They're off!"

'A roar from the stands an' an answerin' roar from the packed course as the bell rang, an' away went the field in a perfect line.

'Baine was on the rails just behind me, an' was readin' the race through his glasses.

' "Bel Mere is makin' the runnin' from Handy Lad, Mosempions, Highbury Boy, an' Cattino," he said.

'They breasted the hill in a bunch, an' came sweepin' to the left to the famous corner.

'They were all together when they turned into the straight, an' then without any glasses I saw Kerslake prepare to take his position.

'Bel Mere was leadin' an' already stands an' course resounded with the yell: "Bel Mere wins!"

'Then Kerslake went after the leader, caught him an' passed him in with one run an' down below in the ring a bookmaker shouted:

' "I'll back Highbury Boy!"

'Up went the whip of Bel Mere's rider, but he could get no nearer, an' Highbury Boy came with his devastatin' strides nearer an' nearer the post.

'Then he stopped . . .

'There is no other word to describe what happened.

'Stopped as dead as that horse did that was shot by the anti-gamblin' fanatic; then swerved right across the course, stopped again an' went down all of a heap as Bel Mere flashed past the post an easy winner.

'I saw Kintock's white face on the Members' stand as I ran across to the horse.

'Baine was at the horse's side first, an' with another policeman helped to lift the unconscious jockey. He was badly shaken by his fall, but was not seriously injured.

'But Highbury Boy was finished, you could see that, long before the vet came with the horse ambulance.

'Kintock, very quiet and self-possessed, directed operations.

'As it happened there were two famous veterinary surgeons on the course an' they accompanied us back to the house – the Captain, Baine, Inspector Carbury an' me.

'Highbury Boy was taken from the ambulance an' collapsed on the grass as we gathered round him.

'Very carefully one of the surgeons made his examination.

' "Has he been shot?" asked Kintock, but the doctor shook his head.

'He continued his examination; then asked if we had a microscope.

'Baine went into the town to borrow one, whilst the vet applied one or two rough an' ready remedies to the horse. By-an'-by he rose an' stood by the horse, eyein' him thoughtfully.

' "Remarkable, very remarkable," he ses; then he asked if he might see the stable.

'He went in by himself an' was there ten minutes, an' when he came out he held in his hand – a matchbox!

'Kintock started back with an oath.

' "Where did you get that?" he demanded.

'The surgeon looked surprised.

' "Out of my pocket," he said, an' just then Baine came back with the microscope.

'The veterinary surgeon took a little blood from the horse with the point of a needle an' adjourned to the house.

'He was back in five minutes.

' "Have you had any person here interested in tropical diseases?" he asked.

'A slow light dawned on Kintock's face an' he nodded.

' "Because," said the vet, "whoever it was must have inadvertently left behind him, these."

'He opened the matchbox he still held in his hand an' produced two dead flies.

'They were a little larger than the house-fly, of a dark-brown colour, an' their wings were folded over their backs in the shape of scissors.

' "This," said the vet, "is the fly which is known to science as the *Glossina morsitans*, or as it is commonly called the 'tsetse fly'. Its bite is almost certain death to a horse, though, curiously enough, the usual symptoms peculiar to the disease are absent in your horse. Do you know who brought the flies here?"

' "I can guess," ses the Captain with a grim smile.'

THE GREAT GENEVA SWEEPSTAKE

GRAESIDE is a very pleasant house in a very pleasant road in the pleasantest suburb of a North of England town. It may be mentioned in passing that the owner of Graeside suffers from some chronic chest trouble, and spends the greater part of the year in the high Alps. Artistically and even comfortably furnished, with an acre or so of excellent garden, it was the source of some bitterness to its wheezy owner that he found some difficulty in letting Graeside furnished at seven guineas a week.

He confided this much to Mr. Burnstid over an after-luncheon cigar in the lounge of the Hotel Bellevue, at Interlaken. The emptiness and desolation of Graeside, the meanness of prospective hirers of furnished houses, and his asthma were Mr. Ferguson's main themes, and Mr. Burnstid, who had listened drowsily to a long dissertation upon what Dr. This had said and Dr. That had advised, and had taken a yawning interest in the various symptoms of the disease which assailed Mr. Ferguson, woke up suddenly when the virtues of Graeside came to be discussed.

Burnstid was a very stout man, with a large, healthy face and a large, healthy nose. He was always well-dressed and even better than that. He wore across his yellow waistcoat an immense chain of gold, and on his plump fingers sparkled and scintillated the products of Kimberley.

'Nice house, eh?' he asked. 'Good neighbourhood, and all that sort of thing?'

'The best,' said Mr. Ferguson emphatically.

'In a road or standing by itself?' asked Mr. Burnstid, and Mr. Ferguson explained that it was not overlooked, that it had electric light and bathrooms of transcendent beauty, that it was honestly worth ten guineas of anybody's money, and that a spirit of meanness and parsimony had swept over the whole of the North Country.

'H'm,' said Mr. Burnstid, and sucked at his cigar, looking at the floor through half-closed eyelids. 'Are you letting this place yourself, or have you got an agent? You always ought to have an agent, you know.'

'I've got an agent,' said the melancholy Ferguson, and gave his name.

At Mr. Burnstid's request he added the address, and remarked in parenthesis that he was probably the most inefficient agent that any house-owner ever had.

Mr. Burnstid grunted, and a little while afterwards went to his room, where his first act was to write down the name of the agent and the place at which he was to be found.

He did not mention Graeside to Ferguson or show the slightest interest, and when, eight or nine days later, the delighted Mr. Ferguson heard from his agent to the effect that Graeside was let, Burnstid was not at Interlaken to hear the good news or to receive the congratulations and thanks of Mr. Ferguson, even supposing Mr. Ferguson had been aware of the fact that it was due to his stout and amiable companion that the letting had been effected.

Mr. Burnstid had indeed gone across country to Lausanne, and thence by boat across the Lake of Geneva, for he had an appointment with his two partners, also stout men who smoked expensive cigars and were girded with large gold cables.

The meeting took place in an airy office on the Rue du Mont Blanc, and was wholly informal. There was Mr. Epsten and Mr. Cowan present in addition to Mr. Burnstid.

'Well?' was Mr. Epsten's first greeting, and he was apparently a person of some importance, 'what's the prospects?'

'The prospects is pretty good,' replied Mr. Burnstid, who was superior to the rules that governed the speech of his adopted country. 'I am sending three-quarters of a million circulars, and they will all be posted in England. We are certain to get in two hundred thousand from our old clients, the fellows we had for the Cesarewitch sweep, and a lot more besides. I haven't wasted the winter.'

'That's good,' said Mr. Epsten, nodding. 'Then you think the Lincoln sweep is going to be a success?'

'Think?' scoffed the other. 'I know. It will be like shelling peas. We ought to get in at least £100,000.'

'What prizes are you offering?' asked Mr. Cowan.

'First prize £20,000,' said Burnstid promptly. 'Wait a bit; I'll give you the full particulars.' He took from his pocket a slip of paper, adjusted a pair of gold-rimmed glasses, and looked down his nose at the document. 'First prize, £20,000,' he read; 'second, £10,000; third, £5,000; fourth; £1,000; ten consolation prizes of £600, and £500 for every horse drawn.'

Mr. Cowan nodded, satisfied.

'That ought to bring 'em in,' he said, 'but wouldn't it be well to make the first prize £40,000?'

Burnstid shook his head.

'You'd scare 'em at £40,000,' he said. '£20,000 is a reasonable sum. You see, the public argue this way: they think we are making a bit out of it, and they don't mind so long as it isn't much. If we offered £40,000 they would smell a fake, because the people who go in for sweepstakes know very well that there ain't a great deal of money going for the Lincolnshire Handicap, anyway. No, we want to put a reasonable prize-list out, and I think this will do.'

'That's all right,' said Epsten. 'Now what about money for preliminary expenses.'

'I reckon it will cost £10,000,' said Burnstid, 'not reckoning my own personal expenses, if I am going to stay to work it as I did last year. I'll put up £2,000, and you two other fellows put up £4,000 each, and we'll split three ways,'

There was some argument as to this division because it was not in the nature of either Mr. Epsten or Mr. Cowan to agree readily any proposal which involved the putting down of hard cash, but eventually the agreement was come to.

'What about a staff?'

'I've got that fixed,' said Mr. Burnstid. 'In fact, I've been very lucky. I have the old war-society offices at a reasonable figure, and I have engaged a bright young man to run the whole thing.'

'A bright young man?' said Mr. Espten suspiciously. 'Where did you get him?'

'He's a young British officer, very well connected, by all accounts,' explained Mr. Burnstid; 'very smart, and willing to do anything. He speaks French, German and English, and he is well in with the authorities here. I am going to fix it up, so that if any trouble comes he will be the mug.'

Mr. Epsten smiled and Mr. Cowan smiled and Mr Burnstid smiled in sympathy.

'Is he straight?' asked the virtuous Mr. Epsten. 'We don't want any crooks in the business, you know, Burnie. I mean, suppose he finds out that none of the big prizes are paid?'

'Leave that to me,' said Mr. Burnstid with confidence. 'I tell you, this lad will do anything for £1,000, and, besides, I can always fake the draw; and, in fact, I have made arrangements already for the awarding of first prize.'

He did not explain what the arrangements were until later, but his companions were satisfied.

They left that night for Paris, leaving Mr. Burnstid to carry out his plans. Mr. Burnstid did not exaggerate the qualities of the young gentleman whose services he had secured. They had met one day on the boat to Ouch and Mr. Burnstid, who never lost an opportunity, nor failed to diagnose the financial conditions of those with whom he was brought into contact, had, as he was subsequently satisfied, accurately placed the bright and talkative young man whom he met in the smoking-room of the boat.

He saw his friends off from the station and then went to the little Café Planet, where he had arranged to meet his new assistant. The new assistant was sitting disconsolately gazing at an empty coffee cup, but brightened up at the sight of his new patron.

'It's all right, Stevens,' said Mr. Burnstid jovially. 'I've fixed up your job with my partners.'

'Oh, I say,' said the grateful young man, 'that is really awfully jolly of you. You are most kind. Really, you are a perfectly dear old thing.'

'Not so old,' growled Mr. Burnstid, with whom age was a sore point. 'Now, you understand that I am putting a lot of confidence in you. This business of ours is not exactly – er – business.'

'Quite so, quite so,' said Mr. Stevens chirpily. 'I think you're a deuced good sportsman, and don't worry about my conscience, because I haven't one. After a fellow has been serving his country in the trenches, and all that sort of thing, he has not many scruples left. I suppose you haven't a son?'

'I have,' said Mr. Burnstid enthusiastically; 'one of the brightest boys in the old country. He is about your age.'

'What was he in?' asked the interested young officer.

'Well, he wasn't in anything,' said Mr. Burnstid carefully; 'he was too valuable a man to risk, if you understand.'

'Quite,' nodded the young man. 'There are people like that.'

'He was in the Ministry of Munitions and did very well indeed, though, of course, the air raids knocked him over a bit.'

'I see,' again the young man nodded. 'Now let's hear what I've got to do.'

Mr. Burnstid told him. Apparently Stevens had to do nothing but sit in a luxurious office and keep an eye upon innumerable young men and women who were opening envelopes containing currency, which would be sent from Britain by even large numbers of other young men and women, desirous of getting rich quick by drawing the winner of the Lincolnshire Handicap.

'You will take charge of all the money and be boss. If anybody comes and wants to know who is running it, remember it is you. You will sign all the cheques.'

The young man purred.

'After I have initialled them,' said Mr. Burnstid. 'I have arranged with the bank manager so that no cheques will be cashed unless my initials are on the left-hand corner.'

'Very proper, very proper,' said the young man.

'Now, you understand,' here Mr. Burnstid became more careful than ever, and spoke slowly and with emphasis, 'that it often happens that we do not get in enough money to pay the big prizes. In that case the prizes are reduced. That's fair, isn't it?'

Stevens agreed.

'And sometimes,' explained Mr. Burnstid further, 'even where there's a lot of money the expenses are so heavy that we have to knock off the first prize to pay our way.'

'I see,' said Stevens thoughtfully.

'When I say knock off the first prize,' said Burnstid, 'I do not mean that we go and tell the people that we have had to knock off the first prize. We award it as though we haven't knocked it off, if you understand.'

'That's a jolly good idea,' approved Stevens. 'I suppose the poor josser who gets it doesn't get it at all. Is that the scheme?'

'Not quite, not quite,' Burnstid rubbed his nose and hesitated. 'Well, you have got to know this, as you are in the game, and you are going to draw £1,000 – a whole thousand army O'Goblins – as your share of the —'

'Loot?' suggested Mr. Stevens.

'That's the word, loot. We may have to elect somebody to take the first prize. You see strictly speaking the draw occurs the day before the race, and the holders of various horses are advertised. Well, you can't do that, because if you planted a man with the favourite, the favourite might lose. So what you do is to announce the names of the people who have drawn the horses after the day of the race and then the thing is simple.'

'Simplicity itself. My dear fellow, I understand the business quite well. What you mean to say is that we are running a commercial concern, and we cannot afford to take uncommercial risks. Ha! ha!'

Burnstid smiled in sympathy.

'Now,' Mr. Burnstid continued, 'I have taken a house called Graeside, in the North of England. I am going to get somebody I can trust to live there till the draw. I need hardly tell you that the first prize is going to the tenant of Graeside. If enquiries are made, there he will be as large as life, ready to answer any questions. Now, I am sending my son, Barney, there. Nobody knows that I am connected with this – this —'

'Swindle?' suggested the other innocently, and Mr. Burnstid frowned.

'That is not the word,' he said sharply; "enterprise" is a better one. Anyway, he will be there. Now you know the whole run of the game. If we have a very successful sweep, I'll give you a little more than the thousand for the season – you will find me pretty generous. If there is any trouble, don't forget that you are the man in charge, and you have got to take whatever medicine is coming to you. That is why I am paying you so high.'

The young man known as Stevens light-heartedly brushed aside the possibility of there being any trouble. If there was, he was quite prepared for all eventualities.

For the next few weeks Mr. Burnstid lived a contented life. He saw his office coming into shape, and was more than satisfied with the adept way in which this young man handled the staff. The sweep had been well advertised and the fruits of the circulars were beginning to appear. The stream of money orders and postal orders and banknotes – the promoters of the Great Geneva Sweepstake accepted no cheques – grew in volume, but never in the busiest time was Mr. Stevens snowed under. Then, when all things were looking serene, a blow fell.

One day Stevens was summoned to the Bellevue Hotel and found his employer pacing the ante-room of his elegant suite.

'Here's a pretty mess,' he said. 'Somebody in England has discovered that Barney is my son, and has advertised the fact – and after Barney had moved into Graeside with his wife!'

'That's pretty bad! You can't award him the prize now.'

Mr. Burnstid did not answer. He was completely occupied in cursing the interfering busybodies on the newspaper Press of Britain, who had stuck their noses into business which did not, from his point of view, concern them.

'This is pretty bad, pretty bad,' he said, shaking his head. 'It's too late to plant another winner.'

'What are you going to do?' asked Stevens again.

'Well,' said Mr. Burnstid, controlling himself with an effort, 'my partner, Mr. Cowan, has got a plan, and it is a very good idea, too. Have you heard of the Three Scallywags?'

'The Three Scallywags?' asked Stevens with a smile. 'I've heard of more than three.'

'I am talking about the famous three,' said Mr. Burnstid impatiently. 'There was a bit in the paper about them. They fooled a crook in London and pinched his money.'

Stevens shook his head.

'No. What are they?'

'Well, according to the newspapers,' said Mr. Burnstid, 'they are three officers who are on the make. They are getting rich by robbing crooks – not,' he added virtuously, 'that crooks shouldn't be robbed. I think it is a very good idea. People who steal money don't deserve to keep it.'

'Well, where do the Three Scallywags come in?' asked Stevens.

'Sit down and I'll tell you.'

Stevens took a seat in a big bow window overlooking the lake and Mr. Burnstid let himself carefully into another chair.

'Suppose after the draw me and you go to London with all the stuff we have collected in a bag?'

'Stuff? You mean money?'

Mr. Burnstid nodded.

'And suppose between Folkestone and London the bag's pinched by the Three Scallywags?'

'Not being pinched at all, but being planted by us at Folkestone or somewhere?'

'That's the idea,' said the admiring Mr. Burnstid. 'My word, you have got a brain! And suppose we put it out that the Scallywags have taken it, and left a note to that effect, and then me and my partners offer to pay half the prizes out of our own pockets?'

'Talking of brains,' said Mr. Stevens, no less admiringly; 'what a head you've got!'

'You see,' said the flattered Burnstid, 'that wouldn't be a bad advertisement for the next sweep. Shows our honesty, and all that sort of thing, and at the same time saves us a matter of about £50,000, which ain't to be sneezed at. To make it more proper, we will have the Press over to see the draw.'

'And to make things more lifelike,' chuckled Mr. Stevens, 'what about getting a couple of detectives from London to accompany us on our way? I know a man who is in that line of business, and he could supply us with a couple of guards.'

To this suggestion Mr. Burnstid at first demurred, but eventually consented, and things fell out as they had planned. There was a draw, conducted with great solemnity, in the presence of representatives of the sporting Press. There were two solemn young men brought from London by Mr. Stevens, who guarded the treasure, and after the Pressmen had been sent on their way rejoicing, and announcements had been telegraphed to London to the effect that the money would be distributed in person by the promoter, Burnstid, his assistant, and the two detectives boarded a through train from Basle to Boulogne.

'To minimise the risk,' said Mr. Stevens, in retailing his plan to the last of the Pressmen.

The scheme as the two had arranged it was simple. The big bag containing the money was to be handed to one of the partners on their arrival at Folkestone, who would give in return a bag of similar size containing old newspapers and who would make his way into

the town and on to London by motor-car. The boat came into
Folkestone Harbour at dusk. There was certain to be a great deal of
confusion at the passengers' landing, and, anyway, Stevens under-
took to allay the suspicions of the detectives.

Everything went without a hitch except that one of the detectives
was so overcome by sea-sickness that he could not come on from
Folkestone. Outside Charing Cross, Mr. Burnstid opened the bag
in the presence of the remaining detective, and, with a simulation
of horror, which was very well done, discovered the substitute.

'We have been robbed, robbed!' he said. 'Look!'

He drew out a card from the top of the bag inscribed:

'With compliments and thanks – The Three Scallywags.'

'This is terrible,' moaned Mr. Burnstid.

'This is horrible,' moaned Mr. Stevens.

There was a small crowd of reporters waiting at Charing Cross
Station, for the arrival of a gentleman with £100,000 in banknotes
and postal orders was, in the romantic circumstances, an event. To
these Mr. Burnstid unfolded his terrible tale of pillage, and the faces
of some of the prize-winners who had gathered to get as near to
their money as was possible, fell in ratio to their hopes.

'But,' said Mr. Burnstid, addressing his small audience in a voice
broken with emotion, 'I am not going to let the prize-winners lose.
Out of my own pocket I am going to pay fifty per cent of the
money due, and you gentlemen of the Press can take that as official.'

They got to their hotel, and, locked in their private sitting-room,
Mr. Stevens and Mr. Burnstid exchanged happy smiles.

'That's all right,' said Burnstid. 'They took it very well and it's
a good ad. for me, old man.' He looked at his watch. 'In a couple
of hours I'll stroll across to Ealing. Cowan will be there with the
money.'

On his arrival at Mr. Cowan's beautiful dwelling, the latter greeted his partner on the doorstep with a look of surprise.

'Have you got the bag?' asked Burnstid without ceremony.

'Bag?' roared Cowan. 'You telegraphed me not to meet you until
the next day.'

'What!' yelled the other. 'You weren't at Folkestone Station?'

'Of course I wasn't,' said Cowan. 'I tell you, you telegraphed
me —'

But Burnstid was making tracks for his taxi, and a few seconds later was being whirled back to his hotel, for he had a few questions to ask Mr. Stevens.

But Stevens, who was called Sam by his confederates, was at that moment in company with the two pseudo detectives, sorting the ill-gotten gains of Mr. Burnstid. The Three Scallywags had turned the pious fraud of the Great Geneva Sweepstake promoters into reality.

'Saul,' he said, 'you count the tenners, Sandy, you make a heap of the money orders – we'll send them on to old man Burnstid. They don't amount to much, anyway, but they will help pay that fifty per cent. which he has promised – officially!'